Foreword

Joe Tiernan
Chairman of HomeBond

A particularly satisfactory aspect of my role, as Chairman of HomeBond, has been the success of our House Building Manual. Since it was first published in late 1993, the Manual has proven to be a remarkable success, exceeding our highest expectations. That a large and expensive technical manual of more than 470 pages, should have achieved a distribution of more than 30,000 copies, speaks volumes for the scale of its success. Not only is this manual a notable success for the house building industry, it is also a significant achievement in the world of Irish technical book publishing.

The decision to go to a third edition was necessitated by changes to the Building Regulations in 2000 whereby Part M "Access for People with Disabilities" and Part D "Materials and Workmanship" were amended.

We are profoundly convinced that we can best serve the Irish house building industry by ensuring that the Manual is kept up-to-date and that in particular it reflects the newly revised Building Regulations.

The previous edition of the Manual was also extended to include a number of new sections. Of these, perhaps the most important one deals with timber frame houses. The popularity of this method of construction makes it imperative that builders of Timber Frame Structures should ensure that the structures conform to our warranty standards.

The Manual deals with the complete house. Houses are much more complex buildings than is commonly realised. Many skills, services and materials are involved, which must be integrated into a single structure, which is soundly built, well lighted, with adequate heating, ventilation and good access. Other essential activities include site selection, planning, design, provision of road works and other services, such as landscaping, dealing with the local authorities and design and property professionals.

Each trade is followed through all stages of construction, making the Manual an indispensable reference on every building site and in places of higher education.

In conclusion, the Manual is a testament to the remarkable skill, quality and professionalism of Irish house builders. Just as we take a legitimate pride in the standard of houses we provide, as house builders, we can also take pride in the HomeBond House Building Manual, as a guarantee that our homes are soundly constructed and that they are fully deserving of the consumer's confidence.

It is the opinion of the Chairman and Board that the Manual will be invaluable for all concerned with good house building.

Joe Tiernan
Chairman of HomeBond

Preface

HomeBond which was established in 1978 has become a most important force in the private sector of housing. The Board involved in producing this Manual is as follows:

Joe Tiernan (Chairman)

Michael Greene, B.L., B.Comm., M.Econ. Sc., (Managing Director and Secretary)

Martin Browne, FCA

Michael J. Coleman

Frank Fahy

Eugene Farrell, B.E., M. Eng. Sc., M.Sc.Mgmt., Ph.D., C. Eng., FIEI

Frank Mc Gee

Sean McKeon

Don O' Brien, FCA

Paddy Raggett

Francis Rhatigan

Jim Wood

HomeBond has been very pleased with the success of the House Building Manual since it was first launched in 1993. We are told that it has assisted builders, architects and engineers in the construction of many houses.

As stated in the preface of the first edition of the Manual, the rules keep changing and to this effect the new editions of both Tecnical Guidance Documents D "Material and Workmanship" and M "Access for People with Disabilities" were issued in 2000.

Due to the new requirements that were contained in these regulations and also revisions of other codes and standards it was felt appropriate that a new edition of the Manual should be launched to incorporate these changes.

In as far as is possible, these changes are covered in this edition of the Manual.

HomeBond and the Department of the Environment and Local Government together inspect dwellings all over the country. As this edition of the Manual goes to print, HomeBond has over 340,000 dwellings registered. These dwellings are all inspected and, in the main, they are found to be well built.

Houses are constructed by various trades working on site with many different materials. They are built in ground which may vary in its geology over a few metres, both horizontally and vertically. There is always something to be learned and there are, unfortunately, times when something goes wrong. This Manual deals with the construction of a house from foundations to chimney pot and it is hoped that implementation of the details given in this Manual will help further in reducing the number of incidents of problems.

In the acknowledgments a list is given of the people who have helped with advice and HomeBond would like to thank them for their cooperation and assistance.

At HomeBond, Dr. Eugene Farrell is the staff member who took the responsibility of editing the Manual. This was in collaboration with John McCarthy, the architect commissioned by HomeBond to produce the Manual and Anthony McFeely who compiled the Manual and produced the illustrations. It is appropriate to congratulate all three for their dedication, hard work and expertise.

This publication is produced as general guidance to members and it is appropriate to indicate that anybody who takes on the responsibility of producing a dwelling must themselves ensure that it is built to correct standards and complies in every way with the Building Regulations and all other requirements that are in force and impact on it. It is also assumed that all work is carried out by competent tradesmen who have an understanding of building construction and with appropriate tools and equipment.

Neither HomeBond, nor the Authors, nor anyone who has assisted in the production of this Manual can accept any liability arising out of reliance on any aspect of this publication. Persons should always obtain professional advice for their specific situation and requirements.

HomeBond reminds all members that the Building Regulations, 2000 ("the Regulations") require that all works to which the Regulations apply must be carried out with proper materials (and in a workmanlike manner).

"Proper materials" are defined in the Regulations as materials which are "fit for the use for which they are intended and for the conditions in which they are to be used". The Regulations also provide that materials are "proper materials" if they:

◆ bear a CE Marking (as per the Construction Products Directive 89/106/EEC)
◆ comply with an appropriate harmonised standard, European technical approval or national technical specification (as per Article 4(2) of the Construction Products Directive)
◆ comply with an appropriate Irish Standard or Irish Agrément Board Certificate or with an alternative national technical specification of any State which is a contracting party to the Agreement on the European Economic Area (as defined in the Regulations), which provides in use an equivalent level of safety and suitability.

Technical Guidance Document D advises that the National Standards Authority of Ireland may be consulted for advice in relation to equivalence.

Acknowledgements

HomeBond gratefully acknowledges the assistance of the following people in the compilation of the Manual.

John McCarthy, Anthony Mc Feely	Coll+McCarthy Architects
Eugene Farrell, Tom Crotty, Kevin Dillon, Mike O'Grady, Tom Cregg, Conor Taaffe, John Keehan, Eugene O'Neill	HomeBond
Pat Murphy	Thomas Garland & Ptnrs, Consulting Engineers
Eoin O'Cofaigh, Caomhán Murphy	Mc Hugh O'Cofaigh Architects
John O'Dea, Seán Wiley, Bill Robinson, Bob Davis, Dermot Murphy	Enterprise Ireland
Hugh Boyd, Michael Weldon	Wavin (Irl.) Ltd
Paul Van Cauwelaert	Roadstone Provinces Ltd
Shane O'Toole, Bobby O'Neill	Tegral Building Products
George Yeates, Tommy Daniel, Tommy Mc Dermott	Gypsum Products Development Association
Seán Hyde, Robert Roe	Health & Safety Authority
Colm Bannon, Brendan Lynch	Irish Cement Ltd
Niall Walsh	Dublin Corporation
Joe Twomey, Nick Ryan, Pat Minogue, Brian Power	Department of the Environment and Local Government
John Holmes	Ormonde Brick
John Maguire, Paul McGarry	Irish Concrete Federation
Eamon Dundon, Jim McBride, Joe Keenan, Roy Dempsey, Tom Meyler, Jim O'Flynn	Irish Timber Frame Manufacturers' Association
Jack Madden, Anne McGarry	Radiological Protection Institute of Ireland
Kevin Hogan	Carey Glass
Domhnall Blair, Tom Davis, Cyril Pearson	Roadstone Dublin Ltd.

WHAT TO DO BEFORE BUYING A SITE
continued

Why has the site not been built on before?

Maps and photographs are a useful source of information about the characteristics and history of a site.

Even if you have a detailed, life-long knowledge of the site, it is wise to see what maps and photographs are available.

Ordnance Survey maps.
Study the current map.
The question of why the site has not already been built on may be critical in an otherwise built-up area. Look also at older Ordnance Survey maps as they may show ponds, hedges, buildings, ditches, rivers etc., now removed but which may have an effect on building.

O.S. maps are available from the Ordnance Survey Office, Phoenix Park, Dublin 8.

Water table.
Avoid building on sites subject to flooding.

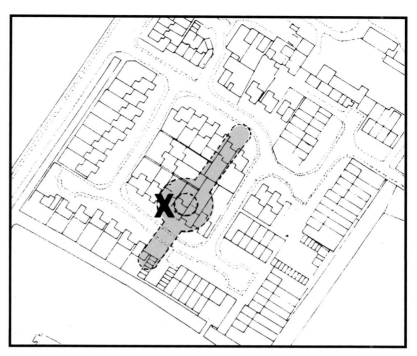

Example:
Settlement occurred in house at **X**. An old map showed that it had been built on the site of a water garden (shown dotted) from a previous era.

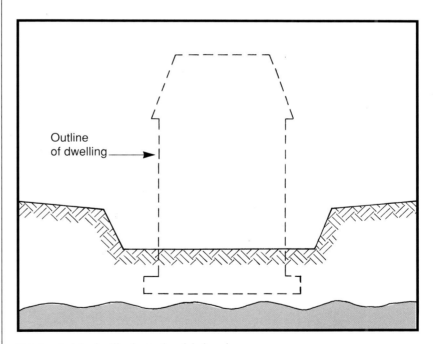

Outline of dwelling

Water table is likely to be high where:

◆ ground is damp in dry weather

◆ the type of vegetation indicates damp ground

◆ the site of the dwelling is surrounded by higher ground.

CHEMICAL HAZARDS AND CONTAMINANTS

A building site may contain hazards and contaminants such as radon, methane, carbon dioxide, sulphates, chlorides or acids. These can be naturally occurring or can occur as a result of the previous use of the site.

This page and the following pages give outline guidance for dealing with such substances.

Radon:

Radon is a naturally occurring radioactive gas which can build up to unacceptably high concentrations in buildings.

Further guidance is given in Appendix A. Additional information is also available from:

- The Radiological Protection Institute of Ireland,
  3 Clonskeagh Square,
  Dublin 14

- The Environmental Information Service (ENFO),
  17 St. Andrew's Street,
  Dublin 2

- Environmental Protection Agency (EPA),
  PO Box 3000,
  Johnstown Castle Est.,
  Co. Wexford

- British Research Establishment (BRE) Report RB211:1991 "Radon Guidance on Protective Measures for new Dwellings"

- "Building on Derelict Land" by B. A. Leach and H. K. Goodger. CIRIA/PSA publication, ref: SP78, 1991.

Methane and Carbon dioxide:

Incidents involving landfill gas in buildings have increased in recent years. The principal components of landfill gas are methane (which is flammable) and carbon dioxide (which is toxic) and so if it enters the building it can pose a risk to both health and safety. These two gases are also associated with coal strata, river silt, sewage and peat.

Specialist advice should be sought, and site investigation carried out if there is a risk of methane or carbon dioxide. Further information may be obtained from the British Research Establishment (BRE) report BR 212: 1991 "Construction of new buildings on gas-contaminated land" available from the British Research Establishment (BRE), Garston, Watford WD2 7JR, England.

Guidance on the appropriate measures to be taken in the design and construction of building on or near sites containing landfill is provided in the Department of the Environment publication "Protection of New Building and Occupants from Landfill Gas", available from Government Publications, Molesworth St., Dublin 2;
Tel: 01 6613111.

Sulphates:

Sulphates can cause expansion and disruption of concrete, particularly on filled sites. Concrete mix specification should take account of the risk, and the concrete mix should be specified by a suitably qualified consulting engineer. Guidance is available in BRE Digest 363 "Sulphate and acid resistance of concrete in the ground".

Chlorides:

Chlorides increase the risk of reinforcement corrosion and chemical attack on concrete. As with sulphates, the concrete mix specification and reinforcement details where a chloride risk exists should be prepared by a suitably qualified consulting engineer. The engineer appointed must be qualified by examination, be in private practice and possess professional indemnity insurance.

CHEMICAL HAZARDS AND CONTAMINANTS
continued

Acids:
High acid content, for example in peat, can damage concrete.

To avoid such damage precautions such as the following may be necessary:

a) Increased cement in mix.

b) Use of special cements.

c) Thorough compaction.

d) Use of a protective layer, such as bituminous or plastic membrane to prevent the contaminants coming into contact with the concrete.

Again, the advice of a suitably qualified person is essential to avoid costly repairs.

Additional information can be found in I.S. 326: 1988 "Code of Practice for the Structural Use of Concrete".

Contamination from a previous use of site:
Contamination arising from a previous use is a possibility requiring investigation on some sites. The table opposite gives some guidance for identifying such risks and possible contaminants.

Further guidance is set out in BS 5930: 1981 "Code of practice for site investigation" and DD 175: 1988 "Code of practice for the identification of potentially contaminated land and its investigation". Both these documents are published by the British Standards Institution (BSI), 389 Chiswick High Rd., London W9 4AL, England.

Sites likely to contain contaminants:

◆ Asbestos works

◆ Chemical works

◆ Gas works, coal carbonisation plants and ancillary by-product works

◆ Industries making or using wood preservatives

◆ Landfill and other waste disposal sites or ground within 250 metres of such sites

◆ Metal mines, smelters, foundries, steel works and metal finishing works

◆ Oil storage and distribution sites

◆ Paper and printing works

◆ Railway land, especially the larger sidings and depots

◆ Scrap yards

◆ Sewage works, sewage farms and sludge disposal sites

◆ Tanneries.

Identifying Contaminants

Signs of possible contamination	Possible contaminant
a) Vegetation (absence, poor or unnatural growth)	Metals, metal compounds, organic compounds, gases.
b) Surface materials (unusual colours and contours may indicate wastes and residues)	Metals, metal compounds, oily and tarry wastes, asbestos (loose), other fibres, organic compounds (including phenols), potentially combustible material including coal and coke dust, refuse and waste.
c) Fumes and odours (may indicate organic chemicals at very low concentrations)	Flammable, explosive and asphyxiating gases including methane and carbon dioxide, corrosive liquids, faecal, animal and vegetable matter (biologically active).
d) Drums and containers (whether full or empty)	Various.

BUILDING ON HAZARDOUS GROUND

Engage an engineer and have a thorough site investigation carried out by a site investigation specialist. The engineer can then design appropriate foundations based on the site investigation findings.

The engineer appointed must be qualified by examination, be in private practice, and possess professional indemnity insurance. The engineer's report could mean that it will pay the builder to use the site differently from his original idea.

Site layout

If any part of the site is hazardous, the best course may be to arrange the dwellings so that the hazardous area is not built on, for example:

A.   Re-site dwelling.

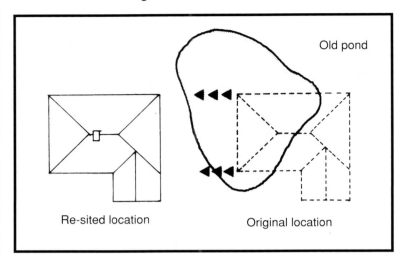

Re-sited location   Original location

B.   Leave an open space.

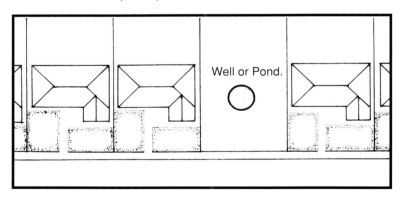

TANKING
continued

Internal tanking: Where the structural wall and floor slab retains the excavation and sandwiches the membrane with an internal skin providing protection.

Of these two methods, external application of mastic asphalt is preferred. It affords protection to the main structure from attack by sulphates in the surrounding soil and groundwater.

Thickness and number of coats

On horizontal surfaces and surfaces sloping up to 30° to the horizontal, mastic asphalt should be laid in three coats to a total thickness of 30 mm.

On vertical surfaces and slopes over 30° to the horizontal, mastic asphalt should be applied in three coats to not less than 20 mm and taken to a height of at least 150 mm above ground level.

Where angle fillets are required they should be at least 50 mm wide and applied in two coats at the junction of two planes forming an internal angle.

It is essential the tanking be applied to clean dry surfaces which should be free from sharp protrusions which could puncture the material and destroy the essential waterproofing integrity.

Backfilling

Backfilling to basement walls should be carefully executed in graded material in layers not exceeding 150 mm and compacted.

Where pitch fibre or PVC/uPVC drains are used it is important that the granular material be well compacted to the sides of the section to prevent deformation.

Note:

Basement design, construction and tanking is a specialised area and an engineer should be engaged. The engineer appointed must be qualified by examination, be in private practice and possess professional indemnity insurance.

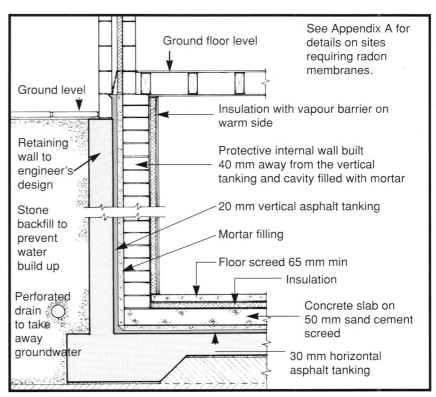

Ground floor level

See Appendix A for details on sites requiring radon membranes.

Ground level

Retaining wall to engineer's design

Stone backfill to prevent water build up

Perforated drain to take away groundwater

Insulation with vapour barrier on warm side

Protective internal wall built 40 mm away from the vertical tanking and cavity filled with mortar

20 mm vertical asphalt tanking

Mortar filling

Floor screed 65 mm min

Insulation

Concrete slab on 50 mm sand cement screed

30 mm horizontal asphalt tanking

Typical internal tanking detail.

Note: If floor screed is laid on top of insulation, screed to be minimum 65 mm thick. It is recommended that light mesh reinforcement is incorporated.

Note:
There is merit in wrapping the perforated drain in a geotextile filter cloth to reduce the risk of clogging by migration of fines.

APPLYING AND LAYING TANKING.

◆ **Protection.**
   Provide protection against damage to the membranes at all times. Provide or ensure the provision of the permanent protective construction as soon as practicable after completion of the damp-proofing membrane. Keep the area which has been overlaid clear of materials used by other trades

◆ **Membrane support.**
   Provide full support without voids over the whole of both surfaces of tanking membranes in a sandwich construction. Where the membrane is applied internally to vertical surfaces, ensure that the protecting inner wall is so constructed as to fully support the membrane

◆ **Externally applied membrane.**
   Provide and maintain effective temporary protection to the membrane at the junction of floor and wall. Do not drive mechanical fixings through the membrane

◆ **Temperatures of heated material.**
   Do not heat bonding bitumens above 260°C. Do not heat asphalt above 230°C for prolonged periods. Measure temperatures with thermometers in the heating cauldrons or in the mastic asphalt immediately after it has been removed from a mixer

INTRODUCTION

Hardcore should be placed and compacted in accordance with the guidance given on these pages. Failure to observe this simple guidance can result in expensive and disruptive remedial work.

Unacceptable fill material.

Failure of fill.

Good quality hardcore: clean, crushed, well graded stone.

Where site conditions require a depth of fill of hardcore in excess of 900 mm, a suspended floor construction should be used. Suspended floors can be of timber, in-situ reinforced concrete or precast concrete.

1

Hardcore material should be clean graded crushed stone, free from shale, 100 mm maximum size. Demolition material, site rubbish or pit run gravel must not be used. Excavated material must not be placed inside line of perimeter walls.

Dry rot material in fill.

2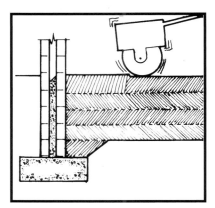

Consolidate hardcore in layers not exceeding 225 mm in thickness. Minimum depth of hardcore 150 mm.

This is essential to avoid subsequent settlement of hardcore. Particular attention should be paid to compacting hardcore where depth increases locally e.g. foundation trenches.

3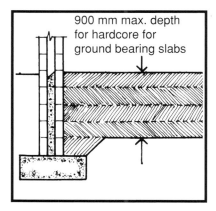

900 mm max. depth for hardcore for ground bearing slabs

Total depth of hardcore should not exceed 900 mm, except where a suspended floor is being used.

BLINDING

Clean hardcore material should be graded crushed stone, free from shale and 100 mm maximum size. Demolition material, site rubbish or pit run gravel must not be used. Excavated material must not be placed inside line of perimeter walls.

Sand blinding.

Typical example of well compacted hardcore

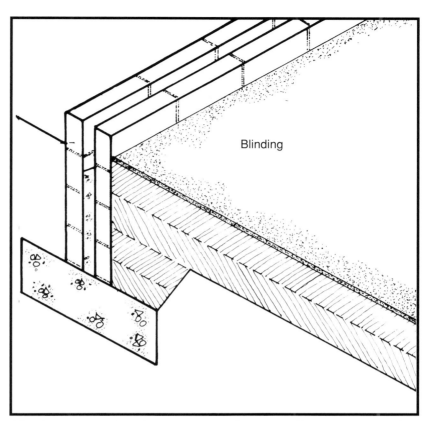

Blinding should be of minimum thickness sufficient only to fill surface voids. For reinforced slabs, blinding should be firm and even to support chairs to reinforcement.

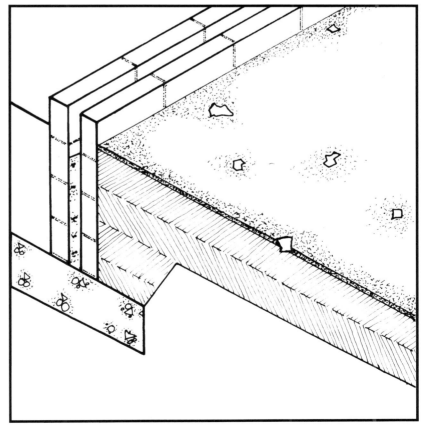

Avoid sharp projections which might puncture the damp-proof membrane.

DAMP-PROOF MEMBRANE

Damp-proof membranes with an appropriate Agrément certificate should be used.

Certain requirements of CP 102: 1973 (Code of Practice for the protection of buildings against water from the ground), with regard to damp-proof membranes are outlined below.

◆ The dpm in the floor should be continuous with or sealed to the dpc in the surrounding walls

◆ Joints in the dpm should be lapped at least 150 mm and sealed

◆ Punctures in the dpm should be patched with the same type of polythene, lapped at least 150 mm and sealed beyond the limits of the punctures.

See Appendix A for guidance on radon membranes.

PROBLEMS WITH CONCRETE GROUND FLOORS
continued

9. Take care with insulation.
To comply with the Building Regulations, insulation is required under the entire area of the floor slab. Thickness of insulation required can be determined from Appendix I. Great care should be taken to ensure this insulation stays in place while the concrete slab is being poured. It may be necessary to weigh down the insulation with bricks, which are then removed while the concrete is poured near to them. To prevent the poured concrete from going under the insulation batts, the batts could be covered with 500 gauge polythene or suitably held down.

10. Take care to avoid cracking.
When laying concrete floor slabs or sand and cement screeds in hot weather it is necessary to protect them from direct sunlight and keep them cool to prevent drying out too quickly which will result in cracking. Detailed guidance on screeds can be found on pages 245 and 246.

RULES TO PREVENT FAILURE OF FLOOR SLABS

◆ Strip ground of all vegetable matter and top soil

◆ Use well graded clean broken stone

◆ Compact hardcore in layers

◆ Do not use deep fill

◆ Blind with quarry dust or sand

◆ Use 1200 gauge dpm

◆ Place dpm and pour slab when walls are at dpc height

◆ Never build walls off the slab – they must have foundations

◆ Floors need insulation under their entire area to comply with the Building Regulations

◆ For rafts, dpm and screed must be on top of raft and screed must be at least 65 mm thick. It is recommended that light mesh reinforcement is incorporated.

See also Appendix A.

Low grade floor fill, this is not acceptable under ground supported slabs.

Sinking floor.

REINFORCEMENT TO SUSPENDED FLOOR SLABS

Reinforcement mesh is available in a range of standard formats. Square mesh with bars at 200 mm centres carries the prefix A. The number following the letter A indicates the cross-sectional area of the steel per metre run of mesh, e.g., A393 mesh is a square mesh with 10 mm diameter bars at 200 mm centres. The standard range of type A meshes is A98 to A393.

Type B meshes have a 200 x 100 mm grid with the main steel at 100 mm centres and the cross reinforcement at 200 mm centres. The range of type B meshes is B196 to B1131.

Type C meshes have a 400 x 100 mm grid with the main steel at 100 mm centres and the cross reinforcement at 400 mm centres. The range of type C meshes is C283 to C785.

Technical Guidance Document C of the Building Regulations recommends that this form of construction should only be used where it is unlikely that a substantial gap will form under the suspended floor due to settlement of the ground under its own weight, thereby creating a risk of explosive gas mixtures accumulating under the floor.

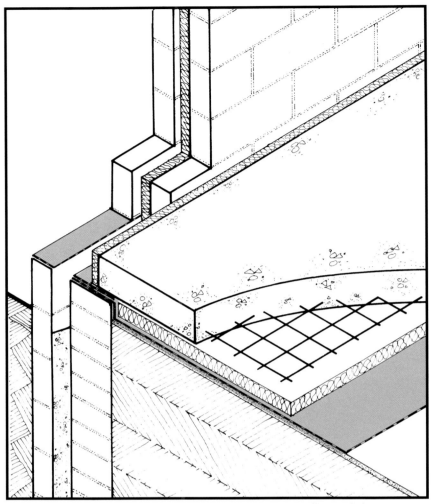

Typical reinforced concrete suspended ground floor slab.

Tabulated below are the appropriate slab depths and reinforcement mesh types for typical domestic ground floor spans. Note that the information given assumes that no internal partitions bear on the slab. The main bars in the mesh should run in the direction of the span and the mesh should be placed so that the main bars are below the secondary bars. There should be a minimum 25 mm nominal cover of concrete between the underside of the slab and the main bars. Concrete mix should be 30N20. Slab bearing on supporting rising walls should be at least 100 mm.

Max. slab clear span (m)	Slab depth (mm)	Reinforcement
3.0	150	B283 mesh
3.3	150	B385 mesh
4.0	175	B503 mesh
4.4	200	B503 mesh

REINFORCEMENT TO SUSPENDED FLOOR SLABS
continued

An alternative bearing detail for suspended floor slabs is shown opposite, and to reduce the risk of cracking, additional reinforcement may be placed in the top of slab at the leading edges and particularly at corners.

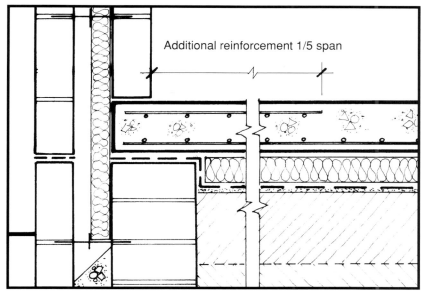

Edge reinforcement.

Where a slab is continuous over a wall, as shown opposite, additional reinforcement should be placed in the top of the slab to reduce the risk of cracking.

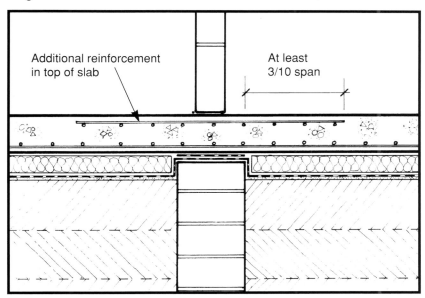

Slab continuous over a wall.

Pipe recesses must only be formed in the perimeter of slabs.

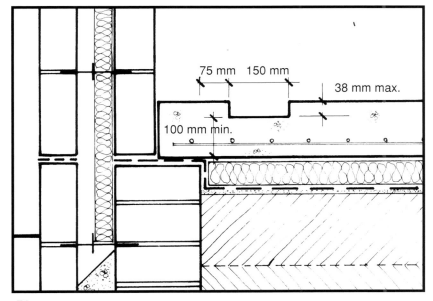

Pipe recesses.

PRECAST CONCRETE FLOORS

As an alternative to the use of suspended timber or suspended in-situ concrete floor slabs, a variety of suitable types of precast concrete floor systems are available for use in suspended floor construction at ground or upper storey level.

Such precast concrete floors fall into three broad categories as follows:

1. Beam and block.

2. Hollow slab.

3. Precast plank or pre-stressed plate with in-situ concrete topping. These types may or may not include infill blocks or void formers.

This and the following page illustrate examples of these floor types. These illustrations do not represent the products of any particular manufacturer but are meant to be indicative of the range available.

See also Appendix A for guidance relating to radon membranes in ground floors.

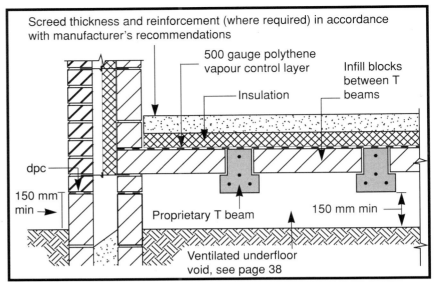

Typical block and beam floor.

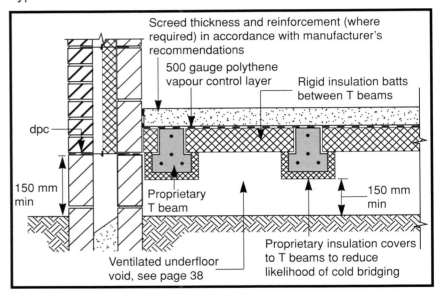

Typical T beam floor.

Typical block and beam floor.

PRECAST CONCRETE FLOORS
continued

Where systems of the type illustrated are being used, the detailed recommendations of the manufacturer should be followed with particular attention being paid to the following aspects of the installation:

◆ Span and supports. Some systems will require propping

◆ Grouting and /or screeding requirements

◆ Reinforcement requirements for screeds

◆ Treatment of point loads such as partitions

◆ Location of damp-proof course

◆ Location, amount and method of installation of insulation to meet the requirements of the Building Regulations and to ensure cold bridging is avoided

◆ Detailing or radon membrane, where required.

It is a requirement of Technical Guidance Document A of the Building Regulations that if the span of suspended concrete ground floors is greater than 5 m, professional guidance is required with regard to the design of the supporting walls.
A similar requirement exists for upper timber floors with a span greater than 5 m.

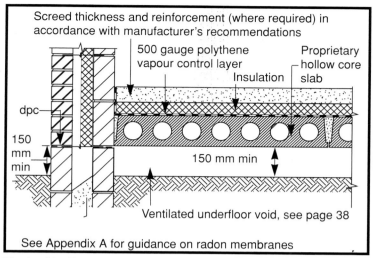

Typical hollow core slab floor.

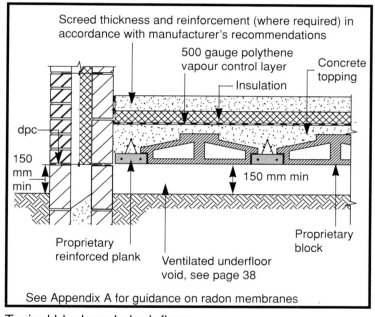

Typical block and plank floor.

PRECAST CONCRETE FLOORS
continued

✳ **HOMEBOND ADVISES THAT THE LEVEL OF THE UNDERFLOOR SHOULD BE LEVEL WITH OR ABOVE EXTERNAL GROUND LEVEL TO PREVENT A SUMP SITUATION ARISING. SEE PAGE 40.**

✳ **TO PREVENT WATER VAPOUR FROM THE GROUND DAMAGING FLOORING MATERIALS AND FINISHES, THE USE OF A DPM OR VAPOUR CONTROL LAYER ABOVE THE STRUCTURAL FLOOR AND BENEATH ANY SCREED OR BOARD FINISH IS RECOMMENDED.**

◆ A ventilated air space should be provided measuring at least 150 mm clear from the ground to the underside of the floor (or insulation if provided in this location). See page 38 for underfloor ventilation requirements.

◆ Take care to avoid overloading the pre-stressed units with blockwork pallets during construction.

◆ Allow concrete finishes adequate time to cure before loading the floor.

Sump found under floor slab.

Cupping of hardwood floor due to water vapour penetrating through the slab.

FROM DPC TO ROOF LEVEL

INTRODUCTION

The function of a lintel is to span an opening in a wall and carry the masonry, then transmit this load from the masonry to the wall on either side. Masonry must not be supported on window or door frames.

Narrow piers between openings give rise to high stress in masonry and the width of the piers must be controlled. For guidance refer to Technical Guidance Document A of the Building Regulations, and to page 82.

Where a lintel span exceeds 3 m the lintel may require calculation by an engineer. The engineer engaged must be qualified by examination, be in private practice and possess professional indemnity insurance.

The two most common types of lintel in current use are:

1. Pressed metal lintels.

2. Precast composite lintels.

Detailed guidance on the construction of composite lintels is given on pages 54 to 61 "construction specification".

Pressed metal lintels.
These should be installed in accordance with the manufacturer's instructions regarding load capacity, corrosion protection, end bearing, water ingress (dpc), fire and thermal properties as set down in the appropriate Agrément Certificate.

The sketches opposite illustrate typical minimum bearing and dpc requirements.

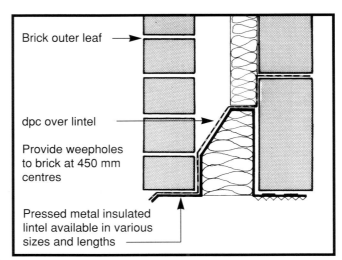

Brick outer leaf

dpc over lintel

Provide weepholes to brick at 450 mm centres

Pressed metal insulated lintel available in various sizes and lengths

Typical pressed metal lintel.

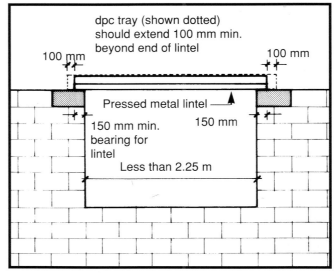

dpc tray (shown dotted) should extend 100 mm min. beyond end of lintel

100 mm

100 mm

Pressed metal lintel

150 mm

150 mm min. bearing for lintel

Less than 2.25 m

Lintel bearings: Pressed metal lintel where span is less than 2.25 m.

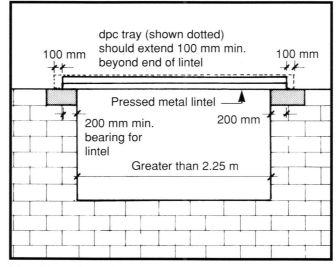

dpc tray (shown dotted) should extend 100 mm min. beyond end of lintel

100 mm

100 mm

Pressed metal lintel

200 mm

200 mm min. bearing for lintel

Greater than 2.25 m

Lintel bearings: Pressed metal lintel where span is greater than 2.25 m. **Note**: Check manufacturer's requirements for bearing conditions. **Note**: Where outer leaf is brickwork or fairfaced blockwork provide weepholes at 450 mm centres (see page 71)

FIRE STOPPING AROUND OPENINGS IN CAVITY WALL CONSTRUCTION

In houses of masonry construction, it is not required to provide fire stopping in the form of a vertical cavity barrier at the junction of party wall and external wall, **provided** that the cavity around doors and windows is closed. This can be achieved using the methods illustrated on this page.

Note:

◆ In all situations the cavity must be closed at wall plate level and along the top of the gables

◆ The details shown here are the standard cavity closing details applicable to semi-detached and terraced houses of one or two storeys in height

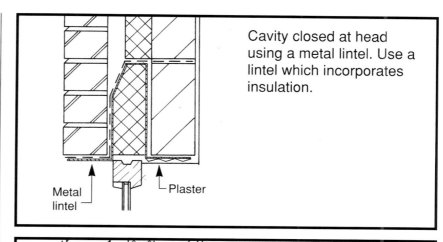

Cavity closed at head using a metal lintel. Use a lintel which incorporates insulation.

Metal lintel — Plaster

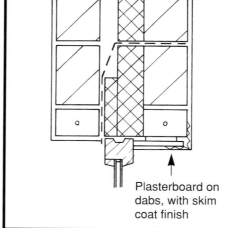

When using pre-stressed concrete lintels, the cavity can be closed by plaster-board fixed by dabs to the underside of the lintel and tight against the window frame with skim coat plaster finish.

Plasterboard on dabs, with skim coat finish

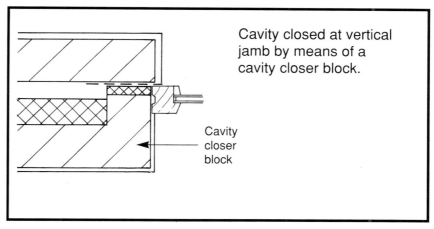

Cavity closed at vertical jamb by means of a cavity closer block.

Cavity closer block

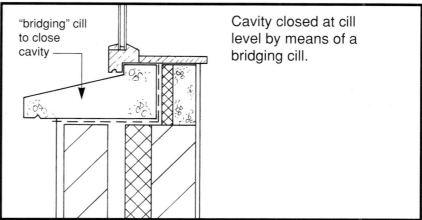

"bridging" cill to close cavity

Cavity closed at cill level by means of a bridging cill.

Typical cavity closing methods.

COMPOSITE LINTELS

Introduction

Composite lintels constructed of prestressed concrete lintels acting together with solid block or in-situ concrete should be designed and constructed in accordance with the guidance on the following pages.

The satisfactory performance of a composite lintel depends on the joint action of the prestressed lintel with a zone of blockwork or in-situ concrete laid on top of the lintel — hence the terms 'composite lintel', 'compression blockwork', 'compression zone'.

In the same way that the steel reinforcement of a reinforced concrete beam resists tensile force, and the concrete resists the compressive force, so in a composite lintel the prestressing tendon in the lintel (i.e. the reinforcing bar) resists the tensile force and the blockwork or in-situ concrete resists the compressive force.

Remember

A prestressed concrete lintel is deemed to have no strength until combined with the blockwork or in-situ concrete built above it.

PRESTRESSED CONCRETE LINTELS

Material specification:

Lintels should be manufactured in accordance with IS 240:1980.

Precast prestressed concrete units for use in composite lintels:

Unit dimensions (mm)	Unit Weight (kg/m)	Initial Prestress (kN)
100 x 65	16	65
150 x 65	24	64
215 x 65	37	130

WALLING MATERIALS:

A. Concrete masonry

Concrete Blocks
Complying with IS 20: 1987 "Concrete Building Blocks Part 1, Normal Density Blocks".
Solid blocks only to be used in the area of composite action.

Concrete Bricks
Complying with IS 189: 1974 "Concrete Building Bricks". Bricks of external quality (i.e. minimum 15 N/mm^2) must be used.

Mortar
Complying with IS 406: 1987 "Masonry Mortars". Mortar designation iii, 1:1:6 Cement : Lime : Sand or, 1:6 Cement : Sand with plasticiser.

B. In-situ concrete

Complying with IS 326: 1988 Code of Practice for the Structural use of Concrete. Characteristic strength: 30 N/mm^2.

CONSTRUCTION SPECIFICATION

◆ **Lintel bearing:**
As specified in IS 240: min. 150 mm for spans up to 1.5 m, 200 mm for spans from 1.5 m to 3.0 m

◆ **Lintel bedding:**
Lintels should be bedded in mortar at supports. The masonry should be constructed so that lintels bear onto whole solid blocks wherever possible

◆ **Propping during construction:**
Lintels must be propped at 1.2 m centres (maximum) until composite masonry or concrete has matured

◆ **Filling of mortar joints:**
Horizontal and vertical joints in the masonry in the composite lintel area should be fully filled. Shell bedding is not allowed in composite lintels

◆ **Placing of in-situ concrete:**
Watertight shuttering for the composite lintel should be wetted before placing concrete. The workability of the mix should be such that it can be fully compacted by the vibration techniques available

◆ **215 mm hollow block walls:**
Solid blocks must be used within the area of masonry required for composite action

◆ **Joist hangers, dpc etc:**
Floor joists, joist hangers, dpc or any other ancillary components must not be allowed to impose a load or interfere with masonry bond within the area of the composite action. Dpc must not be built into compression zone

◆ **Cavity walls:**
Cavity walls should be constructed using a separate lintel under each wall leaf to avoid the cold bridge which a single lintel would create. Additional wall ties at 225 mm vertical centres should be provided within the area of composite action.

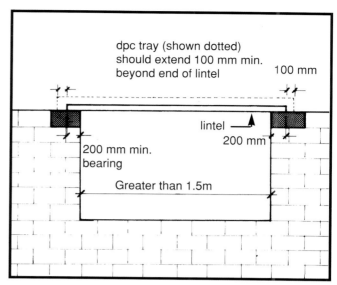

dpc tray (shown dotted) should extend 100 mm min. beyond end of lintel

100 mm

lintel

200 mm

200 mm min. bearing

Greater than 1.5m

Dpc to extend 100 mm min. beyond end of lintel.

Warning.
Never cut out or leave out any openings for services in the blockwork course(s) or in-situ concrete within the compression zone above a prestressed lintel.

DESIGN AND LOAD ASSUMPTION

Timber floor loads:
This design method is suitable for domestic dwellings with timber floors up to three storeys high.

Lintels supporting concrete floors are not covered by this guidance.

In drawing up these design tables the following assumptions have been made:

	Timber floor loads without partition	Timber floor loads with partition
Self weight of floor	0.30 kN/m	0.30 kN/m
Imposed load	1.50 kN/m	2.50 kN/m
Total floor load	1.80 kN/m	2.80 kN/m

The applied load in Table 1 below has been derived by multiplying the total floor load by half the floor span. e.g. The applied floor load for a apan of 6m is:

$(6 \text{ m} \div 2) \times 1.8 \text{ kN/m}^2 = 5.4 \text{ kN/m}$ (without partition)
or
$(6 \text{ m} \div 2) \times 2.8 \text{ kN/m}^2 = 8.4 \text{ kN/m}$ (with partition)

Table 1. Applied floor load on lintel (kN/m run)		
Span of floor	Load on lintel kN/m without partition	Load on lintel kN/m with partition
2 m	1.8	2.8
3 m	2.7	4.2
4 m	3.6	5.6
5 m	4.5	7.0
6 m	5.4	8.4

Pitched roof loads
This design method is suitable for domestic roofs of simple plan form up to three storeys in height.

Roof construction
Modern roof construction with timber trusses spreads all the roof load to the outside supporting walls. Table 2 has been prepared for this arrangement.

In traditional or cut roof construction some of the load is spread through purlins and struts onto the internal walls. Where this occurs the loads given in table 2 may be reduced by one third to allow for this. Where there are no purlins no reduction can be made.

In assessing dead and imposed loads in roof construction the following assumptions were made:

Dead load on slope:
Self weight-concrete tile roof:	0.68 kN/m²
Self weight-fibre cement slate roof:	0.25 kN/m²

Dead load on plan:
Ceiling ties	0.25 kN/m²

Imposed load on plan:
Roof pitch 0° to 30°	0.75 kN/m²
Roof pitch 30° to 45°	0.75 to 0.0 kN/m²

The increase in dead load of the roof with increasing pitch is sufficiently balanced by the decreasing imposed load to allow the roof loads to be simplified to 2.0 kN/m² for concrete tiled roofs and 1.6 kN/m² for fibre cement slated roofs up to 45° pitch.

Note:
The applied load in table 2 has been derived by multiplying the appropriate roof load by half the span, e.g. where a roof with a 20° pitch and concrete tile finish spans 8 m, the applied load on the lintel is 2.0 kN/m² x 4 m (half roof span) = 8 kN/m (as per table 2 below).

Table 2. Applied roof load on lintel (kN/m) For roofs up to 45° pitch		
Roof span on plan	Concrete tiles	Fibre cement slates
3 m	3.0	2.4
4 m	4.0	3.2
5 m	5.0	4.0
6 m	6.0	4.8
7 m	7.0	5.6
8 m	8.0	6.4
9 m	9.0	7.2

COMPOSITE LINTELS OF MASONRY IN CAVITY WALLS

Table 3

Composite depth (D) in mm of 100 mm thick block or brick masonry												
Clear span of lintel in metres	Applied load on lintel from Table 1 and/or 2 (kN/m)											
	1	2	3	4	5	6	7	8	9	10	11	12
0.5	75	75	75	75	75	75	75	75	75	150	150	150
1.0	75	75	75	150	150	150	225	225	225	300	300	300
1.5	75	75	75	150	225	225	300	300	375	375	450	450
2.0	150	150	225	225	300	375	375	450	-	-	-	-
2.5	150	150	300	300	375	450	-	-	-	-	-	-

Note:
1. Only solid concrete blocks or bricks may be used in the area of composite action.
2. Joists, joist hangers, dpc's or flashings must not be built into the zone of composite action of the lintel.

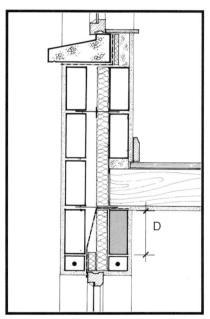

Ground floor window head
Use table 1 to calculate applied floor load on lintel and table 3 to calculate depth of composite blockwork D.

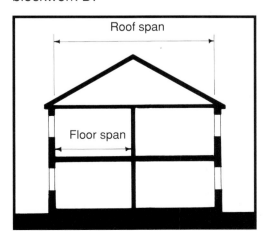

Roof span

Floor span

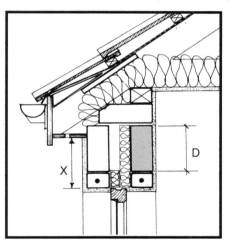

First floor window head
Use table 2 to calculate applied roof load on lintel and table 3 to calculate depth of composite blockwork D.
Note: The solid block cavity closer may be included in the composite depth D.
Note: In exposed conditions or if dimension X exceeds 1 m, use a stepped dpc in this location. Such dpc to be used in all brickwork construction.

Example: Calculate the depth of composite blockwork at (1) ground floor window head and (2) first floor window head, for a dwelling with a roof span of 8 m, concrete tile roof finish, 30° roof pitch, floor span 4 m without partition cavity wall construction and lintels with a maximum clear span of 2 m

1. Ground floor window head: floor span 4 m. So, from table 1:
   Applied floor load on lintel = 3.6 kN/m;
   Lintel span 2 m. So, from table 3 composite depth (D) = 225 mm.

2. First floor window head: roof span 8 m, roof pitch 30°, concrete tile roof finish: So, from table 2:
   Applied roof load on lintel = 8.0 kN/m
   Lintel span 2 m. So, from table 3, composite depth (D) = 450 mm.

COMPOSITE LINTELS OF MASONRY IN 215 mm WALLS

Table 4

Composite depth (D) in mm of solid block or brick masonry												
Clear span of lintel in metres	Applied load on lintel from Table 1 and/or 2 (kN/m)											
	1	2	3	4	5	6	7	8	9	10	11	12
0.5	110	110	110	110	110	110	110	110	110	110	110	110
1.0	110	110	110	110	110	110	110	110	110	110	110	220
1.5	110	110	110	110	110	110	220	220	220	220	220	220
2.0	110	110	110	220	220	220	220	220	330	330	330	330
2.5	110	220	220	220	220	220	330	330	330	330	440	440
3.0	220	220	220	330	330	330	330	440	440	440	-	-
3.5	220	330	330	330	330	440	440	440	-	-	-	-

Note:
1. Only solid concrete blocks or bricks may be used in the area of composite action.
2. Joists, joist hangers, dpc's or flashings must not be built into the zone of composite action of the lintel.

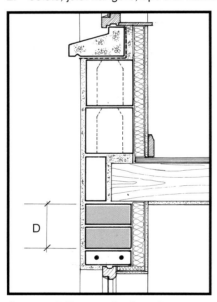

Ground floor window head
Use table 1 to calculate applied floor load on lintel and table 4 to calculate depth of composite blockwork D.

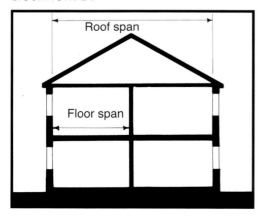

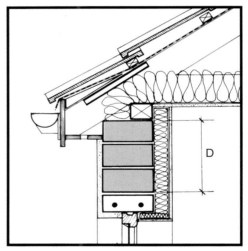

First floor window head
Use table 2 to calculate applied roof load on lintel and table 4 to calculate depth of composite blockwork D.

Example: Calculate the depth of composite blockwork at (1) ground floor window head and (2) first floor window head, for a dwelling with a roof span of 8 m concrete tile roof finish, 25° roof pitch, floor span 4 m with partition hollow block wall construction and lintels with a maximum clear span of 1.5 m

1. Ground floor window head: floor span 4 m. So, from table 1:
   Applied floor load on lintel = 5.6 kN/m;
   Lintel span 1.5 m. So, from table 4 composite depth (D) = 110 mm.

2. First floor window head: roof span 8 m, roof pitch 25° concrete tile roof finish. So from table 2:
   Applied roof load on lintel = 8.0 kN/m;
   Lintel span 1.5 m. So from table 4;
   composite depth (D) = 220 mm.

COMPOSITE LINTELS OF IN-SITU CONCRETE IN CAVITY WALLS

Table 5

Composite depth (D) in mm of 100 mm thick concrete for lintels in cavity walls												
Clear span of lintel in metres	Applied load on lintel from Table 1 and/or 2 (kN/m)											
	1	2	3	4	5	6	7	8	9	10	11	12
0.5	75	75	75	75	75	75	75	75	75	75	75	75
1.0	75	75	75	75	75	75	75	75	75	75	75	150
1.5	75	75	75	75	75	75	150	150	150	150	225	225
2.0	75	75	75	75	150	150	225	225	300	300	375	375
2.5	75	75	150	150	225	300	375	375	375	-	-	-

Note:

1. Concrete of 30 N/mm^2 characteristic strength must be used in concrete composite lintels.
2. Joists, joist hangers, dpc's or flashings must not be built into the zone of composite action of the lintel.

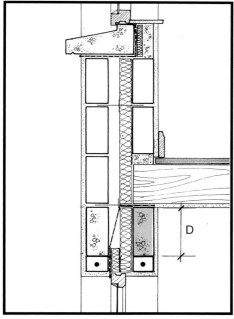

Ground floor window head

Use table 1 to calculate applied floor load on lintel and table 5 to calculate depth of composite in-situ concrete D.

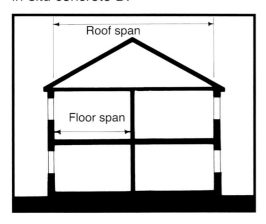

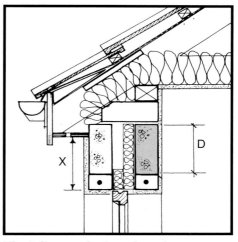

First floor window head

Use table 2 to calculate applied roof load on lintel and table 5 to calculate depth of composite in-situ concrete D.

Note: In exposed conditions or if dimension X exceeds 1 m, use a stepped dpc in this location. Such dpc to be used in all brickwork construction.

Example: Calculate the depth of composite in-situ concrete at (1) ground floor window head and (2) first floor window head, for a dwelling with a roof span 9 m concrete tile roof finish, 20° roof pitch, floor span 4.5 m without partition cavity wall construction and lintels with a maximum clear span of 2 m

(1) Ground floor window head: floor span 4.5 m. So, from table 1:
Applied floor load on lintel = 4.5 kN/m;
Lintel span 2 m so from table 5 composite depth (D) = 150 mm.

(2) First floor window head: roof span 9m, roof pitch 20° concrete tile roof finish. So, from table 2:
Applied roof load on lintel = 9.0 kN/m;
Lintel span 2 m. So from table 5;
composite depth (D) = 300 mm.

COMPOSITE LINTELS OF IN-SITU CONCRETE IN 215 mm WALLS

Table 6

Composite depth (D) in mm of 215 mm thick concrete for lintels in 215 mm walls												
Clear span of lintel in metres	Applied load on lintel from Table 1 and/or 2 (kN/m											
	1	2	3	4	5	6	7	8	9	10	11	12
0.5	75	75	75	75	75	75	75	75	75	75	75	75
1.0	75	75	75	75	75	75	75	75	75	75	75	75
1.5	75	75	75	75	75	75	75	75	75	75	75	75
2.0	75	75	75	75	75	75	75	75	150	150	150	150
2.5	75	75	75	75	75	150	150	150	150	225	300	300
3.0	75	75	75	150	150	150	225	300	300	375	375	375
3.5	75	75	150	150	225	300	375	375	375	-	-	-

Note:
1. Concrete of 30 N/mm^2 characteristic strength must be used in concrete composite lintels.
2. Joists, joist hangers, dpc's or flashings must not be built into the zone of composite action of the lintel.

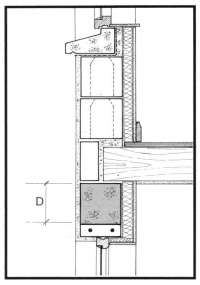

Ground floor window head
Use table 1 to calculate applied floor load on lintel and table 6 to calculate depth of composite in-situ concrete D.

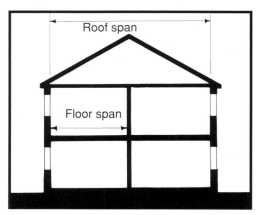

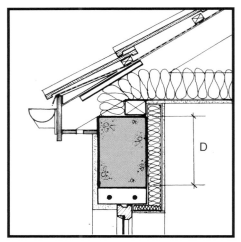

First floor window head
Use table 2 to calculate applied roof load on lintel and table 6 to calculate depth of composite in-situ concrete D.

Example: Calculate the depth of composite in-situ concrete at (1) ground floor window head and (2) first floor window head, for a dwelling with a roof of 8 m concrete tile roof finish, 30° roof pitch, floor span 4 m, with partition hollow block wall construction and lintels with a maximum clear span of 1.5 m.

1. Ground floor window head: floor span 4 m so from table 1:
   Applied floor load on lintel = 5.6 kN/m;
   Lintel span 1.5 m. So from table 6 composite depth (D) = 75 mm.

2. First floor window head: roof span 8 m, roof pitch 30° concrete tile roof finish. So, from table 2:
   Applied roof load on lintel = 8.0 kN/m;
   Lintel span 1.5 m. So, from table 6;
   composite depth (D) = 75 mm.

DORMER ROOF CONSTRUCTION

In houses incorporating accommodation in the roof space (i.e. dormer roof) the lintels in the external walls directly below roof level must carry both roof and floor loads, and where relevant, the floor loads should incorporate partition loads.

The additional load on the lintel from the floor of the dormer accommodation may be calculated from table 1. This should be added to the roof load derived from table 2 and the result used to determine the depth of composite lintel required.

The reduction in load for cut roof construction allowed in table 2 can not be taken into account in the case of dormer roofs.

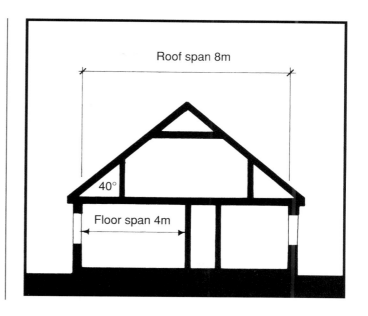

Roof span 8m

40°

Floor span 4m

For example:
Calculate the depth of composite blockwork at roof level for a dwelling with a dormer roof spanning 8 m, concrete tile roof finish, 40° pitch, floor span of 4 m with partition, cavity wall construction and lintels with a maximum clear span of 1.0 m.

Stage 1:
Floor span is 4 m. So, from table 1, the applied floor load on lintel = 5.6kN/m

Stage 2:
Roof span is 8 m, roof pitch is 40° with concrete tile roof finish. So, from table 2, the applied roof load on lintel = 8.0 kN/m.

Stage 3:
Add (applied floor load on lintel) 5.6 kN/m + (applied roof load on lintel) 8.0 kN/m = 13.6 kN/m. Lintel span is 1.0 m. So, from table 3, reproduced below, the depth of composite blockwork D = 375 mm.

COMPOSITE LINTELS OF MASONRY IN CAVITY WALLS

Table 3

Composite depth (D) in mm of 100 mm thick block or brick masonry													
Clear span of lintel in metres	Applied load on lintel from Table 1 and/or 2 (kN/m)												
	2	3	4	5	6	7	8	9	10	11	12	13	14
0.5	75	75	75	75	75	75	75	75	150	150	150	225	225
1.0	75	75	150	150	150	225	225	225	300	300	300	375	375
1.5	75	75	150	225	225	300	300	375	375	450	450	-	-
2.0	150	225	225	300	375	375	450	-	-	-	-	-	-
2.5	150	300	300	375	450	-	-	-	-	-	-	-	-

Note:
1. Only solid concrete blocks or bricks may be used in the area of composite action.
2. Joists, joist hangers, dpc's or flashings must not be built into the zone of composite action of the lintel.

CAST IN-SITU REINFORCED CONCRETE LINTELS

In any situation where cast in-situ reinforced concrete lintels are being used the guidance given in the table opposite, regarding ope span, lintel depth and reinforcement should be used.

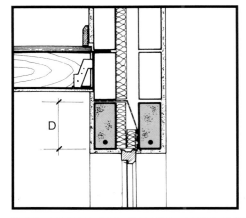

Ope span	Lintel depth(D)	Lintel reinforcement
1.8 m	215 mm	One T16 bar
2.1 m	215 mm	One T20 bar
2.4 m	300 mm	One T20 bar

Note:

1. This guidance should only be used where the roof span is less than 10 m. Where the span exceeds 10 m an engineer should be engaged. The engineer appointed must be qualified by examination, be in private practice and possess professional indemnity insurance.

2	215 mm min. lintel bearing.	Cover to reinforcement: 20 mm for lintels on internal walls 40 mm for lintels on external walls (including lintels on inner leaf of cavity walls)
3	Concrete grade 35N20.	
4	'T' denotes high yield steel.	

METAL SUPPORT ANGLES TO OUTER LEAF

Where metal angles are used to provide support to the outer leaf the guidance given in the table opposite, regarding ope span and angle dimensions should be used.

Alternatively, proprietary galvanised or stainless steel metal lintel angles, used in accordance with the manufacturer's recommendations with regard to span and loading, may be used.

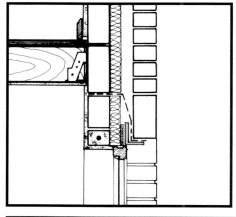

Ope span	Angle required	
	Galvanised mild steel	Stainless steel
1.5 m	90 x 90 x 6	90 x 90 x 6
2.0 m	*150 x 90 x 10	*100 x 90 x 6
3.0 m	*150 x 90 x 10	*150 x 90 x 10

Note:

1. * = Vertical leg of angle.   2. 200 mm min. bearing.

3. Galvanised mild steel to BS 729 and 5493

4. Stainless steel to BS 1449

WALL TIES

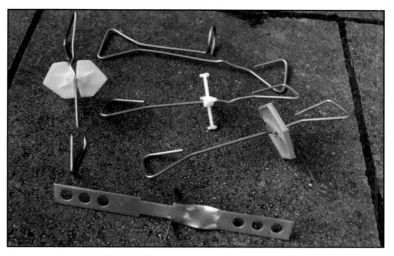

Typical types of wall ties

Wall ties are available in a number of materials and types.

Care should be taken to ensure that:

◆ All wall ties should comply with IS 268: 1986: Metal wall ties for masonry walls. Check that all ties supplied to the site meet the requirements of this standard. The use of austenitic stainless steel ties is strongly recommended and is required in areas of severe exposure. **Note**: The use of plastic wall ties does not comply with the recommendations of Technical Guidance Document A of the Building Regulations or the provisions of IS 268: 1986

◆ Wall ties are long enough to ensure 50 mm embedment into mortar bed in each leaf, i.e. for a 100 mm cavity, use a wall tie at least 200 mm long

◆ Where cavity insulation slabs are used the tie used suits the insulation and holds it firmly in place. Suitable ties are usually available from the suppliers/manufacturers of wall insulation batts

◆ The ties are installed with the drip downward

◆ The ties are installed as work progresses. Do not push ties into mortar after bricks or blocks are laid

◆ There is no backfall (i.e. falling inwards) on wall ties

◆ Double triangle wall ties are used where party walls are of cavity construction; for example, on sloping sites, or at changes of roof level

◆ Both leaves are built up together. No leaf to be more than 1 metre in height above the other.

WALL TIES

Correct spacing and distribution of wall ties is essential for structural stability.
Vertical coursing of wall ties must be staggered.

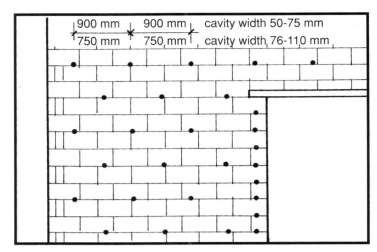

Maximum spacing of wall ties.

MAXIMUM SPACING OF WALL TIES			
Cavity width mm	Horizontal spacing mm	Vertical spacing mm	Number of wall ties per square metre
50 - 75	900	450	2.5
76 -110	750	450	3.0

At unbonded jambs to all openings in cavity walls, provide wall ties at 225 mm vertical centres, located within 150 mm of the opening.

Wall ties should comply with IS 268: 1986: metal wall ties for masonry walls

PROBLEM AREAS

HomeBond has identified a number of recurring problem areas in cavity wall construction associated with damp penetration across the cavity. The seven most common problems are illustrated on the following pages and care should be taken to avoid these.

Keep cavities clean by the use of boards or cavity laths and/or daily cleaning of wall ties. Provide temporary openings at base of wall.

Board across cavity.

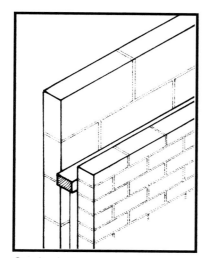

Cavity lath.

Note: All of these recurrent faults can be avoided by care and vigilance on the job.

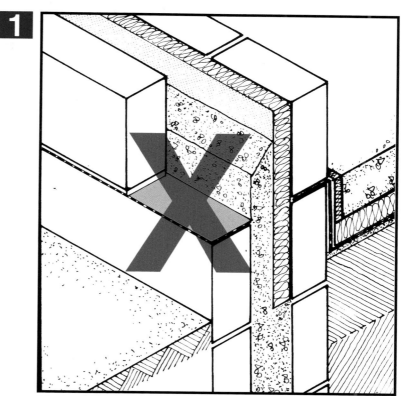

1

Mortar filling to cavity too high: Build up of mortar droppings. Cavity should be kept clear for between 150 mm and 225 mm below dpc level.

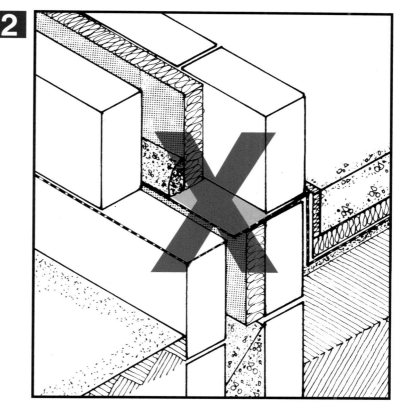

2

Projecting dpc catches mortar:
Ensure that dpc does not project into cavity at ground floor level.

PROBLEM AREAS
continued

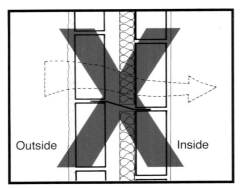

Sloping wall ties act as a bridge across the cavity.

Wall tie sloping inwards and located too close to the reveal.

3

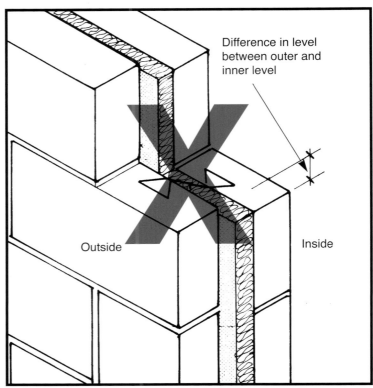

Ties sloping inward act as a bridge across cavity. Take care with coursing of both leaves to avoid backfall on wall ties.

4

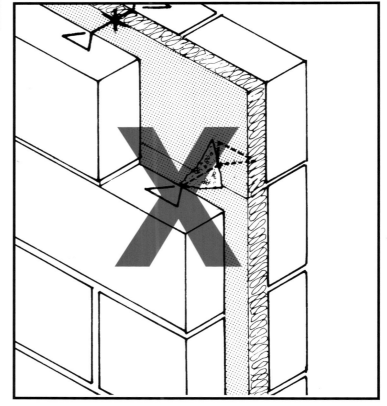

Mortar droppings on wall ties allows penetration of dampness.
Keep cavities and wall ties clean at all times, by using cavity laths and daily cleaning of wall ties as illustrated on page 65.

PROBLEM AREAS
continued

5

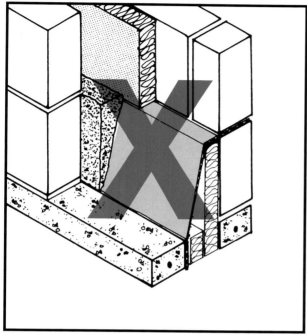

Build up of mortar on trays/lintels over heads.
Keep cavities clean as work progresses.

6

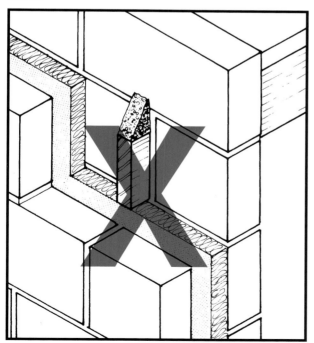

Build up of mortar on joists, purlins,
projections or similar. Avoid such projections.
Note: Treat timber ends with coloured
preservative.

7

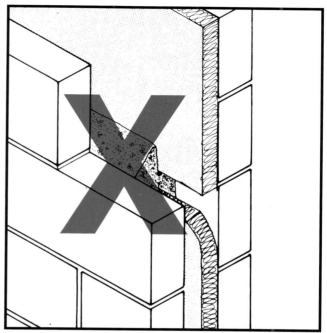

Insulation not restrained against inner leaf.
Use wall ties which are appropriate for the
insulation being used, as per manufacturer's
instructions.

Note:
All of these recurring faults can be avoided by
care and vigilance on the job.

Insufficient wall ties to restrain insulation and
insulation batts missing. This is unacceptable.

STONE CLADDING TO EXTERNAL WALLS

To prevent moisture passing through the wall, stone cladding must not be fixed directly to hollow blockwork or single leaf solid construction.

Stone cladding must only be fixed to the external leaf of a cavity wall, by means of appropriate wall ties, e.g. stainless steel. A minimum of 2.5 ties per square metre is required, spaced at 900 mm max. horizontal centres, 450 mm max. vertical centres and 225 mm vertical centres around opes.

Strips of expanded metal are not considered to be suitable ties.

Typical example of stone cladding.

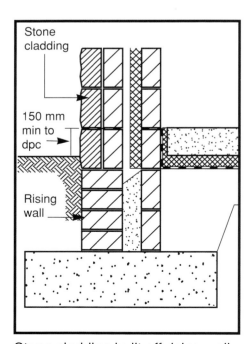

Stone cladding built off rising wall.

Do not fix stone cladding directly to hollow blockwork.

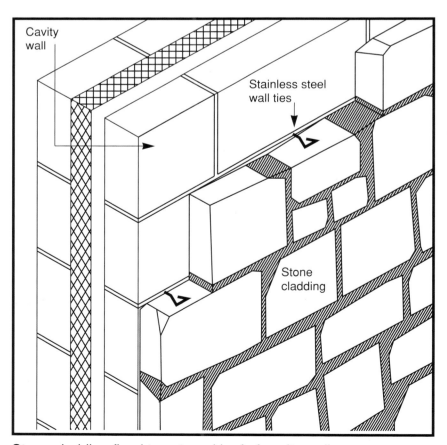

Stone cladding fixed to external leaf of cavity wall.

DAMP-PROOF COURSES

The proper installation of damp proof courses is a key element in cavity wall construction.

The correct use of damp proof courses in cavity wall construction is vital to the satisfactory performance of the building. The following pages highlight some of the principal areas for attention.

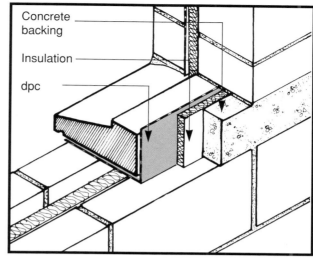

Cill:
Provide dpc to bottom, back, and ends of precast concrete cills.

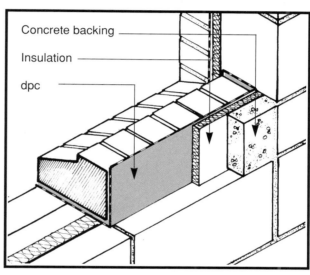

Brick cill:
Provide dpc to bottom, back, and ends of brick cills.

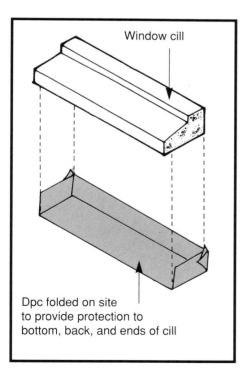

Dpc folded on site to provide protection to bottom, back, and ends of cill

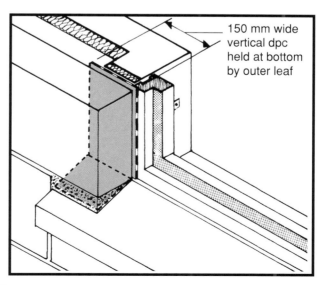

Jamb detail:
Ensure that frames are installed plumb, level, square and fitted to acceptable tolerances. Frame **must** be installed behind the outer leaf.

DAMP-PROOF COURSES
continued

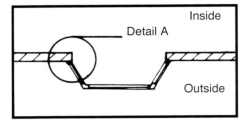

Bay window construction.

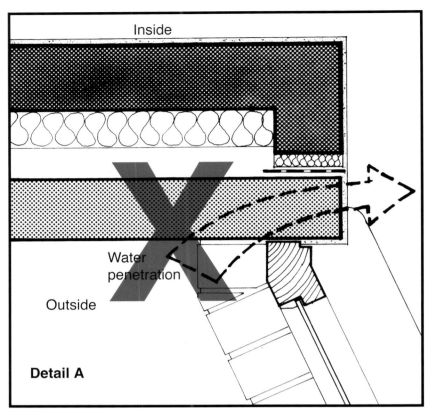

Location of dpc in bay window construction. The above sketch shows an incorrect location of the dpc as it allows moisture from the outside to penetrate to the inside of the building.

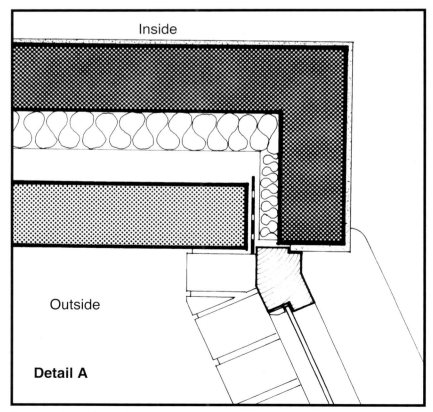

Correct location of dpc where dampness cannot penetrate to inside.

DAMP-PROOF COURSES
continued

The results of the absence of or incorrect installation of damp-proof course and trays.

Pressed metal lintels

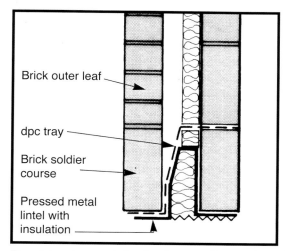

Brick outer leaf

dpc tray

Brick soldier course

Pressed metal lintel with insulation

Provide stepped dpc's above all openings in cavity walls.

Prestressed concrete lintels

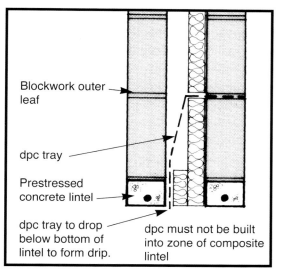

Blockwork outer leaf

dpc tray

Prestressed concrete lintel

dpc tray to drop below bottom of lintel to form drip.

dpc must not be built into zone of composite lintel

Provide stepped dpc's to all openings in cavity walls or proprietary cavity tray dpc's.

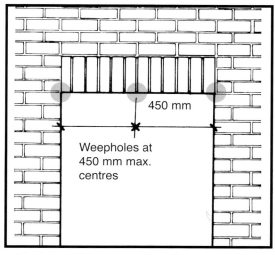

450 mm

Weepholes at 450 mm max. centres

Where outer leaf is unrendered (brick or fairfaced blockwork, for example) provide weepholes at 450 mm max. centres above opening. Avoid any lodging of mortar droppings in dpc tray.

DAMP-PROOF COURSES
continued

Flat roof and mono-pitch roof abutments of the type illustrated can occur at porches, balconies etc., and require careful detailing of damp-proof courses and flashings.

The cover flashings should be built in under the stepped dpc in all cases.

Flashings should be of non-ferrous metal. Where lead is used flashings should be at least code 4 (colour code blue). Individual lengths of flashing in abutments should not exceed 1.5 m with laps not less than 100 mm (150 mm for locations exposed to high wind and rain).

Note: Getting dpc installation right is vital. Otherwise any moisture that drains down the cavity will show as damp on the ceiling of the habitable area of the dwelling.

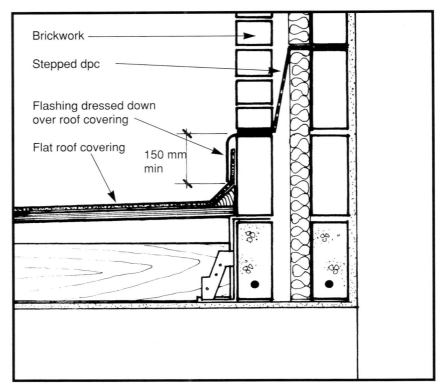

Brickwork

Stepped dpc

Flashing dressed down over roof covering

Flat roof covering

150 mm min

Flat roof abutment.

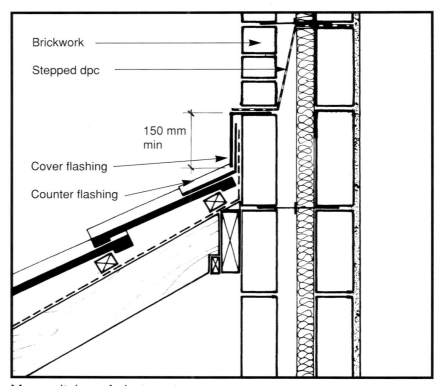

Brickwork

Stepped dpc

150 mm min

Cover flashing

Counter flashing

Mono-pitch roof abutment.

CHANGES IN ROOF LEVEL

Changes in roof level between buildings of different heights or arising from steps and/or staggers in building layout can give rise to an external wall at a higher level becoming an internal wall at lower level. It is vital that adequate damp-proof courses are used in such cases. The use of proprietary cavity trays in such locations is strongly recommended.

The cavity tray is required as flashings and soakers are not sufficient. Below the roof line the external leaf becomes an internal wall, so it is necessary to prevent any moisture that penetrates the outer leaf from running down into the building, as illustrated. This is essential in brickwork outer leaves.

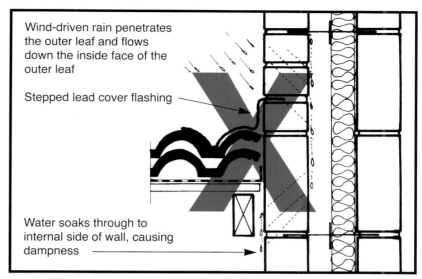

Wind-driven rain penetrates the outer leaf and flows down the inside face of the outer leaf

Stepped lead cover flashing

Water soaks through to internal side of wall, causing dampness

No cavity tray; this construction method is incorrect.

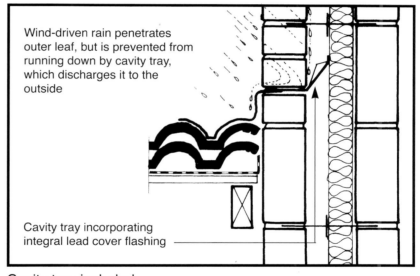

Wind-driven rain penetrates outer leaf, but is prevented from running down by cavity tray, which discharges it to the outside

Cavity tray incorporating integral lead cover flashing

Cavity tray included.

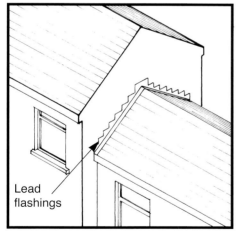

Lead flashings

Location of cavity trays.

Cavity trays with integral lead flashing.

CHANGES IN ROOF LEVEL
continued

Cavity tray range

Catchment tray: This is the first tray to be built into the outer leaf. It should have upstands at both ends and incorporate some sort of discharge unit (integrally designed or by other means) for any water that may run down from higher up. The upstands prevent water from entering the cavity.

Intermediate trays: These trays are handed, with an upstand at one end, and it is recommended that they have 1 weephole per cavity tray to divert water safely to the roof covering. (If this is not possible, provide weepholes at 1 m maximum centres.) Each tray should overhang the one immediately below by at least. 100 mm.

Apex tray: Identical to the catchment tray. However, the shape of the attached lead flashing is different.

When using cavity trays the following points should be considered:

◆ Use purpose-made self weeping trays

◆ Only build trays into the outer leaf

◆ Tray dimensions can vary depending on roof pitch.

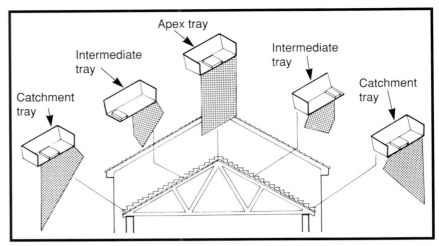

Types of cavity tray.

When built in, each unit discharges individually onto the roof slope. This avoids a build up of water flow towards the bottom of the run.

SETTING OUT

Great care should be exercised when setting out, and the manufacturer's instructions followed carefully.

Note: Where it is necessary to cut bricks to facilitate equal spacing of the trays the cut brick should be covered by the lead flashing from the tray above.

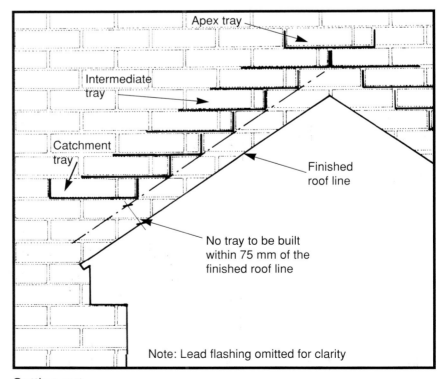

Setting out.

CHANGES IN ROOF LEVEL
continued

Rendered Walls

The same trays that are used for brick walls can also be used for rendered blockwork walls. To facilitate this the region in which the trays are to be inserted must be constructed in concrete brickwork. This ensures proper spacing of the trays.

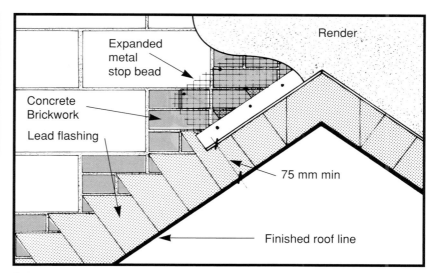

Brickwork trays in rendered walls:
Note the concrete brickwork where the trays are inserted.

Note the patent galvanised/stainless steel render stop bead. Do not nail the render stop bead into the lead flashing.

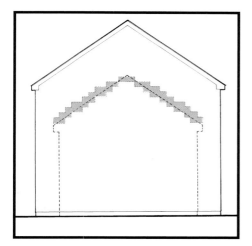

The bricks will be hidden by the flashing and the render; the render can also partly conceal the lead. Rendering should not be applied directly to the flashings, as this restricts movement and may cause splitting of the flashing or detachment of the rendering. Expanded metal mesh should be fixed to the blockwork, extending down to a bellcast stop bead at least 75 mm. off the finished roof line. This provides a key for the render and enables the lead to move. Fixings must not pass through the lead. The render will block the weepholes of the intermediate trays so it is vital to provide a weephole to the catchment tray, to ensure any water collected can drain freely onto the roof surface.

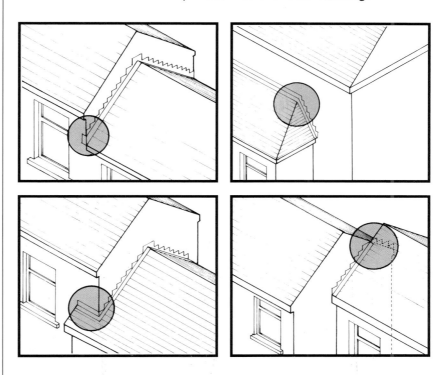

Key junctions: The junctions illustrated above require special care and attention when being constructed. Proprietary purpose made products should be used and the product manufacturer consulted to ensure proper installation.

Note:

It is not normal practice to incorporate cavity trays in rendered blockwork walls. However in areas where there may be exposure to high levels of driving rain the use of such trays should be considered.

Catchment tray incorporating lead flashing.
The first tray to be built in.

Catchment tray built into outer leaf and mortar
bedding provided for the next brick course. Note
the weephole.

No tray to be built within 75 mm
of the finished roofline.

Intermediate tray. This is the next tray to be
built in and should overhang the tray below by
100 mm min. Note the cut bricks which will be
covered by the lead flashing.

Apex tray. Note location in relation to ridge.

The completed cavity tray. The lead flashing is
dressed over the roof finish to ensure proper
weathering.

PROJECTING WINDOWS

The cement render or rough-cast finish is applied to corrosion resistant expanded metal lathing, which is fixed with corrosion resistant nails to the horizontal counter battens. The render should form a key behind the expanded metal. Sarking felt should be provided behind the expanded metal and should be dressed at the window junction as illustrated in details A and B.

As an additional line of defence, it is recommended that a breather membrane is fixed to sheathing material, as illustrated.

A proprietary render stop bead should be provided to bell-cast the render out over the window head.

Two coats of patination oil should be provided to lead flashings to prevent staining of the render finish.

The photo below illustrates cracking of render as a result of incorrect construction. These cracks can allow moisture to penetrate into the fabric of the structure, causing extensive dampness and subsequent deterioration of the timber frame.

Cracking of render.

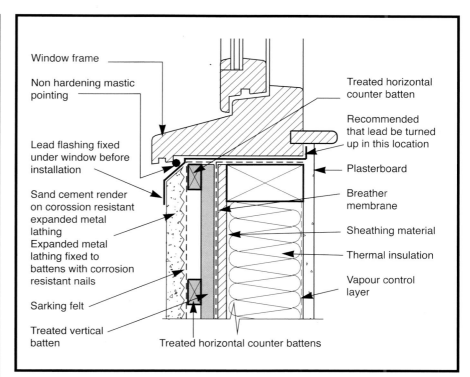

Detail A. Typical first floor window cill.

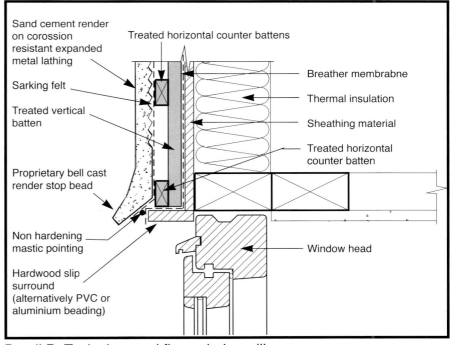

Detail B. Typical ground floor window cill.

INTRODUCTION

The information contained in these pages is for general guidance only. Additional information is contained in BS 5262: 1991: External Rendering. In all cases, the guidance of the building designer should be adhered to.

The properties required of external rendering are that it must be durable, resist moisture penetration, weather uniformly and in addition possess an attractive appearance.

HomeBond recommends the following build-up in external rendering applications: (1) Scud coat (2) Scratch coat (3) Final coat and (4) Finish coat.

Durability:
Durability depends on a number of factors, including proper detailing, the degree of exposure of the building, the proportions of the mix, the bond between the rendering and the wall, and the standard of workmanship.

Resistance to moisture:
Resistance to moisture penetration depends primarily on the detailed design of the building and the mix used for rendering. Water is less likely to penetrate through rendering of an absorbent character than through cracks in the rendering caused by the use of a strong dense mix.

Uniform weathering:
Uniform weathering depends mainly upon the texture of the finished surface, the nature of the mix, and structural details such as cills, copings, eaves etc.

Specification for plain rendering:
Blockwork should be scudded with a mix of 1:1^1/$_2$ to 2, cement : sharp sand, and finished with two coats of render mixed in the proportions 1 cement: ^{1}/$_2$ lime: 4 to 4^1/$_2$ sand. Other acceptable render mixes are described in Table 1: BS 5262: 1991. Where plasticisers are contained in the mix, they must be used in strict accordance with the manufacturer's recommendations. Care should be taken to avoid overdosing or overmixing which may result in excessive air content leading to loss of strength and durability.

Volume batching:
Volume batching should be carried out using properly constructed gauge boxes.

Scud coat:
Rendering should not be applied to blockwork without the provision of an adequate mechanical key to hold the rendering, both during and after its application. Shrinkage of the rendering sets up stress between itself and the background.

The bond must be strong enough to resist separation. The use of a scud coat is recommended as a method of providing a key.

The scud coat should be mixed with just sufficient water to give the consistency of a thick slurry. It is best applied by throwing with a hand scoop to a thickness of approx. 3–5 mm. The surface should be dampened periodically until hardened and then allowed to dry.

First undercoat (scratch coat):
The first undercoat should be combed or scratched after it has been left long enough to set firm, care being taken to leave the scratched marks sufficiently deep to provide a key for the following coat, but not so deep as to penetrate through the undercoat. The first undercoat should be not less than 8 mm nor more than 12 mm thick, except in localised areas when the maximum should be 16 mm.

Second undercoat (final coat):
Before applying the second undercoat the first undercoat should be allowed to harden and dry out sufficiently to provide adequate suction. Where necessary the suction of the first undercoat should be reduced by uniformly wetting. In plain finishes the final coat should be thinner than its undercoat and should be applied with a suitable float e.g. wood. A steel trowel should not be used, and over working should be avoided. Final undercoat between 6 mm and 10 mm thick.

In the case of two undercoat applications, as described above, the nominal overall thickness (excluding texture) should not normally be less than 20 mm.

Successive render coats should be specified as being no stronger than the previous coat or background.

Float ready plaster:

Float ready plaster is a premixed ready to use mortar, specially formulated for external rendering and internal plastering. It is produced in mixing plants and delivered to site in quantities to meet customers' requirements. Its use must be in strict accordance with the manufacturer's instructions.

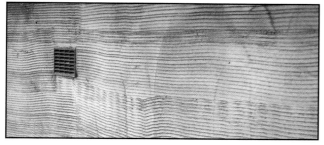

Scratched undercoat to provide a key for the finishing coat.

TYPES OF FINISH

Finishes are the decorative coatings/textures applied on top of the undercoats and as such, cannot be considered as an undercoat.

◆ **General**

In general, textured finishes are less liable to crack and craze than a plain finish, and any cracks that do develop are less likely to be obtrusive. Textured finishes are easier to bring to a uniform appearance; this is an important consideration when the rendering is coloured. Although offering more potential for lodgement of dirt, a rough texture tends to even out any discoloration which makes the dirt less apparent than with smoother finishes. The distribution of the flow of rainwater over a textured surface also reduces the risk of penetration through the rendering.

The finishes for external renderings fall into two broad categories: trowel finishes and thrown finishes.

◆ **Trowel finishes**

i) **Plain finishes**
Plain finishes should be achieved by using a wooden float. This type of finish requires a high standard of workmanship to minimize the risk of crazing and

irregular discoloration. A steel trowel should not be used for finishing an external render.

ii) **Scraped or textured finishes**
Textured finishes should be achieved by working the surface of the freshly applied final coat with a trowel or other hand tool or, alternatively, a textured finish can be applied direct from the nozzle of a rendering machine. Scraped finishes should be obtained by allowing the final coat to harden for several hours and then by scraping it with a suitable tool.

◆ **Thrown finishes**

i) **General**
Under severe conditions of exposure, thrown finishes are generally more satisfactory than trowel applied finishes as regards weather resistance, durability and resistance to cracking and crazing. Roughcast and drydash finishes are normally used on strong backgrounds. Mix properties will need to be modified for use on weaker backgrounds.

ii) **Roughcast**
A roughcast finish should be achieved by throwing on the final coat of rendering as a wet mix and leaving it un-trowelled. The "roughness" is determined by the shape and size of the coarse aggregate in the mix.

iii) **Drydash**
A drydash finish should be produced by throwing crushed rock chippings or pebbles on to a freshly - applied mortar layer (buttercoat) using a small shovel or scoop and leaving it exposed.

TYPES OF FINISH
continued

The risk of crazing should be minimized by:

- The use of properly graded sand, in particular the avoidance of an excessive proportion of very fine material e.g. silty dirty sand

- The use of a mix which is relatively lean in cement

- The avoidance of over working, which causes an excess of laitance to be drawn to the surface

- The avoidance of too rapid drying out of the final coat.

Example of crazing.

Scudding of blockwork

INTRODUCTION

Some buildings may develop cracks in their fabric, usually soon after construction, sometimes later. Much of the cracking is superficial, easily repaired and unlikely to recur to any great extent. Only rarely does cracking indicate serious structural failure. Whether superficial or not, much can be done to minimise cracking by recognising that movement of building materials and components is inevitable and should be allowed for in design.

The following pages address the issue of cracking due to shrinkage and/or expansion, and give guidance on provisions to minimise its occurrence.

There are many reasons for cracking which include settlement of foundations, proximity of trees and spreading of roof structures.

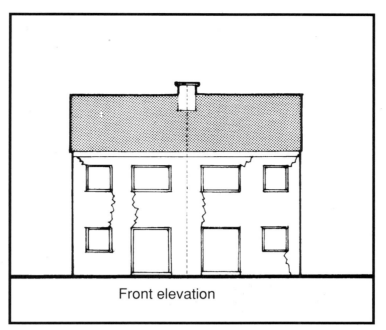

Front elevation

Typical cracking patterns.

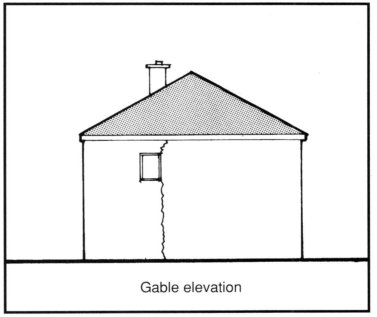

Gable elevation

Cracking patterns commonly encountered in houses built of concrete blocks.

Concrete blocks which are manufactured in the open air have a high moisture content. If not cured properly, they shrink when built into a house, and cracking at the weakest areas such as over and under window openings results. Blocks should not be used until they have been cured adequately. Check that blocks have been stored for at least 4 weeks prior to delivery to minimise the risk of cracking.

Use properly cured blocks to reduce the risk of cracking.

MOVEMENT JOINTS

Long lengths of wall are prone to contraction and expansion with cooling and heating as well as drying. If account is not taken of this, there is a risk of cracking. To reduce this risk, the incorporation of movement joints is necessary. In the case of concrete blockwork, these will be contraction joints, and in the case of clay brickwork, expansion joints.

Codes of practice recommend that spacings of movement joints should be referred to by the building designer. It is not standard practice to incorporate movement joints in semi - detached houses. Based on traditional construction the minimum recommendation of HomeBond is that in terraces of three or more houses, joints should be built in every two houses unless specified more frequently by the designer.

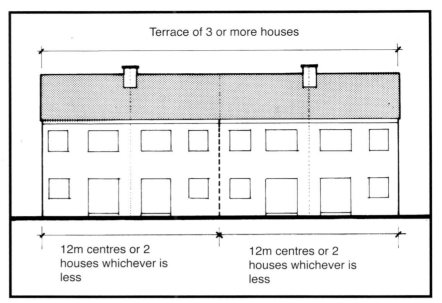

Typical location of movement joints.

Note:
Movement joints are provided to front and back of terraces. Joints are often concealed behind rainwater pipes.

Movement joint in a terrace of houses.

MOVEMENT JOINTS IN CLAY BRICKWORK

Provide ties at 225 mm vertical centres on each side of the joint. The joint should be 18 mm wide minimum.

The joint should be pointed with either one part polysulphide sealant or one part low modulus silicone, on a backing of suitable material which may include flexible closed cell polyethylene, in cord or sheet form.

The joint illustrated on this page (in the outer leaf only) applies to relatively short terraces with brick outer leaves, i.e. terraces of up to four houses. For longer terraces, see page 92.

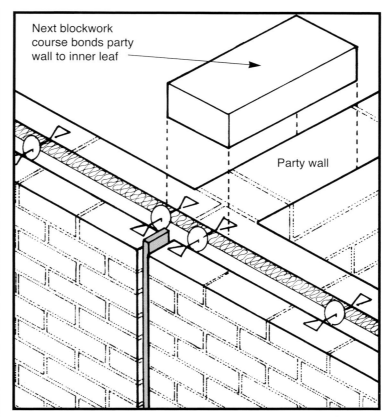

Next blockwork course bonds party wall to inner leaf

Party wall

Typical movement joint in clay brickwork outer leaf.

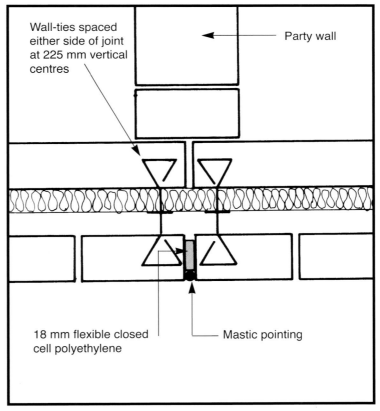

Wall-ties spaced either side of joint at 225 mm vertical centres

Party wall

18 mm flexible closed cell polyethylene

Mastic pointing

Plan view of movement joint in clay brickwork outer leaf.

MOVEMENT JOINTS IN CLAY BRICKWORK
continued

In terraces comprising five or more houses, the provision of control joints to both inner and outer leaves should be considered. This sketch illustrates such a detail, and the sketches on the following pages give further details of such a joint.

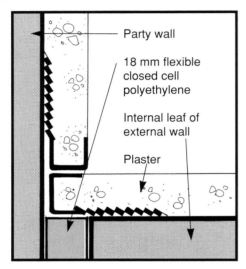

Plan detail of internal corner finished with preformed galvanised or stainless steel plaster stops.

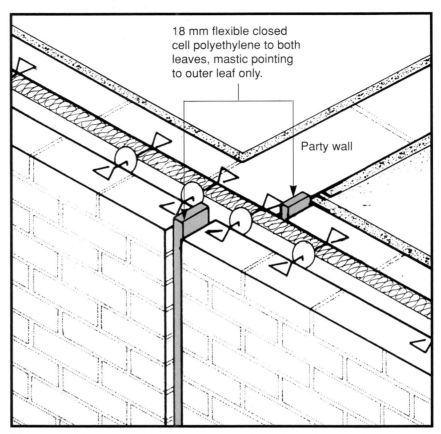

Movement in clay brick outer leaf and blockwork inner leaf. This applies to a terrace of 5 or more houses.

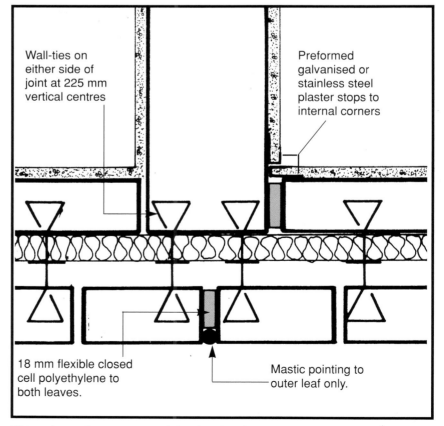

Plan view of movement joint in clay brick outer leaf and blockwork inner leaf.

MOVEMENT JOINTS IN CLAY BRICKWORK
continued

As an alternative to the provision of a joint in the inner leaf of the type shown on the previous page, another approach is to construct the party wall at the movement joint as a cavity wall, with 50 mm cavity.

Note:
Where party wall is of cavity construction, use double triangle wall-ties across cavity of party wall.

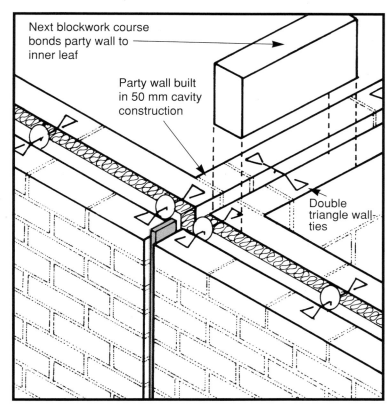

Movement joint to clay brickwork outer leaf.

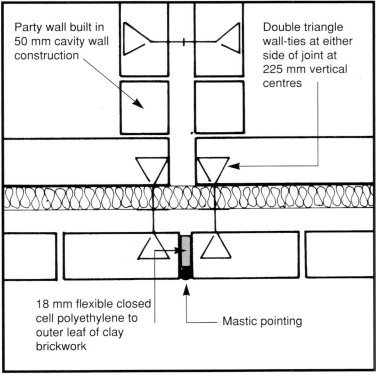

Plan view of movement joint to clay brickwork outer leaf.

MOVEMENT JOINTS IN CLAY BRICKWORK
continued

In the case of stepped blocks / terraces the movement joints are best accommodated in the internal corner of returns as illustrated here.

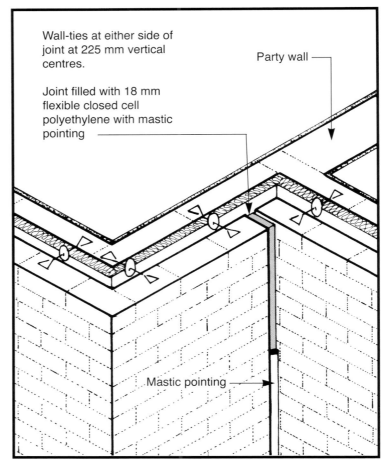

Wall-ties at either side of joint at 225 mm vertical centres.

Joint filled with 18 mm flexible closed cell polyethylene with mastic pointing

Party wall

Mastic pointing

Movement joint in a stepped terrace.

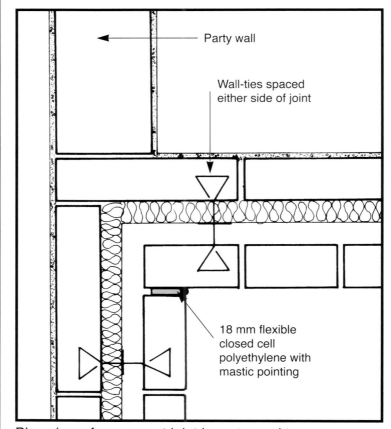

Party wall

Wall-ties spaced either side of joint

18 mm flexible closed cell polyethylene with mastic pointing

Plan view of movement joint in a stepped terrace.

MOVEMENT JOINTS IN CONCRETE BLOCKWORK

As with brickwork, block outer leaves are prone to movement and, in particular, shrinkage. Movement joints are therefore recommended in any block or terrace of three or more houses, where joints in outer leaves should be at 12 m maximum centres, unless specified more frequently by the designer.

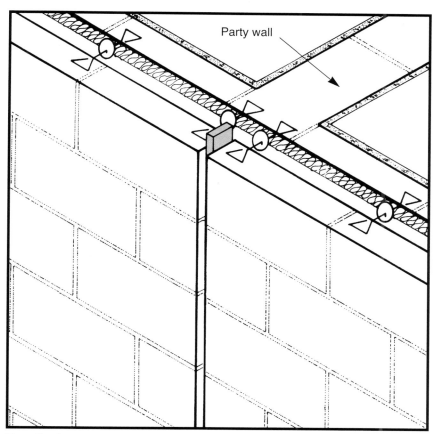

Party wall

Detail of movement joint in blockwork outer leaf.

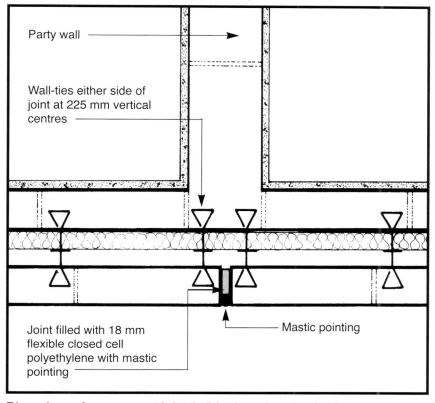

Party wall

Wall-ties either side of joint at 225 mm vertical centres

Joint filled with 18 mm flexible closed cell polyethylene with mastic pointing

Mastic pointing

Plan view of movement joint in blockwork outer leaf.

MOVEMENT JOINTS IN CONCRETE BLOCKWORK
continued

Movement joints are not normally necessary in the inner leaf of a cavity wall, but consideration should be given at the design stage to providing movement joints to the inner leaf of a cavity wall in terraces of five or more houses.

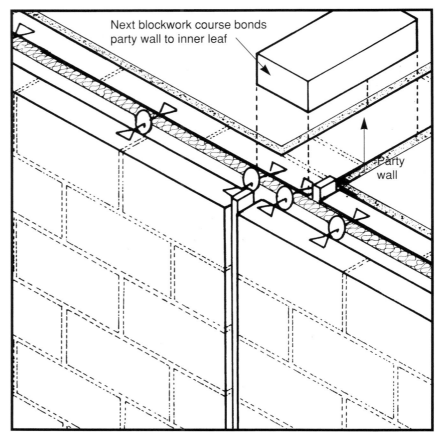

Next blockwork course bonds party wall to inner leaf

Party wall

Detail of movement joint in both leaves of concrete block wall.

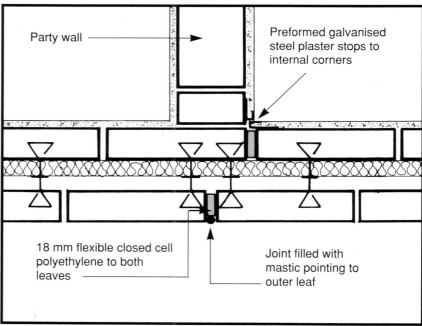

Party wall

Preformed galvanised steel plaster stops to internal corners

18 mm flexible closed cell polyethylene to both leaves

Joint filled with mastic pointing to outer leaf

Plan view of movement joint in both leaves of concrete block wall.

MOVEMENT JOINTS IN CONCRETE BLOCKWORK
continued

Hollow block walls.

As in cavity wall construction where a terrace contains three or more houses, movement joints should be provided at maximum 12 m centres unless specified more frequently by the designer.

The sketch opposite suggests a method of incorporating a movement joint into hollow block wall construction.

Where party wall is of cavity construction, use double triangle wall-ties across cavity of party wall.

Use of hollow blocks:
It should be noted that exposure conditions dictate where hollow blocks may be used in house construction. Advice on this is contained in IS 325: Code of practice for the use of masonry. Part 2: 1995 Masonry construction.

HOMEBOND RULE

NEVER USE LONGITUDINAL TYPE HOLLOW BLOCKS IN AN EXTERNAL WALL

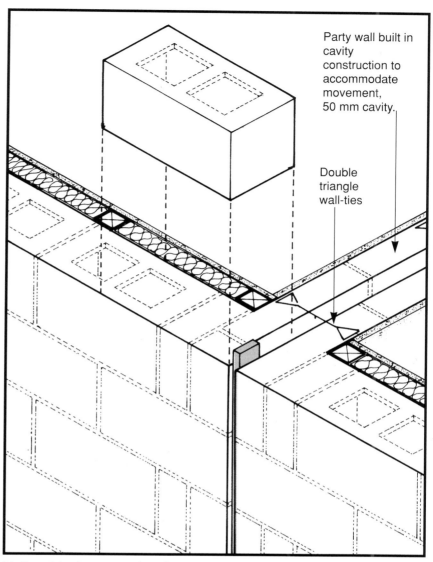

Party wall built in cavity construction to accommodate movement, 50 mm cavity.

Double triangle wall-ties

Hollow block external wall - movement joint.

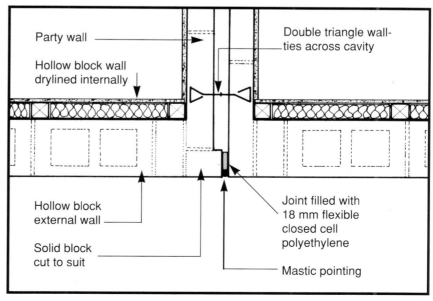

Party wall

Hollow block wall drylined internally

Double triangle wall-ties across cavity

Hollow block external wall

Solid block cut to suit

Joint filled with 18 mm flexible closed cell polyethylene

Mastic pointing

Plan view of movement joint in hollow block wall.

MOVEMENT JOINTS IN CONCRETE BLOCKWORK
continued

Hollow block walls

As an alternative to the movement joint shown on the previous page for hollow block walls, the type of joint illustrated on these pages can also be used in terraces containing three or more houses.

The sketches on this and the following page illustrate the sequence of construction of such a joint, and emphasise that wall-ties be provided at every horizontal bed joint to securely tie the party wall to the external wall.

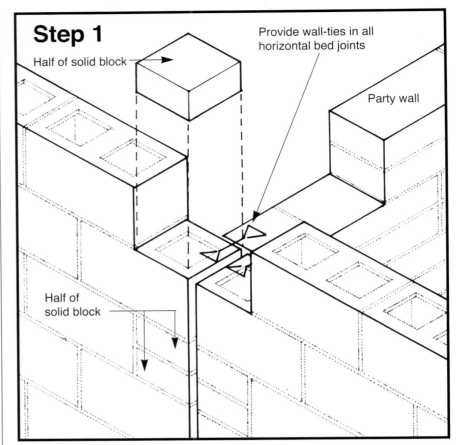

Sequence of construction - hollow block external wall movement joint.

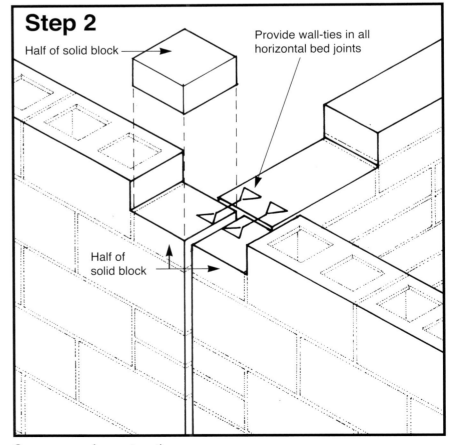

Sequence of construction.

MOVEMENT JOINTS IN CONCRETE BLOCKWORK
continued

Hollow block walls

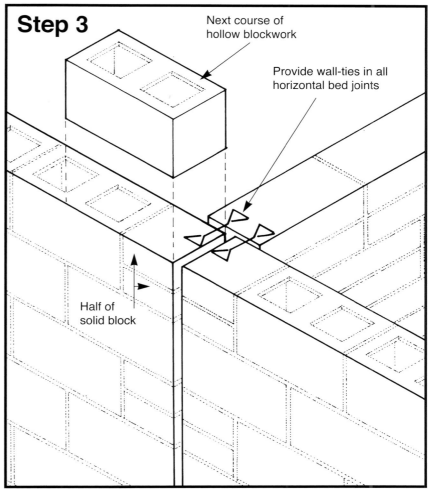

Step 3

Next course of hollow blockwork

Provide wall-ties in all horizontal bed joints

Half of solid block

Sequence of construction.

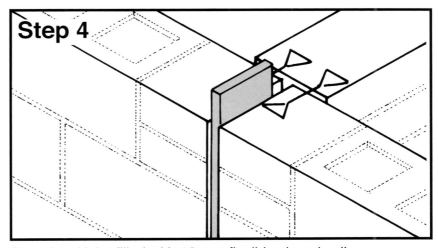

Step 4

Completed joint filled with 18 mm flexible closed cell polyethylene with mastic pointing.

PREFORMED MOVEMENT JOINT BEADS

For use with externally rendered or plastered walls.

The bead consists of two lengths of galvanised or stainless steel plaster stop bead jointed by a PVC extrusion which allows movement across the joint.

The beads are fixed by dabs or by corrosion resistant nails driven through the holes provided to the external surface of the wall across the joint. The face of the PVC extrusion is fitted with a protective tape which is removed after plastering. Ensure that the movement joint bead used is suitable for external use.

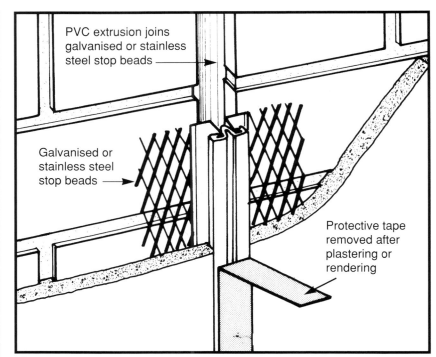

PVC extrusion joins galvanised or stainless steel stop beads

Galvanised or stainless steel stop beads

Protective tape removed after plastering or rendering

Movement joint bead.

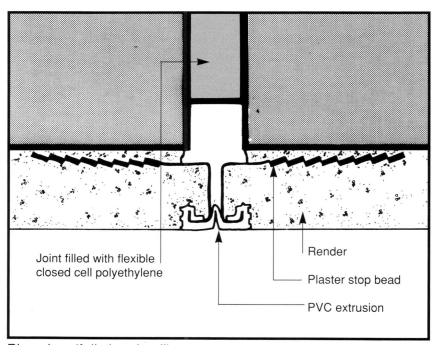

Joint filled with flexible closed cell polyethylene

Render

Plaster stop bead

PVC extrusion

Plan view (full size detail).

BED JOINT REINFORCEMENT

Cracking may be controlled by the use of patent reinforcement in horizontal joints in areas of high stress such as above and below openings. The reinforcement should be long enough, at least 600 mm either side of ope, to distribute the high stress to areas of low stress. The reinforcement used in an external wall should be corrosion resistant, such as stainless steel, and should have at least 20 mm cover from the outer wall face.

Wall panel provisions.

The use of movement joints, as recommended in the preceding pages, will not necessarily eliminate completely the occurrence of shrinkage cracking that extends diagonally from the corner of openings in blockwork walls. There is an increased risk of cracking if the length of a blockwork panel exceeds twice the height, and the shape is often more critical than size.

For example, a large square gable may remain free of cracks while a low panel below a long window may crack.

In any bungalow built of blocks the incorporation of movement joints is recommended wherever the length of uninterrupted wall exceeds twice the height.

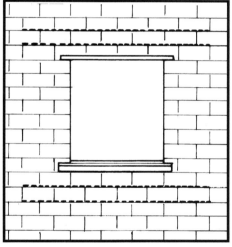

Typical bed joint reinforcement at openings (shown dotted).

Typical example of shrinkage cracking under window cill.

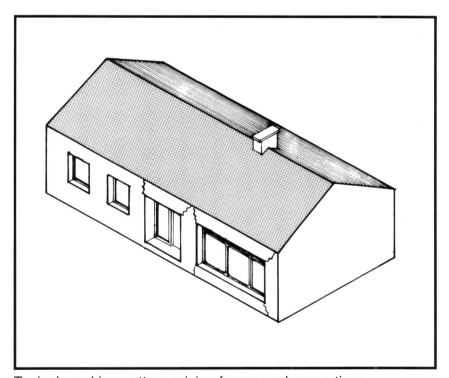

Typical cracking pattern arising from panel proportions.

CORBELLING OF BRICKWORK AND BLOCKWORK

When it is proposed to provide a corbel in wall construction, the extent of the overhang should not exceed $\frac{1}{3}$ of the original wall thickness - or in the case of cavity wall construction $\frac{1}{3}$ of the thickness of the leaf containing the corbel, as illustrated, unless the corbel detail is designed to take account of the specific circumstances. Design guidance on this matter is given in clause 27.8, BS 5628: Pt. 3: 1985 – Code of practice for use of Masonry.

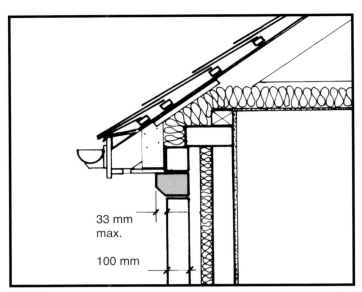

33 mm max.

100 mm

Corbel at eaves, maximum projection should be 33 mm.

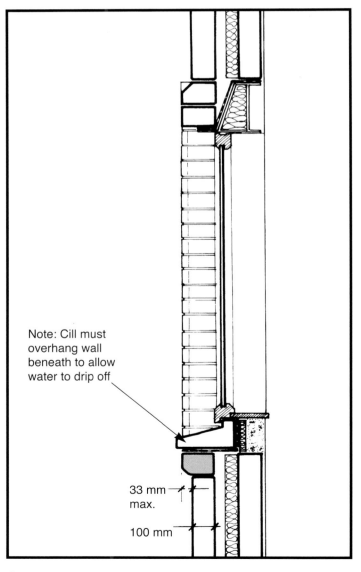

Note: Cill must overhang wall beneath to allow water to drip off

33 mm max.

100 mm

Corbel above and below window ope — maximum projection should be 33 mm.

PARTY WALL CONSTRUCTION

Attention to detail is important in this area to ensure avoidance of

1. Excessive sound transmission;
2. The risk of fire spread.

Building Regulations Technical Guidance Document E for sound insulation states that joists at right angles to a party wall should be fixed with single joist hangers.

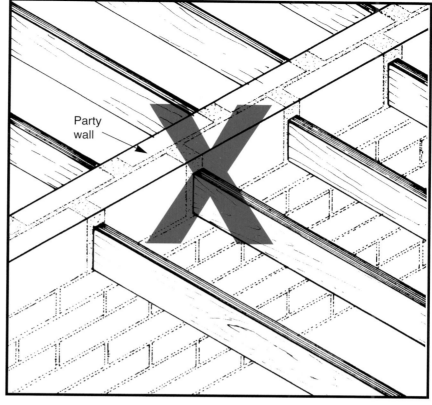

DO NOT BUILD JOISTS INTO PARTY WALL

Where possible, joists should span from front to back of house. Where this is not possible, and joists must span on to the party wall, use single joist hangers. All joints to be filled to avoid excessive noise transmission and risk of fire spread.

Note:

◆   Ensure hangers are correct size

◆   Ensure hangers are tight against blockwork

◆   Ensure joists are securely nailed into hangers.

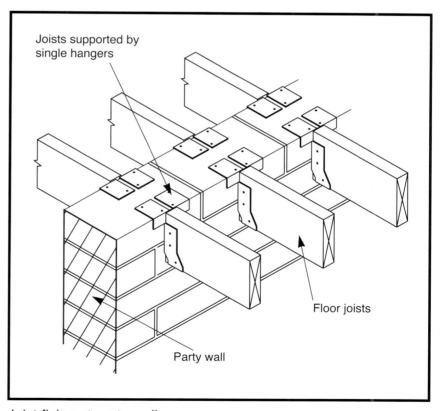

Joist fixing at party wall.

PARTY WALL CONSTRUCTION
continued

In forming the top of party wall at its junction with the roof, ensure that the party wall is completed along the line of the slope of the roof – this is to reduce the risk of fire spread.

The junction between the party wall and the roof of a dwelling should be capable of restricting fire spread between dwellings.

The party wall should be taken up to meet the underside of the roof covering and fire stopped where necessary along the wall/roof junction.

Typical details in common use are illustrated in Technical Guidance Document B of the Building Regulations and opposite.

Technical Guidance Document B also allows any other system which has been shown by test to be equally effective in restricting the spread of fire at a party wall/roof junction.

Cut blocks and pack with mortar raked off smooth to follow line of roof. Leave 25 mm approx. gap between top of mortar and top of rafter to allow for roof settlement. This gap will be packed with compressible material (e.g. mineral fibre quilt) at the roofing stage.

Note: Ensure that there are no holes or opes in party wall.

Typical party wall fire stopping detail.

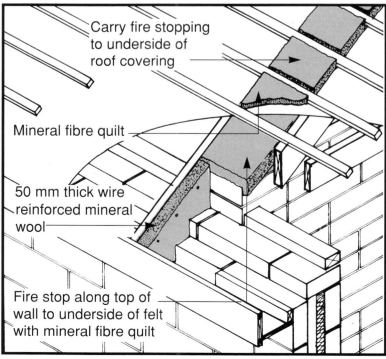

Carry fire stopping to underside of roof covering

Mineral fibre quilt

50 mm thick wire reinforced mineral wool

Fire stop along top of wall to underside of felt with mineral fibre quilt

Typical party wall fire stopping detail.

INTRODUCTION

Mortar quality is an important consideration in the design and construction of brickwork and blockwork. A good mortar is easy to work with, not likely to cause efflorescence in brickwork and provides the required strength necessary to support the brickwork or blockwork. The type of mortar used may also have an effect on shrinkage/expansion cracking. Weak mortars will allow a very slight change in dimensions in each joint, where strong mortar will hold the units together and possibly eventually result in a large crack in one location.

Mortar is made from an aggregate, binder and water. The aggregate is sand with suitable grain consistency and the binder is usually a mixture of lime and cement. Other ingredients can be added such as plasticiser in place of lime or colouring agents to achieve the required colour in the case of brickwork. Plasticising agents are often used instead of lime to give improved workability. These additives entrain small air bubbles which act as a lubricant. The air bubbles serve to increase the volume of the binder paste, filling the voids in the sand and this improves the working qualities. Several types of plasticiser are available and should only be used in accordance with manufacturer's instructions.

A good mortar should cling to the trowel, spread easily and not stiffen too quickly. The basic rule for mortars is: cement provides strength, lime or plasticisers improve workability.

Generally about one volume of binder is needed for three volumes of sand to give a workable mix, but cement mortar of this kind is stronger than necessary for most uses. For weaker mortars, lime or plasticisers are needed to maintain workability.

TYPES OF MORTAR

Cement: sand mortar

Adequate strength in the fully hardened mortar, combined with a rapid development of strength in the early stages, is most conveniently attained by the use of Portland cement, but it is not practicable to adjust the strength simply by varying the ratio of cement to sand, because lean mixes of cement and sand are harsh and unworkable.

Cement: lime: sand mortar

Mortars made with appropriate proportions of Portland cement (including sulphate-resisting Portland cement) and lime, take advantage of the useful properties of each. Cement: lime: sand mortar is designed on the principle that part of the cement is replaced by an equal volume of lime so that the binder-paste still fills the voids in the sand. In this way good working qualities, water retention, adhesion and early strength can be secured without the mature strength being too high. The lime used should be non-hydraulic (high calcium or magnesian) or semi-hydraulic.

Air-entrained (plasticised) mortar

Mortar plasticisers which entrain air in the mix provide an alternative to lime for imparting good working qualities to lean cement: sand mixes. In effect, the air bubbles serve to increase the volume of the binder paste, filling the voids in the sand. This correspondingly improves the working qualities.

Ready-to-use retarded cement: lime: sand mortar and cement: sand mortar

When ready-to-use retarded cement: lime: sand mortar and cement: sand mortar are used, care should be taken to follow the manufacturer's instructions for their use.

Mortar mix

The designer should select the mortar designation with reference to the structural requirements and the degree of exposure, taking into account the type of masonry unit, the type of construction, the position in the building and the possibility of early exposure to frost.

The mortar mixes indicated on the following page are suggested to provide the most suitable mortar that will be readily workable to allow the block/brick layer to produce satisfactory work at an economic rate, to be sufficiently durable and to be able to assist in accommodating strains arising from minor movements within the wall.

Further information is available in:

I.S. 325 Part 1: 1986: Structural use of Unreinforced Masonry

I.S. 406: 1987: Masonry Mortars.

Mortar mixes using ordinary Portland cement
or sulphate resisting cements when required.

Location	Recommended Cement : lime : sand mix	Recommended Cement : sand mix with plasticiser
General wall area above dpc . Brickwork and fairfaced blockwork only in areas of very severe exposure.	1 : 1/2 : 4 to 4 1/2	1 : 3 or 4
General wall area above dpc. Brickwork and blockwork: other exposure categories.	1 : 1 : 5 or 6	1 : 5 or 6
Below dpc level, and in chimney stacks, cappings, copings, cills and free standing walls.	1 : 1/2 : 4 to 4 1/2*	1 : 3 or 4

* Also recommended in areas of high water run-off in brickwork and fairfaced blockwork, e.g., under
large expanses of glazed area.

INTRODUCTION

Fireplaces and chimneys are a standard item in house construction. Fireplaces can be constructed to accommodate an open fire or closed appliance, of which there is a variety in common use. For a fireplace and chimney to function correctly, basic good building practice needs to be executed. The following pages set out these basics – careful adoption of these practices will avoid the risk of costly remedial measures.

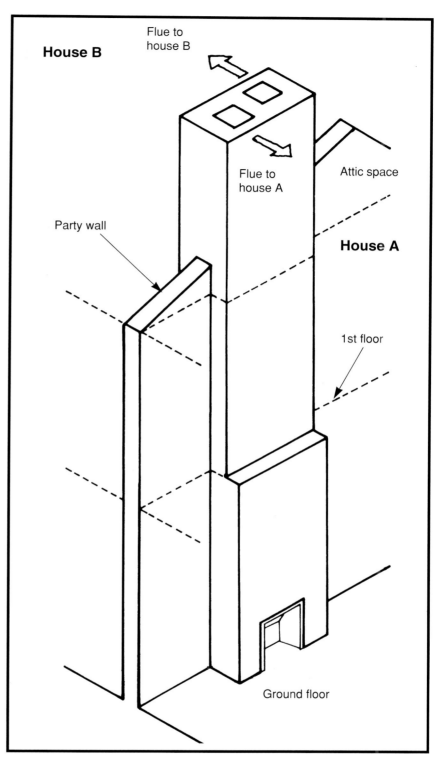

Typical back to back chimney arrangement from ground floor through to roof level.

FIREPLACE RECESSES

Party wall

Where fireplaces are on a party wall, the thickness of the wall between the fireplaces must be at least 200 mm.

Note:

Where two fireplaces occur within the same house, the thickness of the dividing wall between the two fireplaces and flues throughout their height must be at least 100 mm.

Where pipes pass from a boiler through opes in blockwork, the opes should be fully sealed to prevent smoke escape into the pipe duct as this is frequently a cause of smoke ingress to first floor rooms.

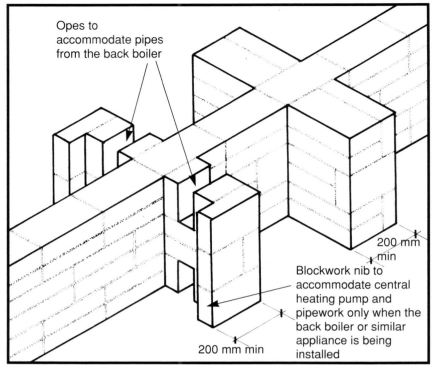

Fireplace recess in party wall (back to back).

Note: Blockwork to chimney stacks must be carried up with all other blockwork. Subsequent "toothing in" is not permitted.

Fireplaces on external walls

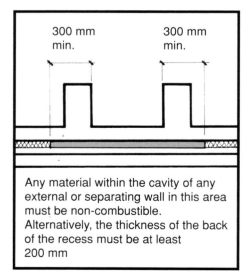

Any material within the cavity of any external or separating wall in this area must be non-combustible.
Alternatively, the thickness of the back of the recess must be at least 200 mm

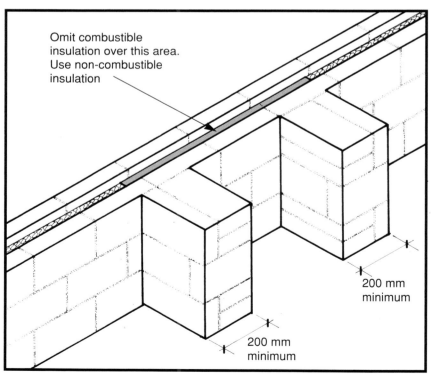

Fireplace recess on external wall.
Maintain cavity where fire place backs on to external wall.

DIMENSIONS OF FIREPLACE OPENINGS

Note: Where a fireplace opening is too high the chimney will not draw properly. A badly formed throating will cause draught problems.

Flue liners

Flue liner installation:
Good practice.

1. Use precast flue gatherers.
2. Use spigot and socket flue liners with socket upwards, or rebated flue liner with socket upwards. Liners should be jointed with fire resistant mortar all round.
3. Pack flue liners as each liner is built in, with:

Cement	Lime	Sand mix.
1	1	12

   or insulating concrete
4. Mix to be wetted with water. Do not use dry fill. Flue liners must not touch the surrounding blockwork.
5. 194 mm minimum flue diameter (or square section of equivalent area).

DO NOT PACK AROUND FLUE LINERS WITH DRY SAND. USE WETTED CEMENT : LIME : SAND MIX.

The result of packing the flue liner with unsuitable material.

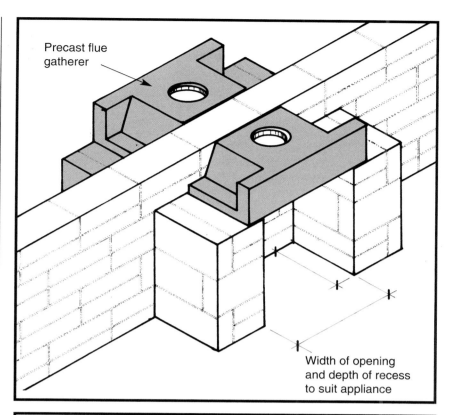

Precast flue gatherer

Width of opening and depth of recess to suit appliance

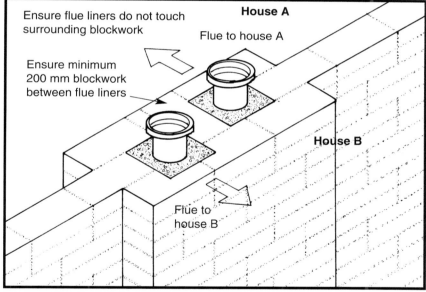

Ensure flue liners do not touch surrounding blockwork

House A

Flue to house A

Ensure minimum 200 mm blockwork between flue liners

House B

Flue to house B

View of chimney breast at first floor level. Install flue liners as work progresses. Pack around flue liners as each is built in.

Brick/block chimneys should be lined with liners of an appropriate class in accordance with the requirements of I.S. EN 1457: 1999 Chimneys - Clay/Ceramic Flue Liners - Requirements and Test Methods. Class A1 N1 would be the most appropriate class.

I.S. EN 1457: 1999 requires that all flue liners be marked with:
◆ EN 1457
◆ Manufacturer's identification and date of manufacture; and
◆ Class number(s)

FIREPLACE CONSTRUCTION

For a chimney to draw properly the formation from the top of the fireplace into the flue (the throat) should be properly formed. It is strongly recommended that a pre-formed flue-gathering lintel be used for this purpose to ensure a satisfactory throat arrangement.

Fireplace dimensions should be controlled to avoid the risk of smoking in the finished construction. The height of the fireplace opening measured vertically from the top of the grate to the underside of the flue gathering lintel should not be greater than 550 mm.

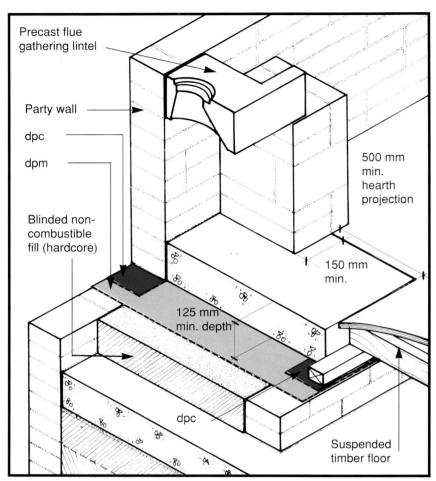

Precast flue gathering lintel

Party wall

dpc

dpm

Blinded non-combustible fill (hardcore)

500 mm min. hearth projection

150 mm min.

125 mm min. depth

dpc

Suspended timber floor

Cut-away view of a typical fireplace and suspended timber floor.

The result of packing the flue liner with unsuitable material.

INSTALLATION OF COOKERS

If an oil fired or solid fuel cooker is installed, the installation should be in accordance with the manufacturer's instructions. In particular the connection to the chimney and the chimney construction must be as required by the manufacturer, so that the cooker has sufficient draw and the risk of condensation in the flue is reduced.

Oil fired cookers

In the case of an oil fired cooker, particular attention must be given to the manufacturer's instructions with respect to connection to a standard 200 mm flue, as it may be required to line the existing flue with a 150 mm rigid or flexible stainless steel flue liner in order to reduce condensation in the flue. Check with the manufacturer of the cooker.

Solid fuel cookers

In the case of solid fuel cookers the correct construction and location of the soot box is essential. Particular attention must be paid to the type of fuel used in order to avoid condensation in the flue, as this could result in a liquid tarry substance running down the chimney. If wood or turf with a high moisture content is used, a great deal of moisture is emitted into the flue and the risk of condensation is greatly increased.

It should be noted that if the appliance is run for extended periods at a low heat, especially when burning wood or peat, the flue can cool down to such an extent that vapour in the flue gases may condense. This will make the inside of the flue damp so that the soot sticks to the flue and the tarry mixture formed may drip down into the appliance. It is always best to run at a high rate of heat whenever possible. In the summer, it is better to run the appliance at a high rate to heat the water, and let the fire die and re-light, rather than running a low fire continuously.

Gas appliances

Where gas appliances are used they must be installed by appropriately qualified personnel and in accordance with manufacturer's instructions.

Ventilation Note

The ventilation requirements for rooms are specified in Technical Guidance Document F of the Building Regulations and in Appendix C of this publication, and must be adhered to in the construction of dwellings. HomeBond also advise that if new windows, whether single or double glazed, are installed in existing houses, it is vital that there is sufficient ventilation for the room, particularly those with fireplaces, to ensure that the fire, whether an open or closed appliance, has sufficient air to draw and that there will not be a build up of the products of combustion which could be a health hazard.

TRIMMING AT FIRST FLOOR LEVEL

Floor joists running parallel or perpendicular to a chimney stack must be trimmed around the stack. Combustible materials **(excluding floorboards, skirting, dado or picture rail, mantleshelf or architrave)** should be separated from a brick or blockwork chimney by at least:

a) 200 mm from a flue, or
b) 40 mm from the outer surface of a brick or blockwork chimney or fireplace recess if blockwork or brickwork is 100 mm. Metal fixings in contact with combustible materials should be at least 50 mm from a flue.

If using a pair of joists to form trimming / trimmer joists, they should be nailed at 450 mm centres 20 mm from top and bottom edges of the joist. Alternatively, they can be bolted on the centreline at approx. 1 m centres. If using this method it is difficult to obtain joist hangers to accommodate the off-standard width of two joists together.

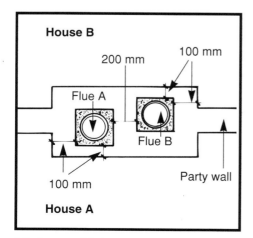

Minimum thickness for back to back chimneys.

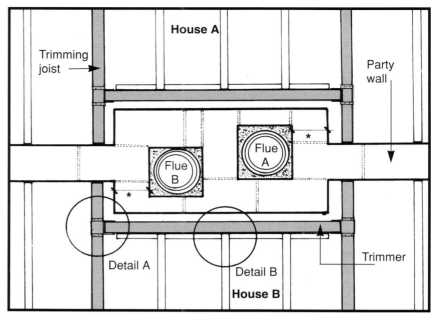

Joists perpendicular to chimney stack.

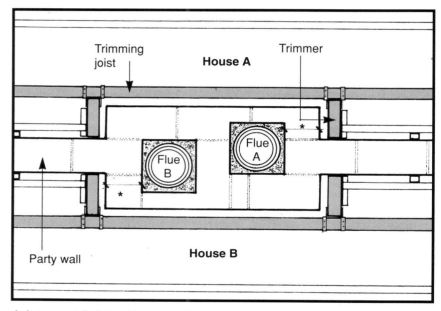

Joists parallel to chimney stack.

Note:

1. Joists are not built into the party wall - they are supported on single steel hangers. See page 103.

2. The chimney breast dimensions illustrated on this page should be maintained up to the level of the roof covering. Above that, the 200 mm dimension between flues and around flues can reduce to 100 mm, subject to structural stability.

3. * This dimension is illustrated as 200 mm for the purpose of facilitating blockwork coursing and setting out. However it may actually be reduced to 100 mm.

BRICK CHIMNEY STACKS

The discharge of any water collected on the tray is achieved by means of weepholes, located at the front of the stack. Weepholes may be formed by leaving open perpend joints in the brickwork. Alternatively, proprietary plastic weephole vents can be used, inserted in the perpends as the brickwork is constructed. By keeping the drainage channels and weepholes free from mortar, water collected will be allowed to drain freely over the lead flashing. If the weepholes are blocked and the drainage channel filled with mortar, water can to build up on the tray and discharge into the attic space.

Weepholes provided in brick joints. Perpends left open.

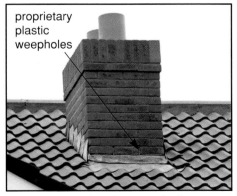

Proprietary plastic weepholes installed in brick joints.

Dampness, the result of an inadequately installed dpc tray in a brickwork chimney stack in a dormer roof.

In dormer roof construction, where the back of the tray is in the habitable area, an additional upstand is required in this location in order to prevent any water ingress into the room. Alternatively two dpc trays can be installed, as illustrated on the previous page.

AVOIDING DEFECTIVE AND SMOKING CHIMNEYS

The table on this and the following page highlights the ten most common faults in fireplace and chimney construction and the steps that should be taken to avoid them. Repairs to chimneys are costly.

See Appendix C for recommended levels of ventilation for rooms in dwellings. Technical Guidance Document F of the Building Regulations advises that all habitable rooms must have background ventilation openings of not less than 6500 mm² in addition to some form of rapid ventilation. This includes rooms with a fireplace.

Defect	Causes	Prevention
1 Blockages	Mis-aligned flue lintels and liners. Mortar joints protruding into flue. Debris in flue.	Care in workmanship and supervision. Proper packing of flue liners as work proceeds. Clean and test flue thoroughly on completion of construction.
2 Air starvation	House too well sealed. Note: Many builders fit underfloor air feed pipes to sunken ash box type fires to avoid air starvation problems.	Ensure adequate air supply. If there is insufficient air supply, air speed through the flue will be inadequate for proper draught. If opening a door or window on a calm day stops the fireplace smoking, this usually indicates air starvation. Form throat properly – the throat should be approximately 300 mm wide by 100 mm. These are the smallest dimensions that will allow a chimney brush to pass through.
3 Badly-formed throat	Poor workmanship / supervision.	Care in workmanship / supervision. Use a precast flue-gathering lintel to ensure smooth flow to the flue.
4 Steady downdraught	Top of chimney too low, e.g. not above ridge. Chimney too short (e.g. in bungalow).	Carry chimney above ridge level in all cases. Ensure that stack extends at least 4.5m above the top of the fireplace.
5 Intermittent downdraught	Chimney near higher building or trees. Chimney located on a sheltered hillside or in a valley.	Where practical, build chimney to a level where down draught is overcome. Where this is not practical, incorporate a draught-inducing cowl into the chimney construction (See illustrations on Page 122).

**AVOIDING DEFECTIVE
AND SMOKING CHIMNEYS**
continued

Defects	Causes	Prevention
6 Fireplace opening too high	Opening such that top is more than 550 mm above level of grate.	Care in setting-out opening. Care in workmanship and supervision. Use standard sizes for fire openings.
7 Badly-built offset	Offset too long, too shallow or too close to throat.	Care in workmanship and supervision. Angle of offset should be no shallower than 52.5° to the horizontal. The straighter the chimney, the better the draw.
8 Wrong size flue	Too big – chimney does not warm up. Too small – not permitted due to fire risk.	Use standard flue liners of 200 mm nominal internal diameter for open fires.
9 Air leaks	Open joints in blockwork. Flue liners not properly packed. Boiler pipes not sealed where they leave chimney.	Seal joints in flue liners with fire resistant mortar. Pack flue liners fully with weak wetted mortar mix having cement content. Fill all joints in blockwork to chimney. Apply coat of sand / cement render to chimney blockwork at ground floor level and at first floor level. Pay particular attention at ceiling/floor joist level to ensure all joints are adequately sealed. Seal thoroughly primary and secondary circuit pipes from back boilers and room heaters where they pass through the side of the chimney. It is a fallacy that a chimney with bends draws better than a straight flue. The straighter the chimney is, the better it draws. Never fix dry lining to a chimney breast unless the breast has been first rendered in sand/cement. An unrendered breast can allow smoke to leak from the fire and enter habitable areas. Any drylining fixed to a chimney breast must be fully sealed at mantel and ceiling level in the room containing the fireplace.
10 Unsuitable chimney pot	Pot smaller than flue or tapering to a diameter less than of the flue liner.	Use a standard flue liner as the flue terminal, or alternatively use a terminal having a minimum diameter at least equal to that of the flue liner.

AVOIDING DEFECTIVE AND SMOKING CHIMNEYS
continued

As stated in item (5) of the preceding table, the incorporation of a chimney cowl may help in overcoming downdraught in chimneys. The sketches on this page illustrate typical purpose made cowls which can be used in such circumstances. Proper design and construction of the chimney should overcome the need to have recourse to such devices in the majority of cases.

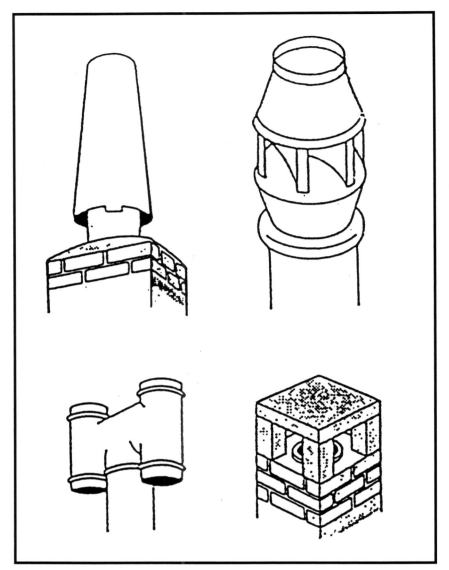

Typical draught-inducing cowls.

IMPORTANT NOTE

At the time of publication of this document, IS 444: 1998: The use of structural timber in buildings, had just superseded SR 11: Structural timber for domestic construction. SR 11 has been withdrawn and should no longer be used.
To aid the transition between these documents this publication reproduces extracts from both. See Appendix J.

INTRODUCTION

IS 444: 1998: The use of Structural Timber in Buildings is the standard that must be used for structural timber applications.

The standard provides span tables for various joist sizes across a range of strength classifications and spacings. Joist size is referred to as "target size", which is the desired size at 20% moisture content.

The average actual thickness and width of timber members should not be less than the target size, making allowance for changes in size due to changes in moisture content.

The moisture content at the time of construction should not normally exceed 20% with no value exceeding 24%.

For the design of timber outside the scope of IS 444 an engineer should be engaged. The engineer appointed must be qualified by examination, be in private practice and possess professional indemnity insurance.

IS 444 is available from: National Standards Authority of Ireland, Glasnevin, Dublin 9.

The following pages 123 to 126 explain IS 444, give worked examples and reproduce some of the tables.

STRENGTH CLASSIFICATION

IS 444 divides timber in ascending order of strength into six strength classes (C14, C16, C18, C22, C24, C27) depending on the species and grade of timber.

The common species and grades of Irish and imported timber that fall into these strength classes are set out below.

Combinations of species and visual strength grades.

Softwood Species	Strength classes				
	C14	C16	C18	C22	C24
Irish Timber:					
Sitka Spruce	GS		SS		
Norway Spruce	GS		SS		
Lodgepole Pine	GS		SS		
Douglas Fir	GS		SS		
Larch		GS		SS	
Scots Pine		GS		SS	
Imported Timber:					
European Whitewood		GS			SS
European Redwood		GS			SS
Douglas Fir-Larch*		GS			SS
Spruce-Pine-Fir*		GS			SS
Hem-Fir*		GS			SS

*Source, Canada or USA

Note: NSAI/Enterprise Ireland should be contacted for the designation of other species and visual grades into an appropriate strength class. IS/EN 1912 lists visual strength grades, species and sources of timber and strength class from IS/EN 338 into which they are assigned.
All structural timber may be machine graded to the strength classes listed above, and in addition to strength class C27 as defined in table 2 of IS444.

TIMBER STRENGTH GRADES

The strength grade abbreviations in the above table are as follows:

GS - general structural grade, visually graded.
SS - special structural grade, visually graded.

Visual grading in accordance with IS127.
Mechanical grading in accordance with IS/EN 519.

TIMBER IDENTIFICATION MARKS

In order to comply with the requirements of IS 444, timber must be marked with the following information which will identify:

◆ Appropriate strength class and/or species grade

◆ Design standard (IS 444).

The grading and marking of timber by individual companies is subject to the supervisory control of The Timber Quality Bureau of Ireland, Enterprise Ireland, Glasnevin, Dublin 9.

Outlined opposite are typical examples of the visual and maching strength grading stamps which must occur on timber complying with the requirements of IS 444. Other combinations of species, grade and strength class are possible.

Species & Source Codes

Softwood Species	Source	Code
Species group 1 Sitka/Norway Spruce Lodgepole Pine Douglas Fir	Ireland	WE[1]/SGI
Species group 2 Larch Scots Pine	Ireland	WE[1]/SG2
Sitka/Norway Spruce Douglas Fir	UK UK	B[2]/S B[2]/DF
Whitewood Redwood Whitewood & Redwood combined	NNE Europe[3] NNE Europe[3] NNE Europe[3]	EW ER EW/ER
Douglas Fir-Larch Spruce-Pine-Fir Hemlock Fir	North America North America North America	NA/DFL NA/SPF NA/HF

1 WE = Western Europe. This also includes timber grown in Britain.
2 B = British. A designation used in BS4978 which includes timber grown in Ireland.
3 Northern and North Eastern Europe, which includes the Scandinavian countries and Russia.

Visual Strength Grading Stamps

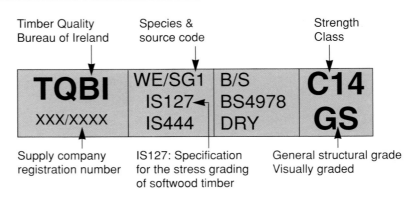

Timber Quality Bureau of Ireland

Species & source code

Strength Class

| TQBI XXX/XXXX | WE/SG1 IS127 IS444 | B/S BS4978 DRY | C14 GS |

Supply company registration number

IS127: Specification for the stress grading of softwood timber

General structural grade Visually graded

SG1 = Sitka Spruce, Norway Spruce, Douglas Fir, Lodgepole Pine

| TQBI XXX/XXXX | WE/SG1 IS127 IS444 | B/S BS4978 DRY | C18 SS |

SG1 = Sitka Spruce, Norway Spruce, Douglas Fir, Lodgepole Pine

| TQBI XXX/XXXX | EW/ER IS127 IS444 | EW/ER BS4978 DRY | C16 GS |

EW/ER = European Whitewood and Redwood

| TQBI XXX/XXXX | EW/ER IS127 IS444 | EW/ER BS4978 DRY | C24 SS |

EW/ER = European Whitewood and Redwood

Machine strength grading stamps

| TQBI XXX | WE/SG1 ISEN519 | B/S DRY BSEN519 | C16 IS444 |

Structural grading requirements for machine strength graded timber and grading machines

SG1 = Sitka Spruce, Norway Spruce, Douglas Fir, Lodgepole Pine

| TQBI XXX | WE/SG2 ISEN519 | B/S DRY BSEN519 | C18 IS444 |

SG2 = Scots Pine, Larch

TRIMMING AROUND OPENINGS

Stairwell opes:

Trimmer and trimming joists may require specialist design by an engineer. The engineer appointed must be qualified by examination, be in private practice and possess professional indemnity insurance.

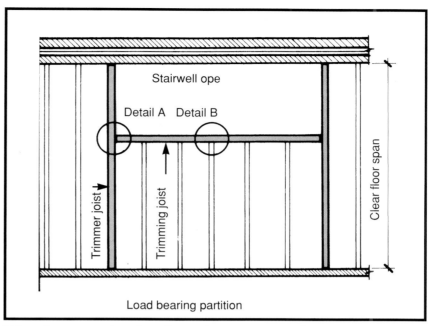

Trimming around stairwell ope (see page 113 for details A and B).

ENSURING RIGID FLOORS

To generally stiffen the floor and to reduce the risk of joists twisting, it is essential to provide adequate bridging. Bridging should be solid timber at least $^3/_4$ the depth of the floor joist. For timber sized in accordance with IS 444, bridging is required for all floor joists with a span greater than 2.7 m. Bridging should be provided at 1350 mm centres.

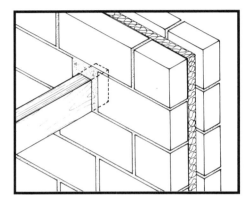

Where joists are built into walls ensure a minimum. bearing of 90 mm, and the space between the joists and the blockwork should be packed solidly with mortar to ensure rigidity as illustrated above.

Other acceptable means of providing adequate lateral stability at the point of support include; fixing end bridging between joints or appropriate joist hangers built into the masonry.

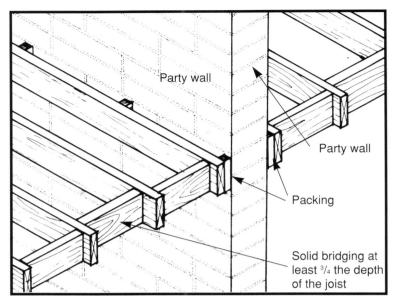

Provide packing and bridging.

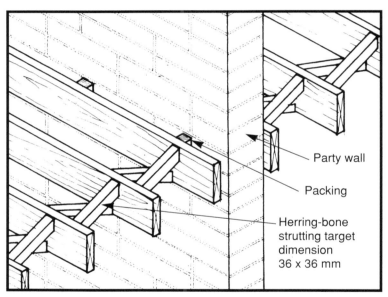

Alternative to solid bridging: herring-bone strutting and packing. Such strutting should only be used where the spacing of the joist does not exceed three times the joist depth.

Example of solid bridging between floor joists.

NOTCHING AND DRILLING REQUIREMENTS OF 1S 444

Extreme care should be taken when notching and drilling joists. They should generally only be notched and drilled in the locations shown and to the extent illustrated opposite.

NOTCHES SHOULD ONLY BE MADE IN THE TOP OF THE JOIST

Care must be taken when notching to ensure that the depth of the saw cut, does not exceed the depth of the notch itself.

Plumbers and electricians should be made aware that they must not weaken joists by inappropriate notching and drilling.

Excessive notching is not allowed.

The horizontal distance between any hole and notch should not be less than the depth of the joist.

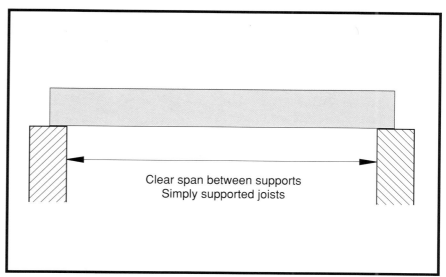

Notching and drilling simply supported joists

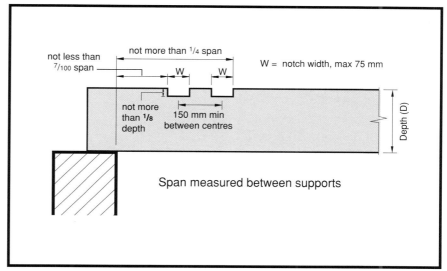

Limitations for notching

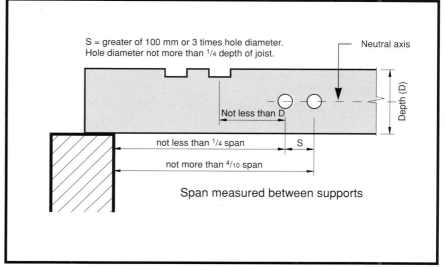

Limitations for drilling

PLYWOOD

General Information:
The following types of plywood are suitable for domestic flooring.

American plywood:
Grades C-D and C-C, exterior, unsanded.
Typical markings:
C-D. Exposure 1, PS1-85.
C-C. Exterior, PS1-83.

Canadian plywood:
Grades B-C and exterior, unsanded.
Typical markings:
Exterior. DFP or CSP. (Douglas Fir Plywood & Canadian Softwood Plywood)

Finnish plywood:
Birch and Conifer plywood, Grades III and IV, sanded.
Typical markings:
Exterior WPB. Finnish Birch-Faced, Exterior, WBP. Conifer, WBP.

Swedish plywood:
Spruce or Pine, Grade P30, Unsanded.
Typical markings:
S15. Trident symbol.

Note:
The above list is not exhaustive, other plywood types are acceptable subject to appropriate approval.

Plywood Type	Thickness (mm)	Max. joist centres (mm)
American	15.0 18.0	450 600
Canadian DFP	15.5 18.5	450 600
Canadian CSP	15.5 18.5	450 600
Finnish Birch & Conifer	15.0 18.0	450 600
Swedish softwood (P30 Grade)	16.0 16.0	450 600

Moisture content:
The maximum moisture content at the time of fixing should not exceed 16%. It is recommended that plywood be conditioned to the expected in-service moisture content level prior to fixing.

Laying and fixing:

◆ Plywood panels should be laid with the face grain at right angles to the direction of the floor joists

◆ All end joints should occur over joists and be staggered transversely across the floor

◆ All longitudinal joints should be kept in line

◆ Where boards are square edged (ie, not tongued and grooved), the edges should be supported by noggings.

Expansion gaps:
A gap should be left between the edges of the sheets and the wall. Allow 2 mm width of gap for each metre across the floor with a minimum gap of 10 mm. Intermediate gaps may be required in large floor areas.

PLYWOOD
continued

Typical fixing:
Flat head 3 mm dia. x 50 mm long (or 2.5 times board thickness, achieving 32 mm penetration into support) annular ring shank nails.

Nails at 150 mm centres to perimeter and 300 mm centres to intermediate supports, (BS 8103: Pt 3: 1996).

The use of other fixings is not excluded: manufacturer's guidance should be sought.

Areas of application:

◆ Timber frame prefabricated floor panel: Type C-D Exposure 1

◆ Suitable for all locations in both timber frame and masonry construction: Type C-C Exterior or type C-D Exposure 1.

CHIPBOARD

General Information:
Only flooring grade chipboards are suitable for use as floor decking. The following grades are suitable for use.

Chipboard:
Type C4 (moisture resistant) and C5.
Typical markings:
C4 - red and green stripes.
C5 - yellow and green stripes.

Chipboard:
Type II/III (C4 equivalent).
Typical markings:
Type II/III (C4), green code mark on the underside.

Board thickness for domestic floor loading

Thickness (mm)	Max. joist centres (mm)
18.0	450
22.0	600

Moisture content:

The maximum moisture content of chipboard flooring at the time of fixing should not exceed 15%. The moisture content of the chipboard should be allowed to adjust to the expected in-service conditions prior to fixing.

Laying and fixing:

◆ Square edged boards should be laid with the long edges parallel with and butt-jointed over the joists

◆ End joints should be staggered and supported by noggings

◆ Tongued and grooved boards are normally laid at right angles to the joists with the short edges butt-jointed over the joists

◆ No support is necessary under the long edges of tongued and grooved boards set between correctly spaced joists. Joints along the shorter edges should be staggered.

CHIPBOARD

Laying and fixing:
continued

◆ It is essential that board edges around the perimeter of the floor are continuously supported by joists or noggings.

Expansion gaps:
A gap should be left between the edges of the boards and the wall. Allow 2 mm width of gap for each metre across the floor with a minimum gap of 10 mm at the perimeter of the floor. Tongued and grooved boards are manufactured with an expansion gap on the underside of the joint. This accommodates intermediate expansion across the floor.

Typical fixing:
Flat head 3 mm dia. x 50 mm long (or 2.5 times board thickness, achieving 32 mm penetration into support) annular ring shank nails.

Nails at 300 mm centres to perimeter and 300 mm centres to intermediate supports, (BS 7916: 1998 & BS 8103: Pt 3: 1996).

The use of other fixings is not excluded: manufacturer's guidance should be sought.

Gluing of joints:
All tongued and grooved joints should be glued to prevent creaking. Poly Vinyl Acetate (PVA) type adhesives conforming to BS 4071, are suitable for this purpose.

Areas of application:

◆ Timber frame prefabricated floor panels must be: Type P5 to EN 312 (BS ref. C4)

◆ Timber frame flooring: Type P4 to EN 312 (BS ref. C2), fixed on site in a dwelling completely enclosed from the elements. Type P5 (C4) for kitchens, bathrooms and wet areas

◆ Masonry construction: Type P4 (C2) for general areas. Type P5 (C4) for kitchens, bathrooms and wet areas.

Note:
Care should be exercised to ensure that chipboard flooring is not exposed to wet weather. Excessive exposure can cause damage, even to moisture resistant chipboard.

ORIENTED STRAND BOARD

General Information

Oriented Strand Board (OSB) is a structural panel board manufactured from softwood flakes bonded with phenolic resin adhesives, chemical binders and wares. It is produced in a range of thicknesses and grades.

A voluntary colour coding system exists for OSB. Two colours are used in each case. The first colour defines the panel as either intended for general purpose use or load bearing applications (either one or two stripes of this colour are used). The second colour identifies the panel as being suitable for use in either dry or humid conditions.

The colours used are as follows.

First colour	white	general purpose
	yellow	load bearing
Second colour	blue	dry conditions
	green	humid conditions

Voluntary colour coding for OSB

OSB type	Colour code
OSB 2	yellow, yellow, blue
OSB 3	yellow, yellow, green

In addition, OSB decking will be printed with the following typical markings:
OSB 2 EN 300 or OSB 3 EN 300

These markings in conjunction with the colour coding will allow easy identification on site.

Note: Guidance on colour coding and markings should be sought as these may vary between manufacturers.

Board thickness for domestic floor loading:

Thickness (mm)	Max. joist centres (mm)
15.0	450
18.0	600

Moisture content:

OSB 3 is factory conditioned to a moisture content in excess of 5%, but less than 13%. It is recommended that the panels should be allowed to adjust to the expected in-service conditions prior to fixing.

Laying and fixing:

◆ All boards must be laid with the long edges at right angles to the floor joists

◆ Cross joints should be staggered

◆ All cut edges which are not supported on joists and all edges of square edged boards should be supported on noggings

◆ All board edges must be supported at the perimeter of the floor.

Expansion gaps:

Expansion gaps are required between each floor panel (3 mm), and at the perimeter of the floor (10 mm). Generally allow for a possible overall expansion of 2 mm per metre length of floor. Intermediate gaps may be required in large floor areas.

Typical fixing:

Flat head 3 mm dia. x 50mm long (or 2.5 times board thickness, achieving 32 mm penetration into support) annular ring shank nails.

Nails at 150 mm centres to perimeter and 150mm centres to intermediate supports, (Irish Agrément Cert. 97/0093).

The use of other fixings is not excluded. Manufacturer's guidance should be sought.

Areas of application:

◆ Timber frame flooring including prefabricated floor panels: OSB 3

◆ Timber frame flooring: OSB 3 or OSB 2, fixed on site in a dwelling completely enclosed from the elements. OSB 3 for kitchens, bathrooms, wet areas, and where there is a risk of wetting on site

◆ Masonry construction: OSB 2 or OSB 3 for general areas. OSB 3 for kitchens, bathrooms and wet areas.

Note:

Care should be exercised to ensure that OSB flooring is not exposed to wet weather. Excessive exposure can cause damage, even to moisture resistant OSB.

TIMBER STUD PARTITIONS

A typical timber stud partition consists of a layer of plasterboard nailed to each side of a framework of timber.

The plasterboard for this partition is supplied with tapered edges for flush jointing.

It is essential that the timber framing be accurately spaced and aligned. The timber used should be straight and properly dried (not normally exceeding 20% moisture content) so as to prevent warping or distortion, which can cause cracking of the joints.

Non-loadbearing timber stud partitions (such as those used at first floor level in two-storey housing) should be of kiln dried timber and should comprise 36 mm x 75 mm minimum studs at 400 mm centres.

Loadbearing timber stud partitions, when used, should comprise timber of at least strength class C14 and incorporate studs of 44 x 100 mm min. at 400 mm centres, with double header and sole pieces. Load-bearing partitions may require fire resistance if carrying floors. See Appendix H, Fire.

For timber stud partitions comprising of 75 x 36 mm studs or less, 2438 m in height, two rows of noggings are recommended. For larger studs, one row of noggings is generally sufficient. Noggings are required to all board edges in fire rated partitions and where vapour check plasterboard is used.

Proprietary metal stud partitioning systems should be installed in accordance with the manufacturer's recommendations.

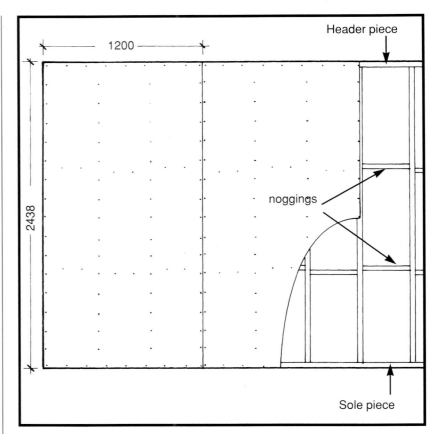

Typical timber stud partition (Non-loadbearing).

Supporting members	Board Thickness (mm)	Board width (mm)	Recommended Max. centres (mm)
Studs	9.5	900	450
		1200	400
	12.5	900	450
		1200	600

The table above sets out the recommended maximum spacing of studs for the range of standard plasterboard thicknesses and sheet widths.

CERAMIC WALL TILING

Plasterboard may receive ceramic tiles in localised areas such as splash-backs, behind kitchen units and wash hand basins. In other areas where there is splashing of surface water, as in the case of showers, plasterboard treated on the face with two coats of dual purpose pigmented primer or, preferably, moisture resistant plasterboard should be used.

FIXING OF PLASTERBOARD

The common sizes of plasterboard used in domestic construction are 9.5 mm and 12.5 mm in thickness and 2438 mm high x 1200 mm wide.

The face of the board is the surface on which the paper extends continuously to cover the edges i.e. ivory face. The back is that surface having a double thickness of paper along the two edges i.e. grey face.

Nails for fixing gypsum plasterboard should be hot dip galvanised, zinc electroplated or sheradized steel. Nails should have a shank of minimum finished diameter 2.5 mm and a head of minimum diameter 7.0 mm.

Nail the boards to every support at approx. 150 mm centres (8 nails per linear metre), working from the centre of the board outwards. Nails should be driven home firmly without the head fracturing the paper surface, but leaving a shallow depression to facilitate spotting. In non-loadbearing non-fire rated partitions, the long edges of the board should be fixed parallel with the studs, so that the bound edges are joined on a stud.

Screws used for fixing should be zinc electroplated or block phosphate oiled steel self drilling and tapping drywall screws, having trumpet countersunk and cross punched heads. Provide screws at 230 mm centres (5 no. screws per linear metre). The minimum lengths for nails and screws are outlined in the table opposite.

The length of screws for fixing thermal laminate boards to metal and timber studs should be at least 10 mm and 25 mm greater, respectively, than the total laminate thickness.

Board thickness	Min. Nail Length (mm)	Min. Screw Length (mm)	
		Metal	Timber
9.5 mm	30	N/A	32
12.5 mm	40	22	36
15 mm	40	25	36
19 mm	50	32	42
12.5 mm on 12.5 mm	50	36	50
12.5 mm on 19 mm	65	42	60
15 mm on 15 mm	65	42	60

Minimum nail and screw lengths.

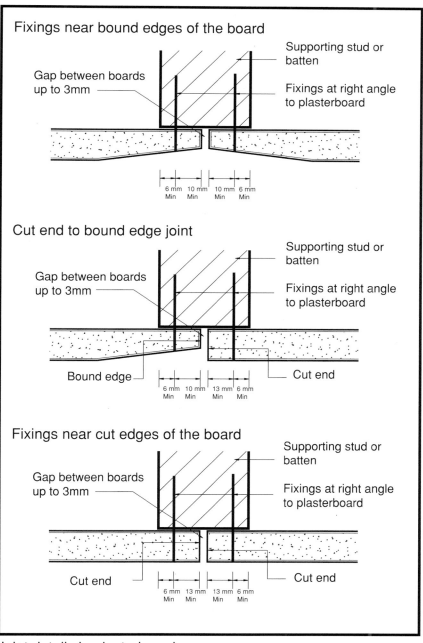

Joint details in plasterboard.

FIXING DETAILS

Stud partition construction: typical fixing details.

Buttressing

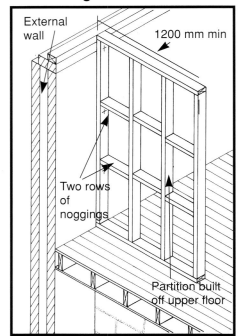

Internal buttressing to external walls in upper floors may be provided by stud partitions providing that:

- The partition is not less than 1200 mm long

- Kiln dried studs are used, 75 mm x 35 mm min., at 400 mm max. centres

- Two rows of noggings are provided

- The end stud is fixed to the wall using drilled screw fixings at the top, and at each of the noggings.

Sound insulation

Improved sound insulation can be provided to bathroom, WC and ensuite partitions by the use of 12.5 mm plasterboard, used in conjunction with sound insulation quilt material placed between studs.

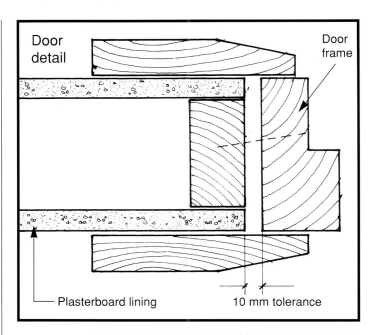

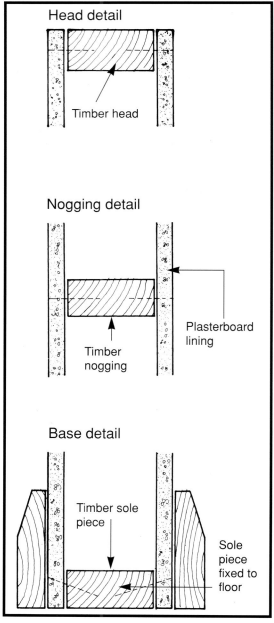

CONSTRUCTION

Non-loadbearing stud partitions should be built off double joists to avoid the risk of ceiling deflection and cracking, or, alternatively, above an extra joist placed directly under the line of the partition.

Note:

If the partition is load bearing (e.g. carrying roof loads) a specially designed member such as an RSJ or universal beam may be required to support it.

DO NOT LOAD ROOF UNTIL PARTITIONS ARE PROPERLY SECURED INTO PLACE.

Support must be provided directly beneath the partition. The photo highlights unacceptable practice.

NOTCHING AND DRILLING OF STUDS

Studs should not normally be notched.

Services should be run in holes drilled on the centreline of the stud. Hole diameters should not exceed 0.25 times the depth of the stud. Holes should only be drilled in the zones indicated opposite.

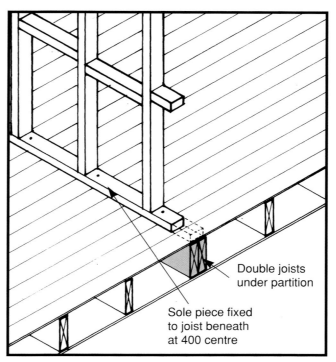

Typical non-load bearing stud partition built off timber floor, with double joists beneath.

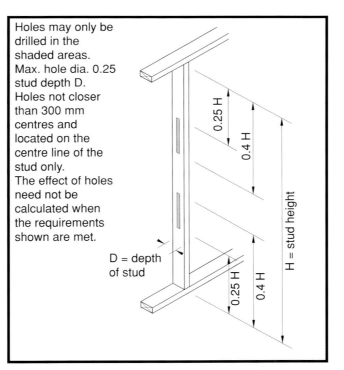

Location and extent of drill holes in studs.

CONSTRUCTION
continued

It should be noted that where partitions run at right angles to the joists, the design of the joists should take into account the point load imposed thereby. Any partition at right angles to the joist should incorporate a double sole piece.

Loadbearing stud partition.
Note the double sole pieces.

The heads of partitions should be fixed to the ceiling joists if the partition is at right angles to the joists. If the partition is parallel to the joists, it should be fixed to nogging placed between the joists. The noggings should be spaced at 400 mm centres.

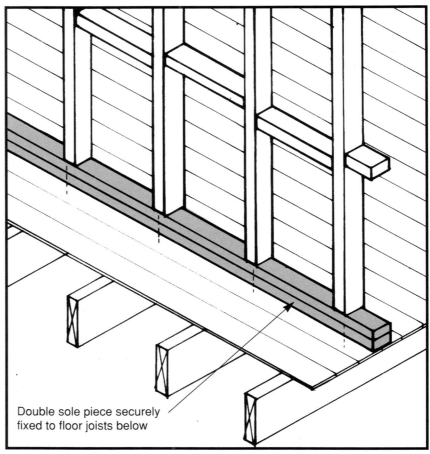

Double sole piece securely fixed to floor joists below

Partition at right angles to joist – note that joist sizing should take partition load into account. Note also double sole piece.

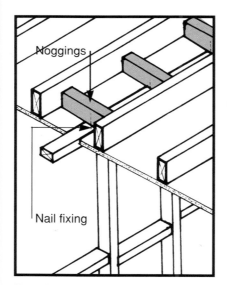

Noggings

Nail fixing

Nail fixing

Details at head of partition.

Note:
The sketches above illustrate stud partitions under a cut timber roof construction, where the ceiling material is fixed after the partition is erected. However, with prefabricated trussed roof construction, the ceiling material is often fixed before the partition is erected. See also page 311.

INTRODUCTION

A stairway may be constructed with steps rising without a break from floor to floor, or with steps rising to a landing between floors, with a further series of steps rising from the landing to the floor above. The most common type in domestic construction is the straight flight stair consisting of a straight flight of parallel steps.

Definitions:

"**flight**": a part of a stairway which consists of a step or consecutive steps between landings;

"**going**": the horizontal distance between the nosing of a tread and the nosing of the tread or landing next above it;

"**pitch**": the angle between the pitch line and the horizontal;

"**rise**": the vertical distance between the top of a tread and the top of the tread, landing or ramp next above or below it;

"**tread**": the upper surface of a step within the width of a stairway;

"**string**": sloping board at each end of the treads housed or cut to carry the treads and risers of a stair. A string can be either a wall string or an outer string and either a closed string or a cut string.

Note: In any single flight of stairs the rise and going of each step must be consistent.

There should not be more than sixteen risers in any one flight.

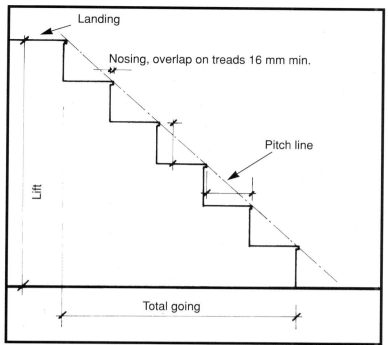

Straight flight stairs.

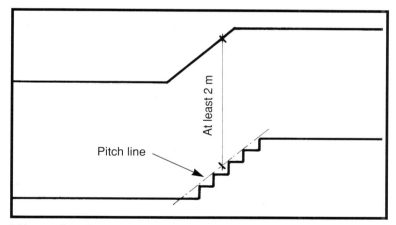

Measuring headroom.
Headroom over the whole width of any stairs, measured as shown above, should generally be not less than 2 m.

Relationship between rise and going.

In order to ensure steps are suitably proportioned, the sum of twice the rise plus the going (2R +G) should be between 550 mm and 700 mm, with an optimum of 600 mm.

Dimensions for going: 220 mm min. (250 mm optimum).

Dimensions for Rise: 220 mm max. (175 mm optimum).

Angle of pitch: 42° max. (35° optimum).

WIDTH OF STAIRS

Technical Guidance Document K of the Building Regulations recommends a minimum clear width (clear of handrails and other obstructions) of 800 mm for domestic stairs.

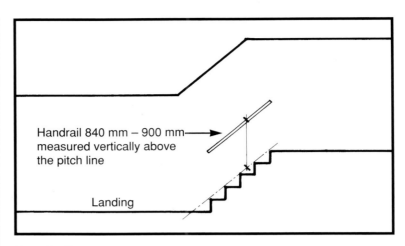

Handrails

A stairs should have a handrail on at least one side if it is 1000 mm wide or less, and should be designed and constructed to ensure: (1) firm support, (2) secure fixing, (3) it may be easily gripped, (4) it may be safely used, (5) that trapping or injuring of the hand is prevented, (6) that the handrail does not project to catch clothing etc., and (7) that the handrail allows uninterrupted hand freedom along the length of the flight. Note that a handrail may form the top of a guarding if the height is suitable. Handrails may not be necessary beside the two bottom steps of a domestic stairs.

Landings

A landing should be provided at the top and bottom of every flight. A landing may not be necessary between a flight and a door if the total rise of the flight is not more than 600 mm and the door slides or opens away from the stairs. The landing may include part of a floor. The width and going of the landing should be at least as great as the smallest width of the flight.

Landings should be clear of permanent obstruction. A door opening onto a landing should be positioned so that there will be a clear space of at least the the full width of the flight between the door swing and the flight.

In the case of domestic stairs, the landing at the bottom of a flight may be reduced in length, provided a clear space of at least 400 mm is maintained between the flight and the door swing, as illustrated opposite.

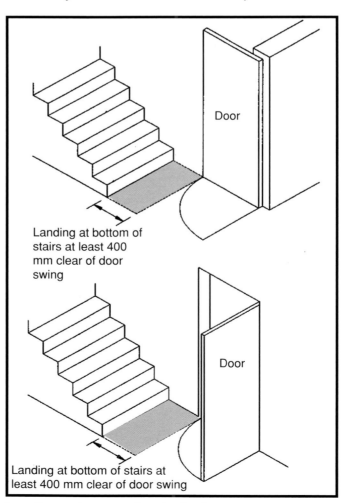

Landing at bottom of stairs in domestic construction.

GUARDING REQUIREMENTS

◆ Stairs should be guarded at the sides, (except where the total rise is no more than 600 mm in which case guarding may not be essential)

◆ Suitable guarding materials include: a wall, screen (incl. glazing), railing and balustrade

◆ Guarding should be designed and constructed in such a way that it will not present unacceptable risk of accidents in service

◆ Where guarding contains glazing, it should be in accordance with the recommendations of BS 6262: Part 4

◆ Guarding should not be readily climbable by children

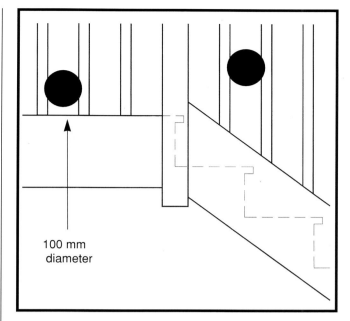

100 mm diameter

◆ Guarding should be constructed so that a 100 mm diameter sphere cannot pass through any openings in the guarding

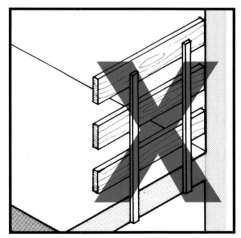

This type of guarding is not acceptable as it can be easily climbed by children.

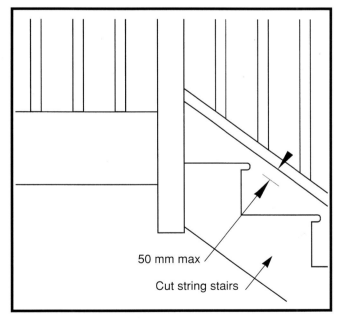

50 mm max

Cut string stairs

◆ Where a cut string is used, the triangular space formed by the tread and riser is allowable provided that the bottom edge of the balustrade is not more than 50 mm above the nosing line

GUARDING REQUIREMENTS
continued

◆ Guarding should be provided at the sides of any part of a:

◇ raised floor (guarding may not be essential where the total difference in level is 600 mm or less),

◇ balcony,

◇ roof,

◇ or other place to which people have access (unless access is only for the purpose of maintenance or repair).

◆ Height of guarding depends on location, see table opposite

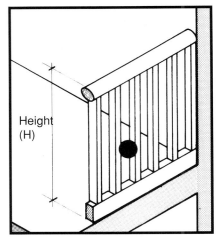

Balustrade or railing type guarding.

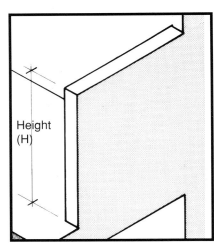

Solid guarding.

Location of guarding	Min. height (H) of guarding
stairway	840 mm (measured vertically above pitch line)
landing	900 mm
raised floor balcony roof	1100 mm

Height requirements for guarding

◆ Guarding should be capable of withstanding the following minimum imposed loads

Location of guarding	Horizontal uniformly distributed line load (kN/m)	Uniformly distributed load applied to the infill (kN/m²)	Point load applied to part of the infill (kN)
All areas within or serving one dwelling, including stairs and landings but excluding external balconies and roof edges	0.36	0.5	0.25
External balconies and roof edges	0.74	1.0	0.5

For design purposes, the uniformly distributed line load should be considered to act at a height of 1.1 m above datum (i.e. finished floor level) irrespective of the actual height of the guarding.

TIMBER STAIRCASE CONSTRUCTION

String: The string is the inclined member which supports the ends of treads and risers.

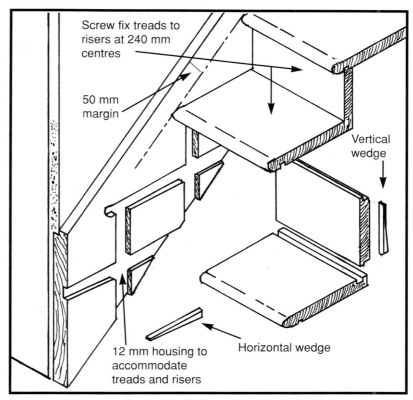

Detail of typical closed string stairs.

Closed string: (as illustrated) an outer string with parallel edges into which the treads and risers are housed.

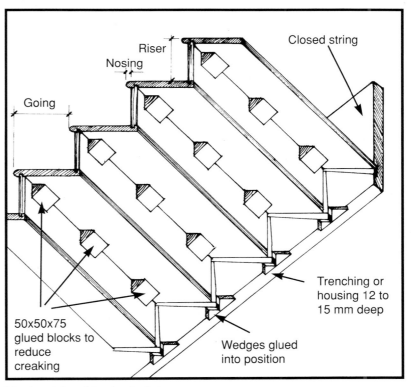

Underside of typical staircase.

CILL HEIGHT

Where a window cill is less than 800mm in height above floor level, guarding is required irrespective of the location of the window within the dwelling.

If the window is capable of being opened, the guarding should still remain effective while the window is in the open position.

In the case of fixed low level glazing, safety glass in accordance with the requirements of BS 6262: Pt. 4, may be considered as an alternative to barrier type guarding.

CRITICAL LOCATIONS

Robust glazing i.e. glass that must break safely, resist impact or be protected by permanent guarding, should be used in the critical locations illustrated opposite. Typical critical locations include door side panels and glazed screens. The glass used in these areas should meet the requirements of BS 6262: Pt.4 and be marked in accordance with BS 6206.

Small panes of 6 mm annealed glass are suitable in critical locations, if the area of the single pane does not exceed 0.5 m² and the width of each pane is no more than 250 mm.

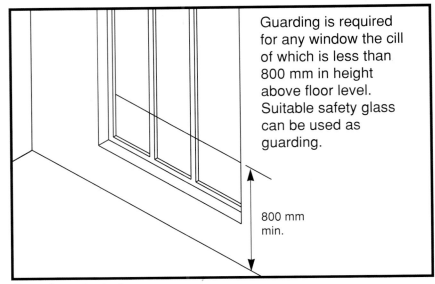

Guarding is required for any window the cill of which is less than 800 mm in height above floor level. Suitable safety glass can be used as guarding.

800 mm min.

Guarding at windows.

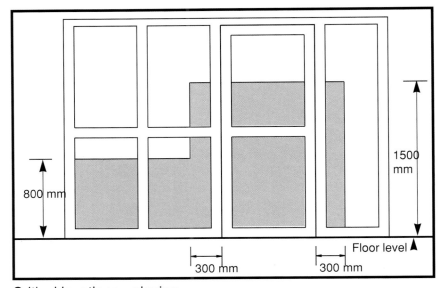

1500 mm

800 mm

Floor level

300 mm   300 mm

Critical locations - glazing.

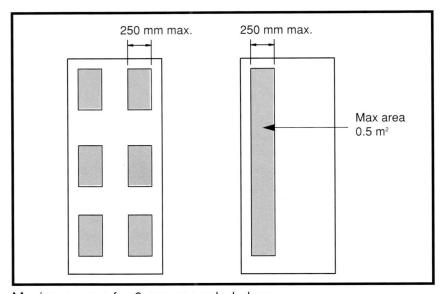

250 mm max.   250 mm max.

Max area 0.5 m²

Maximum area for 6 mm annealed glass.

ROOF CONSTRUCTION

INTRODUCTION

The fundamental requirements of a properly constructed roof, apart from prevention of moisture penetration, are that it must be built to prevent excessive deflection and to transfer properly the roof loads to the load-bearing walls of the house. The underlying principles of roof construction are relatively simple and they are outlined on the following pages for prefabricated trusses, traditional cut roofs, and flat roofs.

Roofs under construction.

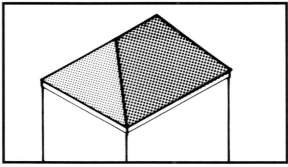

Pitched roof with hips.

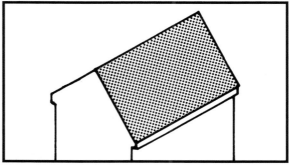

Standard pitched roof with gable end.

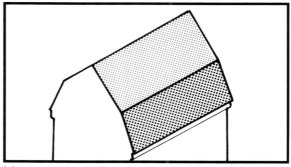

Mansard roof (Dutch gable).

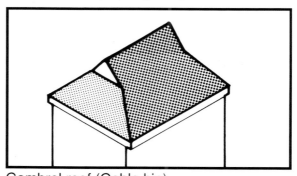

Gambrel roof (Gable hip).

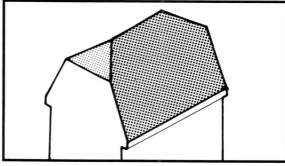

Dutch hip.

INTRODUCTION

The vast majority of modern houses are built using prefabricated trussed rafters, usually placed at 600 mm centres. These trusses rely on a number of factors for their successful performance, as follows:

◆ Proper design and fabrication by the manufacturer for the roof in question
◆ Galvanised punched metal plate fixings at joints
◆ Adequate bracing
◆ Adequate provision for holding down
◆ Proper distribution of point loads such as water tanks.

The appropriate standard for roof construction incorporating such trusses is 'Irish Standard 193: 1986: Timber Trussed Rafters for Roofs' published by the National Standards Authority of Ireland and available from N.S.A.I., Glasnevin, Dublin 9.

Prefabricated trusses must bear the Timber Quality Board of Ireland (TQBI) approval tag. A selection of typical tags and an explanation of their markings are illustrated opposite.

When ordering trusses, design drawings and details of the roof should be provided to the suppliers to facilitate design and manufacture of the trusses.

Note: When measuring the span of trusses, measure from the outside of the wall plate on one side to the outside of the wall plate on the other side, and add 25 mm.

Typical approval tags

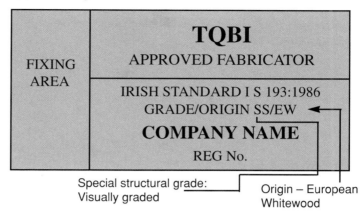

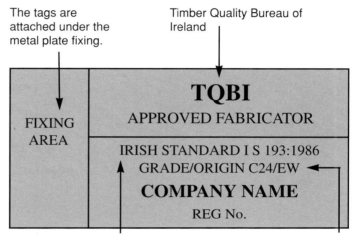

Location of tags

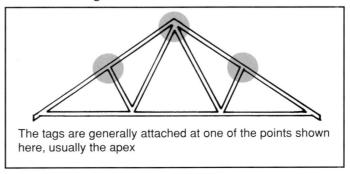

The tags are generally attached at one of the points shown here, usually the apex

TRUSS BEARING

The truss must be supported directly on the ceiling chord immediately below the point of intersection of joist and rafter, unless the trusses are specifically designed. Special design must be carried out in accordance with the approval of the truss manufacturer.

Prefabricated trusses nailed to wall plate/head binder/top rail.

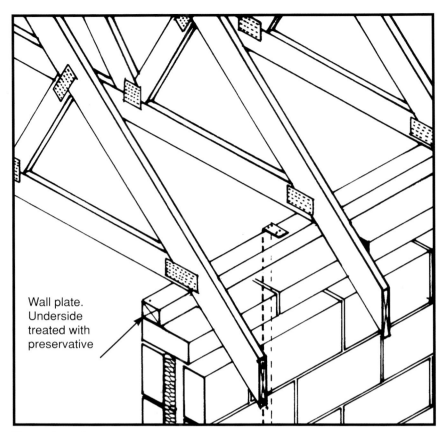

Wall plate. Underside treated with preservative

Truss bearing.

Overhangs of the type illustrated opposite are acceptable if the rafters and joists are braced in accordance with the manufacturer's recommendations.

Note:
The truss shown opposite is a specially designed and manufactured cantilever truss.

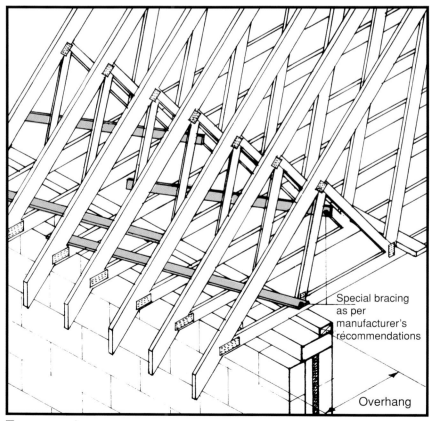

Special bracing as per manufacturer's recommendations

Overhang

Truss overhang.

HOLDING DOWN METHODS

Trusses should be securely tied down to the walls to resist uplift by the wind. Fixing by proprietary clips or straps is the preferred method. Alternatively, fixing by means of nails may also be considered. At least two wire round nails, each not less than 3.75 mm in diameter and not less than 85 mm in length, should be used to secure each truss to the wall plate in such a way as to prevent damage to the plate connectors. The nails should comply with IS 105, be staggered in position and be fixed on either side of the truss member.

DO NOT NOTCH RAFTERS TO SEAT TRUSSES ON WALL PLATE.

Truss clip can be used to fix each truss to the wall plate.

Additional holding down straps may be necessary if the roof has a pitch of less than 15° and is in wind zone C. See map on page 116.

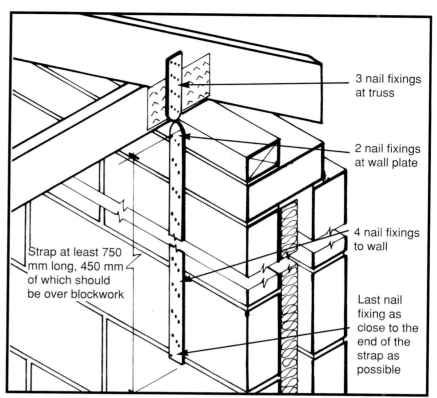

3 nail fixings at truss

2 nail fixings at wall plate

Strap at least 750 mm long, 450 mm of which should be over blockwork

4 nail fixings to wall

Last nail fixing as close to the end of the strap as possible

Twisted galvanised vertical restraint straps, generally 30 x 2.5 mm in cross section, tying trusses down to blockwork in external wall. Starting at truss nearest gable/party wall and then at 2 m max. centres.

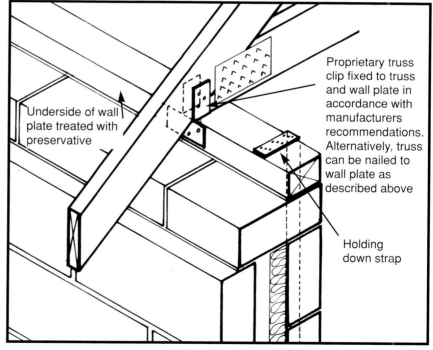

Underside of wall plate treated with preservative

Proprietary truss clip fixed to truss and wall plate in accordance with manufacturers recommendations. Alternatively, truss can be nailed to wall plate as described above

Holding down strap

Alternative means of holding down the truss is by fixing directly to the wall plate using proprietary truss clips. The wall plate should be fixed to the masonry by means of galvanised straps at 1.8 m centres or bolts at 1.2 m centres. Where wall plates are butt joined, holding down straps must be provided at no more than 400 mm centres on either side of the joint. The wall plate should have a target width of 100 mm and target depth of 75 mm

BRACING

It is vital for the satisfactory performance of a prefabricated trussed roof that the trusses be tied together and braced properly so that the roof structure acts as a unit.

The minimum bracing details illustrated on this page are appropriate for the majority of roofs. Roofs of irregular or unusual design, or having a large span, will require additional bracing which should be designed by an appropriately qualified person.

The following pages illustrate some typical examples of such additional bracing.

Detailed design guidance on the bracing of trusses is given in I.S. 193: 1986: Timber Trussed Rafters for Roofs, published by the N.S.A.I., Glasnevin, Dublin 9.

NOTE: BRACING DETAILS MUST CONFORM TO THE TRUSS MANUFACTURER / ROOF DESIGNER'S RECOMMENDATIONS.

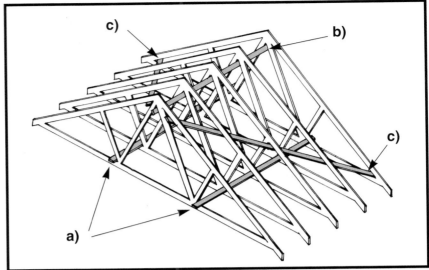

This sketch illustrates the minimum standard bracing of a pre-fabricated trussed roof.

a) At ceiling level, at the intersection of ceiling joist, tie and strut i.e. node point. These bracing timbers are called "longitudinal binders"
b) At ridge level—these are also termed "longitudinal binders"
c) From eaves to ridge on both sides of roof—this is called "rafter diagonal bracing".

Bracing timbers must be at least 100 x 22 mm (minimum size), free from major defects and fixed with two 75 mm galvanized nails of 2.65 mm diameter at every point of contact with a truss. Where a single length of timber is not used, lengths must overlap across two trusses.

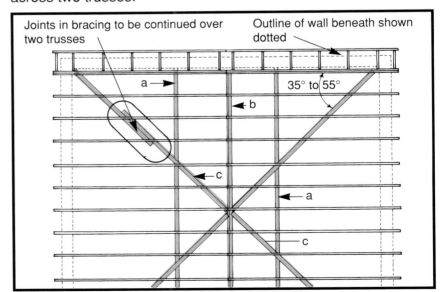

Rafter diagonal bracing should be fixed at an angle of approximately 35° to 55° on plan to the rafters and should repeat continuously along the roof. The end of all longitudinal bracing timbers should tightly abut the gable or separating wall. The lower ends of diagonal rafter bracing members should abut the end walls as closely as possible to the intersection between the wall and the wallplate.

BRACING
continued

Where a roof has a long span, bracing additional to the standard longitudinal and rafter diagonal bracing becomes necessary. The illustrations on this page and the following pages highlight such additional bracing. As is the case for standard bracing, bracing timber must be 100 x 22 mm minimum size, free of defects and nailed twice with 75 mm galvanised nails of 2.65 mm diameter at each point of contact with the truss.

The following table sets out the conditions under which bracing additional to the minimum standard is required.

		Roof pitch in degrees					
		22.5	25	27.5	30	32.5	35
Brace internal tie where span exceeds		10.2 m	9.5 m	8.7 m	8.0 m	7.5 m	7.0 m
Brace internal strut where span exceeds		–	–	–	–	10.7 m	10.0 m

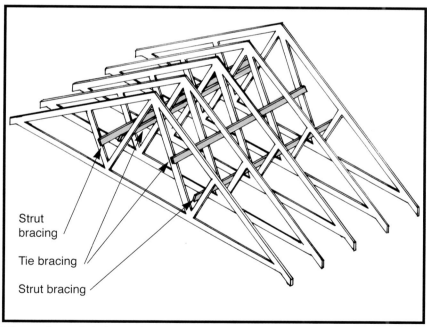

Strut bracing

Tie bracing

Strut bracing

View of pre-fabricated trussed roof highlighting additional bracing to internal truss members. (See also additional note on page 154.)

BRACING
continued

If it is necessary to brace ties or struts as illustrated on the previous page, it is also required that additional bracing timbers (chevron bracing) be fixed as illustrated in the sketches opposite, repeated without interruption along the length of the roof.

BRACING MUST NOT CROSS A PARTY WALL

Typical "fink" truss bracing members. Longitudinal, rafter diagonal and strut bracing can be clearly seen.

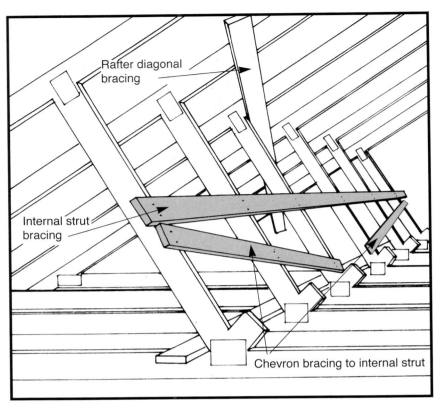

Rafter diagonal bracing

Internal strut bracing

Chevron bracing to internal strut

Chevron bracing to internal strut.

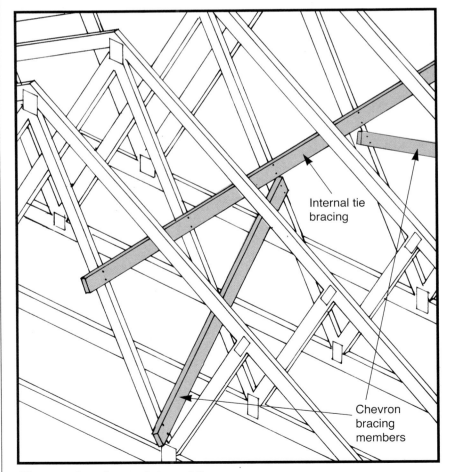

Internal tie bracing

Chevron bracing members

Chevron bracing to internal tie.
Note: In the interest of clarity some bracing members have been omitted from this sketch.

BRACING
continued

The guidance outlined on pages 152, 154 and in IS 193 deals only with "fink" trusses. Where trusses of other types, such as those illustrated below, are used, the Trussed Rafter Association (TRA) has standardised the locations in which chevron bracing may be required. This chevron bracing may be required in addition to longitudinal and rafter diagonal bracing.

If specified by the truss manufacturer or roof designer, lateral web bracing may be required to prevent sideways buckling of the internal webs.

BRACING DETAILS MUST CONFORM TO THE TRUSS MANUFACTURER/ROOF DESIGNER'S RECOMMENDATIONS.

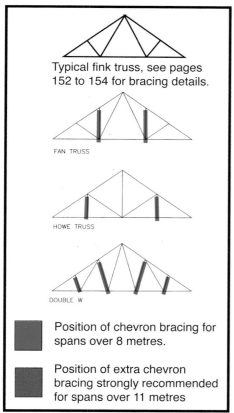

Typical fink truss, see pages 152 to 154 for bracing details.

FAN TRUSS

HOWE TRUSS

DOUBLE W

Position of chevron bracing for spans over 8 metres.

Position of extra chevron bracing strongly recommended for spans over 11 metres

Summary of Trussed Rafter Association bracing recommendations for non fink trusses.

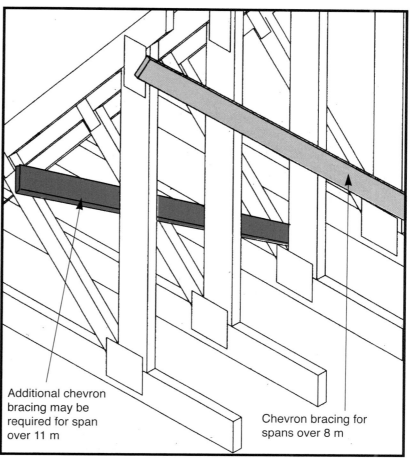

Additional chevron bracing may be required for span over 11 m

Chevron bracing for spans over 8 m

Typical example of chevron bracing. All other bracing members omitted for clarity.

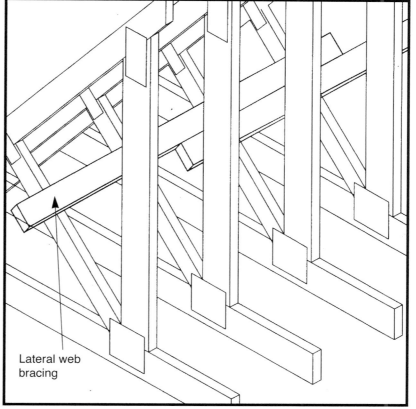

Lateral web bracing

In certain situations, lateral web bracing may be required, if specified by the designer.

MONO TRUSS BRACING

The following pages give general guidance on web chevron bracing from mono trusses. The chevron bracing may be required in addition to longitudinal and rafter diagonal bracing.

BRACING DETAILS MUST CONFORM TO THE TRUSS MANUFACTURER/ROOF DESIGNER'S RECOMMENDATIONS

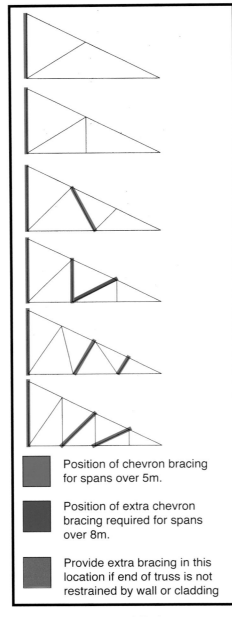

■ Position of chevron bracing for spans over 5m.

■ Position of extra chevron bracing required for spans over 8m.

■ Provide extra bracing in this location if end of truss is not restrained by wall or cladding

Summary of Trussed Rafter Association bracing recommendations for mono trusses.

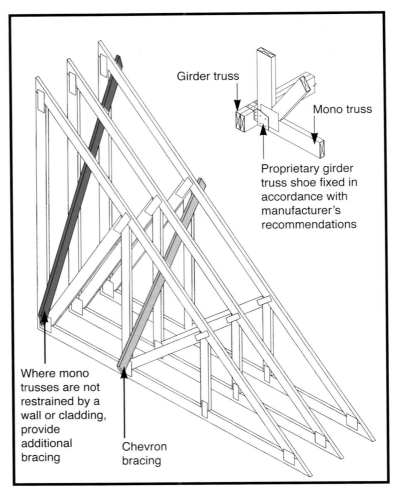

Girder truss

Mono truss

Proprietary girder truss shoe fixed in accordance with manufacturer's recommendations

Where mono trusses are not restrained by a wall or cladding, provide additional bracing

Chevron bracing

Example of chevron bracing for mono trusses.

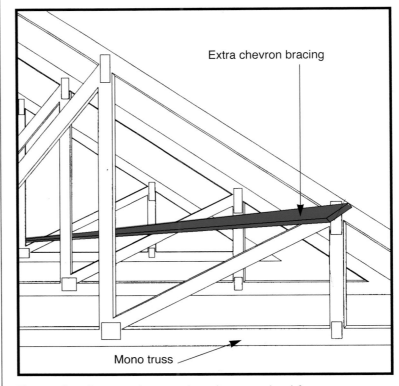

Extra chevron bracing

Mono truss

Example of extra chevron bracing required for mono trusses with a span greater than 8m. Other bracing members omitted for clarity.

HATCH AND CHIMNEY OPENINGS
continued

Note: When infill rafters and ceiling joists are required, support for these members should be provided in accordance with the guidance on page 162.

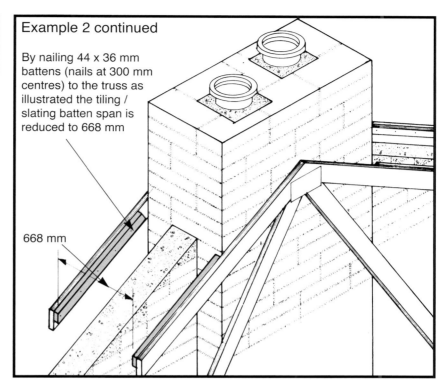

Example 2 continued

By nailing 44 x 36 mm battens (nails at 300 mm centres) to the truss as illustrated the tiling / slating batten span is reduced to 668 mm

668 mm

Detail at party wall to avoid excessive spans of tiling / slating battens.

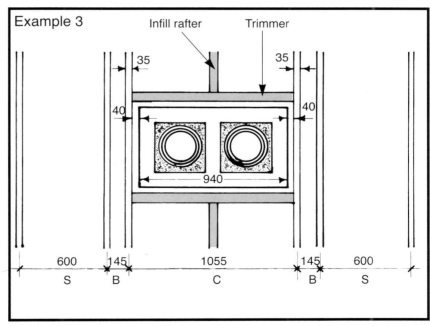

Example 3

Infill rafter   Trimmer

35   35

40   40

940

600   145   1055   145   600
S   B   C   B   S

Truss spacing dimensions for a standard block chimney with two flues, both within same house. i.e. not on a party wall as derived from condition 2 on page 158.

TRIMMING AROUND CHIMNEYS
continued

Where truss spacings are increased to accommodate chimneys, in some cases, trimming may be unavoidable.

When this occurs, increased truss spacing must be in accordance with the preceding pages. The sketches on the following pages illustrate the correct procedure for providing support to the infill timbers which support the tiling battens and ceiling materials.

Note: For fire safety reasons, all timbers must be 40 mm clear of chimney where blockwork or brickwork is less than 200 mm thick. See also page 112.

Infill timbers sized in accordance with IS 444 and at least 25 mm deeper than rafter member of roof truss.

DO NOT NAIL TIMBER DIRECTLY TO CHIMNEY

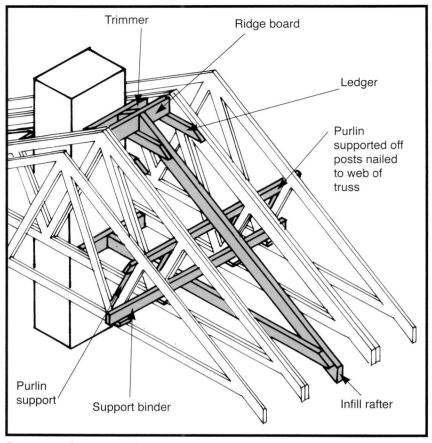

Support of loose timbers.

Care should be taken when nailing the purlin and purlin support to the trussed rafter strut in order to avoid damage.

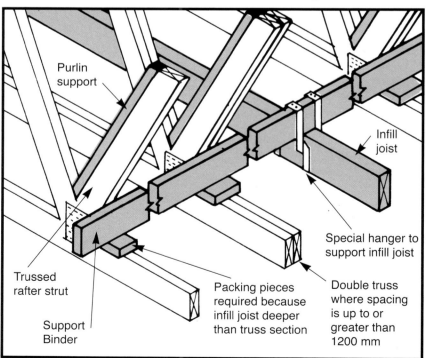

Detail showing arrangement of truss and cut timbers in a typical trimming arrangement around stack.
Note that the loads on the infill timbers are transferred to the double-trusses either on side and also to the next adjoining truss.

TRIMMING AROUND CHIMNEYS
continued

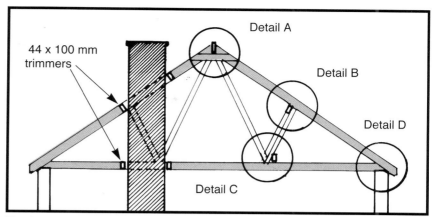

Detail A

Detail B

Detail D

44 x 100 mm trimmers

Detail C

Typical section through chimney trimming.

Note: This sketch is not illustrating a cut truss, it is a section through the infill timbers between trusses.

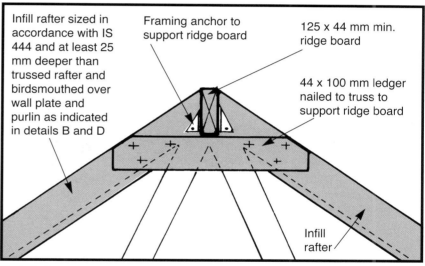

Infill rafter sized in accordance with IS 444 and at least 25 mm deeper than trussed rafter and birdsmouthed over wall plate and purlin as indicated in details B and D

Framing anchor to support ridge board

125 x 44 mm min. ridge board

44 x 100 mm ledger nailed to truss to support ridge board

Infill rafter

Detail A

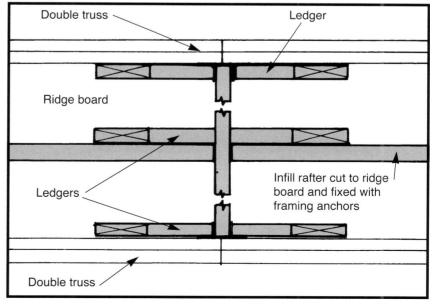

Double truss

Ledger

Ridge board

Ledgers

Infill rafter cut to ridge board and fixed with framing anchors

Double truss

Plan view of Detail A.

TRIMMING AROUND CHIMNEYS
continued

As an alternative to using loose timbers as trimming, a specially designed and fabricated 'stubbed' truss can be used as illustrated below.

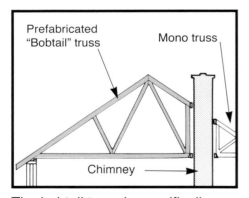

The bobtail truss is specifically designed and fabricated for such situations and is not adapted from an ordinary truss by site cutting. The bobtail truss must be erected in accordance with the manufacturer's instructions.

All timbers to be kept 40 mm clear of chimney, where blockwork is less than 200 mm thick.

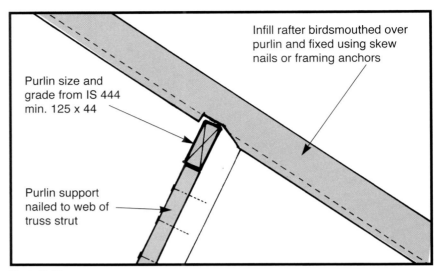

Purlin size and grade from IS 444 min. 125 x 44

Infill rafter birdsmouthed over purlin and fixed using skew nails or framing anchors

Purlin support nailed to web of truss strut

Detail B.

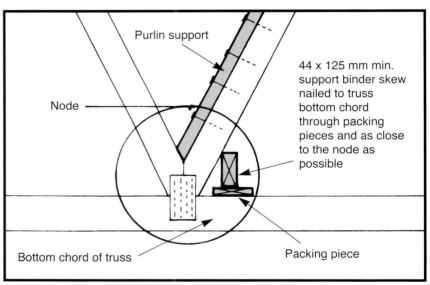

Purlin support

44 x 125 mm min. support binder skew nailed to truss bottom chord through packing pieces and as close to the node as possible

Node

Bottom chord of truss

Packing piece

Detail C.

Note: Support binder size and grade designed to suit span.

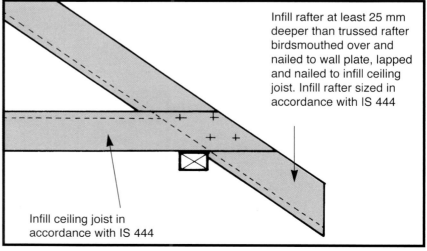

Infill rafter at least 25 mm deeper than trussed rafter birdsmouthed over and nailed to wall plate, lapped and nailed to infill ceiling joist. Infill rafter sized in accordance with IS 444

Infill ceiling joist in accordance with IS 444

Detail D.

WATER CISTERNS

It is essential that the weight of the water cistern be spread over a number of trusses. Failure to do this will lead to local deflection and cracking of the ceiling below the cistern. Dimensions for the support members can be taken from the table on this page.

Water storage capacity:

Minimum actual capacity 212 litres for a three bedroomed house; minimum actual capacity 340 litres for other dwellings.

Cistern cover:

Cover the cistern with a suitable rigid, but not air-tight, lid.

Note:

For cisterns with a nominal capacity greater than 270 litres, special design is required by I.S.193: 1986.

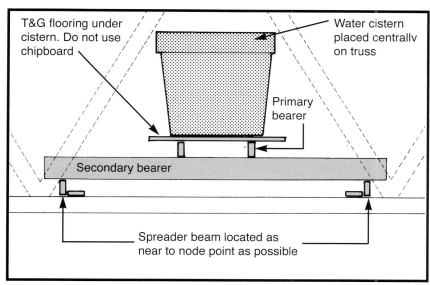

Water cistern support.

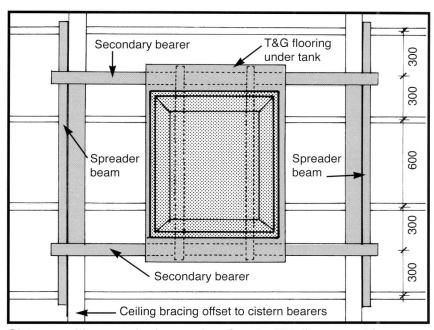

Cisterns with a nominal capacity of up to 270 litres must be spread over **four** trusses. Where more than one cistern is required, the load from more than one cistern must not be carried by any truss.

Limit of span trussed rafter	Primary bearers	Secondary bearers	Spreader bearers
m	mm	mm	mm
8.0	36 x 100	44 x 175	44 x 100
11.0	36 x 100	75 x 150	44 x 100

Minimum size of cistern support members, for nominal capacity up to 270 litres.

INSULATION AROUND TANKS AND AT ROOFLIGHTS

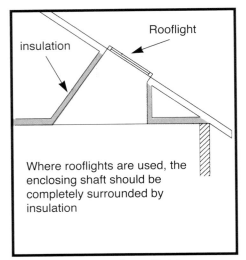

Where rooflights are used, the enclosing shaft should be completely surrounded by insulation

Insulation around rooflight.

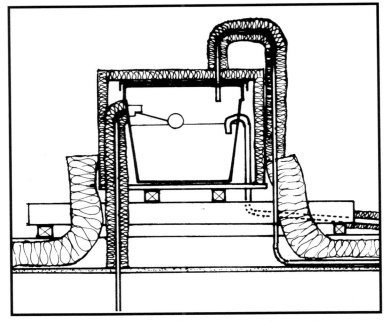

Insulation around tank and associated pipe work.

The tank should be properly covered but not airtight, accessible for cleaning and replacement and fitted with an overflow pipe so located as to discharge in a manner that will give ready warning of the occurrence of overflow, without causing any nuisance or any dampness in the dwelling. Insulation should be omitted under the tank to expose the water to the heat from within the house and thus reduce the risk of freezing.

Trap doors

The standard spacing between prefabricated trusses will accommodate the trap door. Under no circumstances should the trussed rafter be cut to make space for a larger opening.

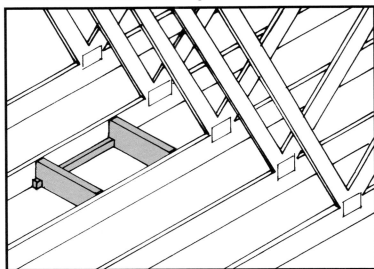

Trap door accommodated in standard spacing between trusses. Framing members notched over battens and fixed.

GABLE LADDERS

Gable ladders are used where a roof overhang is required at a gable end, and must be securely nailed directly to the last truss.

The gable ladder must be evenly supported by the gable blockwork. Barge boards and soffits can be nailed directly to the gable ladder. Special design will be required for gable overhangs in excess of 300 mm from the outside face of the wall.

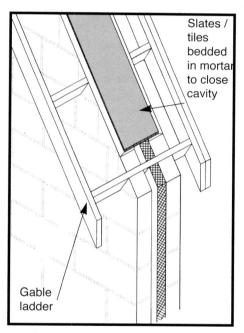

Cavity must be closed along the verge.

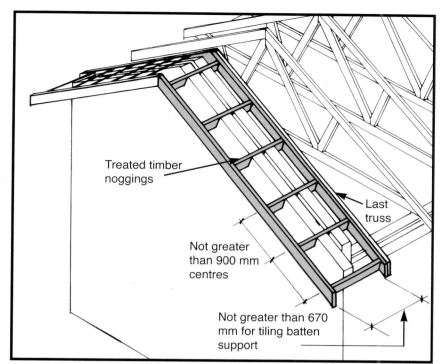

Typical gable ladder.

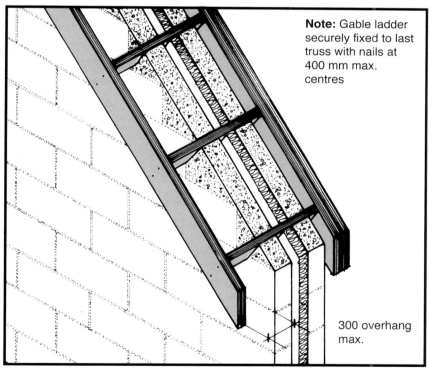

Overhang must not be greater than 300 mm.

FORMING HIPPED ENDS

Forming hips in a roof with prefabricated trusses can be done in two ways.

1. Using cut timbers to form the hipped section of the roof and/or

2. Using mono trusses specially designed and manufactured to suit the roof.

Note:
If a cut hipped end is used and loading is transferred to a load bearing partition wall, the partition must have a separate foundation because it is load bearing.

Sizes of ceiling joists and rafters from IS 444.

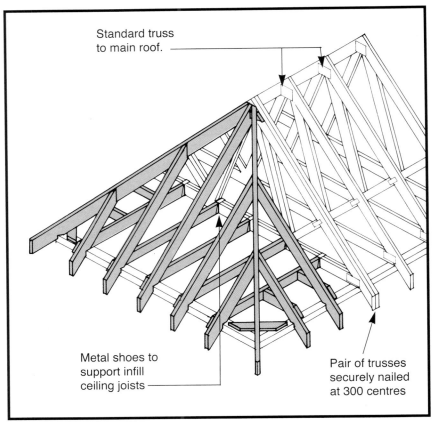

View of a hipped roof with prefabricated trusses and cut timber hips. **Note:** This method should only be used where the length of the gable does not exceed 5m. When this dimension exceeds 5 m the method of forming the hipped end illustrated on page 169 can be used.

Individual truss manufacturers can also provide appropriate hip details and components as part of the roof design and manufacture.

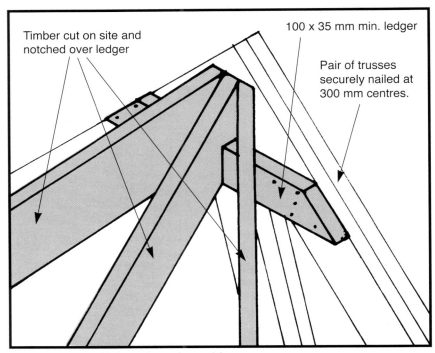

Detail at top of hips: Junction with trusses.

FORMING HIPPED ENDS
continued

Option 2:
Using specially designed girder truss and mono trusses, together with cut infill timber, to form the hip.

Infill hip rafter birdsmouthed over girder truss.

If using this method to form the hipped end, note the following:

◆ Ensure that the girder truss* contains the correct number of flat top plies (usually 2 or 3 fixed together) in accordance with the manufacturer's instructions

◆ Bearing details must conform with manufacturer's instructions

◆ Brace the top chord of the flat top trusses to the girder truss in accordance with the manufacturer's instructions

◆ Use truss shoes to support the mono trusses at the girder truss

◆ Birdsmouth the hip rafter over the girder truss to ensure support.

*Girder truss: A truss comprising two or more individual trusses (plies) fixed together and designed to carry exceptional loads such as those imparted by other trusses.

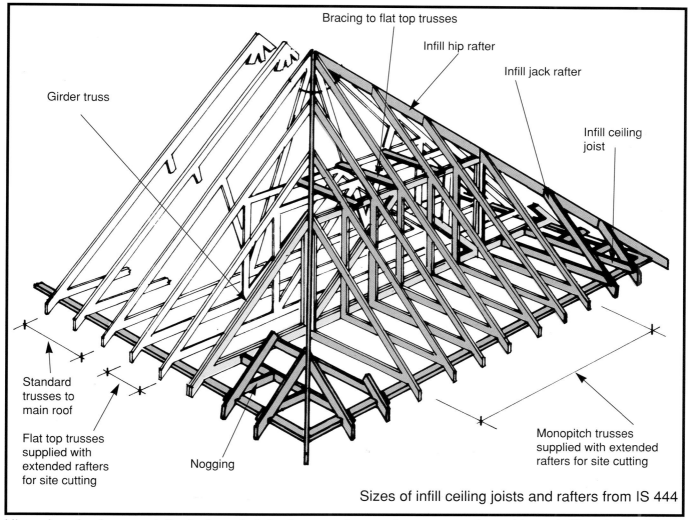

Hipped roof using specially designed girder truss and mono trusses together with cut infill timber to form the hip.

FORMING HIPPED ENDS
continued

A large proportion of the load of a hipped roof is transferred to the walls at the corner. To avoid "kicking" of the roof at the feet of hips, care must be taken with the fixing and joining of the wallplate. For further details of good practice in this area see pages 175 to 177.

HANDLING OF TRUSSES

Trusses are designed to be loaded in a particular way when erected. They must be handled carefully so as to avoid damaging the fixing of the truss plates. They must be stored carefully (see page 252) and when being erected they must be put into place without being strained.

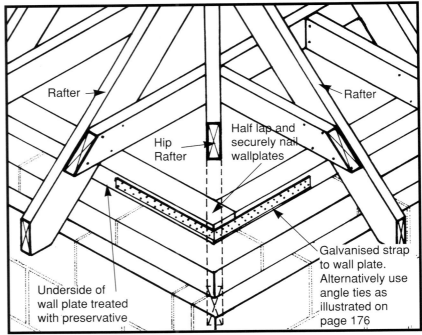

Typical detail at foot of hip. (Showing cut-away hip rafter). In heavily loaded hips, an angle tie and dragon tie should be used as an alternative. See page 177.

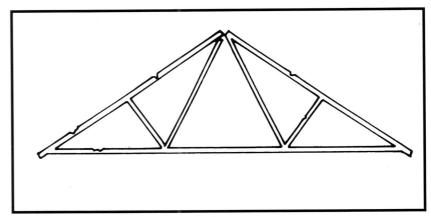

Care in handling trusses is vital:
REJECT ANY DAMAGED OR DISTORTED TRUSSES

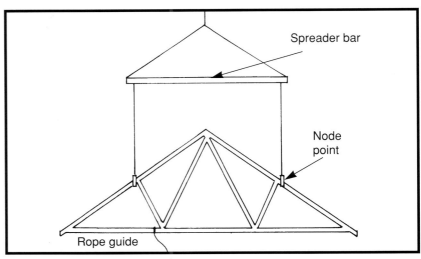

Mechanical handling technique.

INTRODUCTION

The essence of good traditional cut roof construction can be summarised as requiring:

◆ Properly sized timber - use IS 444 to select timber sizes

◆ Full triangulation of the roof - if the joists and rafters do not meet at wall plate level, there is a consequent risk of roof spread and thus an engineer's design will be required. Inadequate triangulation is a significant source of problems in cut roofs. The engineer appointed must be qualified by examination, be in private practice and possess professional indemnity insurance

◆ Proper transfer of purlin loads either to load bearing walls or specially designed joists.

Proper cut roof construction.
The sketches on these pages show the parts of a well designed and constructed cut roof. Note the triangulation at eaves level, and the purlin strutted on to a load bearing wall.

Note:
Cut roofs should be strapped to external walls in accordance with the guidance on pages 151 and 157.

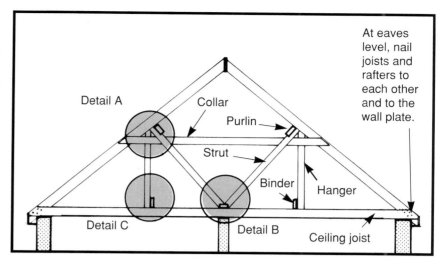

Typical section through a cut roof.

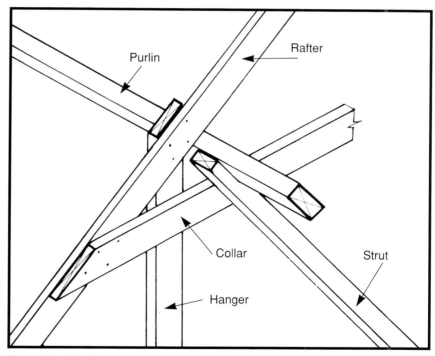

Detail A: Typical arrangement at junction of rafter, purlin, collar, hanger and strut.

PROPER CUT ROOF CONSTRUCTION
continued

Where steel members are used to provide support to ceiling joists, continuity of triangulation is lost when the joists are notched into the web of the beam. This can be overcome by strapping the joists to either side of the steel as illustrated below. The straps must be at least 30 mm x 2.5 mm and adequately nailed to the joists.

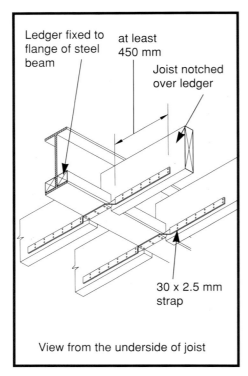

Ledger fixed to flange of steel beam

at least 450 mm

Joist notched over ledger

30 x 2.5 mm strap

View from the underside of joist

Typical fixing detail viewed from underside of ceiling joists. Beam size and fixing details in accordance with engineer's detail. The engineer appointed must be qualified by examination, be in private practice and possess professional indemnity insurance.

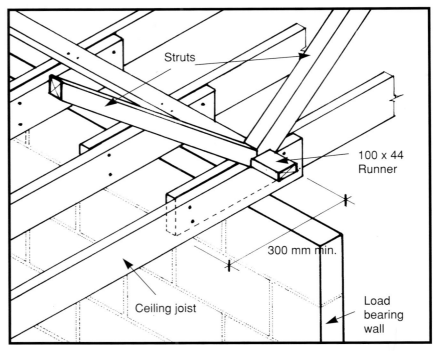

Struts

100 x 44 Runner

300 mm min.

Ceiling joist

Load bearing wall

Detail B: Arrangement of struts at ceiling level.

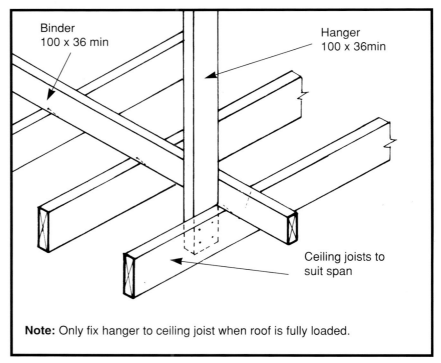

Binder 100 x 36 min

Hanger 100 x 36min

Ceiling joists to suit span

Note: Only fix hanger to ceiling joist when roof is fully loaded.

Detail C: Hanger and joist arrangement.

Note: Traditional cut roof construction assumes that the binder/hanger supports the ceiling joist. The binder is securely fixed to each ceiling joist, and the hangers (which are provided every third or fourth rafter) are nailed to the ceiling joists after the roof is loaded.

PURLINS

Purlins are horizontal members which give intermediate support to the rafters. The purlins are in turn supported by struts which must bear onto a load bearing partition or specially designed ceiling joist.

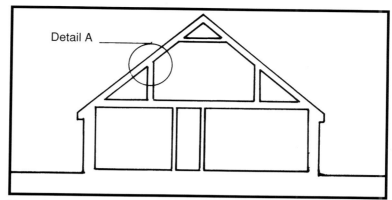

Key sketch – location of purlin.

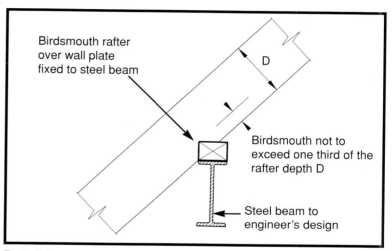

Detail A .
Rafters to purlin: A birdsmouth joint should be used if the purlin is to be fixed vertically.

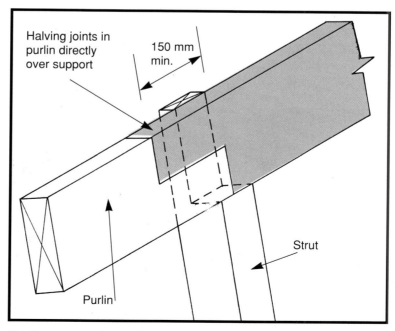

Purlin connections: Support must be provided directly under the joint. Cut purlins to suit strut positions.

PURLINS
continued

It is essential to prop purlins at regular intervals.

For example a 75 x 175 mm purlin of Strength Class C18, with a rafter span of 1.75 m and a pitch of 30°, would normally require to be propped at 2.42 m. A 75 x 255 mm purlin of Strength Class C24, with a rafter span of 1.5 m would require to be propped at 3.52 m.

Note: rafter span is measured on the slope: see pages 201 and 202.

NEVER PROP A PURLIN OFF A CEILING JOIST UNLESS THE CEILING JOIST IS DESIGNED TO CARRY THE LOAD

Purlin and struts supported by specially designed timber beam.

Struts supported by specially designed timber beam.

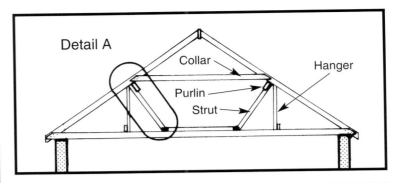

Detail A

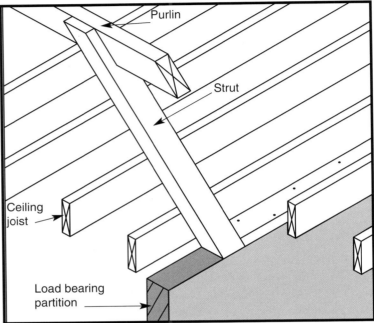

Detail A: Detail of strutting purlin onto a load bearing wall
Note: For clarity the hangers have been omitted from this sketch.

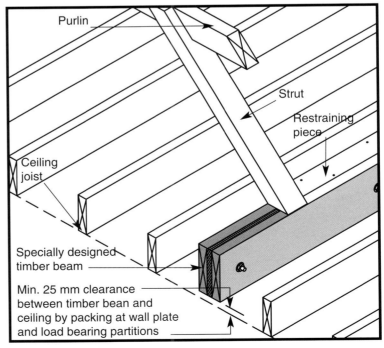

Alternative detail A: Where a purlin cannot be propped onto a wall, it may be propped onto a specially designed timber beam, (but not an ordinary ceiling joist), or onto a steel beam, see page 179.

Hipped ends

See comment on pages 168 and 169 with regard to the construction of hips.

Hip rafter and purlin connection:
It is vital that the hipped rafter in this location be notched over and securely nailed to the purlins. The purlins must be mitred and supported at or close to their intersection and the struts themselves must be supported.

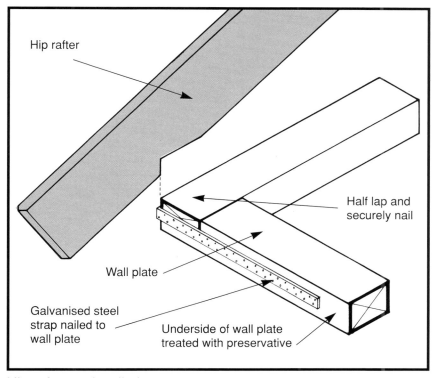

Hip rafter and wall plate.

Hip rafter

Half lap and securely nail

Wall plate

Galvanised steel strap nailed to wall plate

Underside of wall plate treated with preservative

HIPPED ENDS
continued

To reduce outward thrust at the corner under the hip, it is necessary, at the intersection of the wall plates, to half lap and securely nail them and then:

1. Reinforce the corner with a galvanised steel strap as illustrated in Fig. 1, or

2. Reinforce the corner with an angle tie securely nailed to the wall plates as illustrated in Fig. 2.

Additionally, in the case of heavily loaded hips, securely fix a galvanised steel dragon tie to both angle tie and hip rafter as illustrated on page 177.

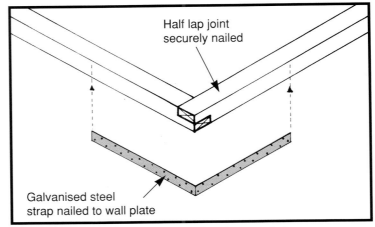

1 Use of galvanised steel strip to reinforce corner. This method is strongly recommended.

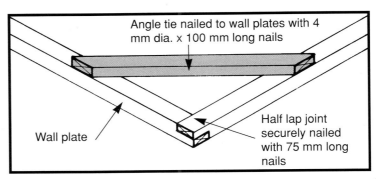

2 Angle tie nailed securely to wall plates.

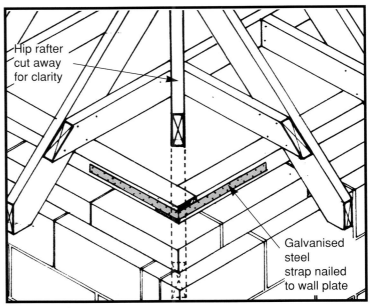

'Cutaway' view of typical detail at foot of hip.

HIPPED ENDS
continued

Hips: See commentary on pages 168 and 169 with regard to the construction of hips.

Angle tie at corner – note wall plate tying down straps.

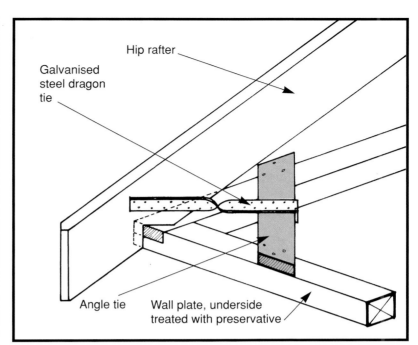

Use, in the case of heavily loaded hips, of a galvanised steel dragon tie securely fixed to the hip rafter and the angle tie.

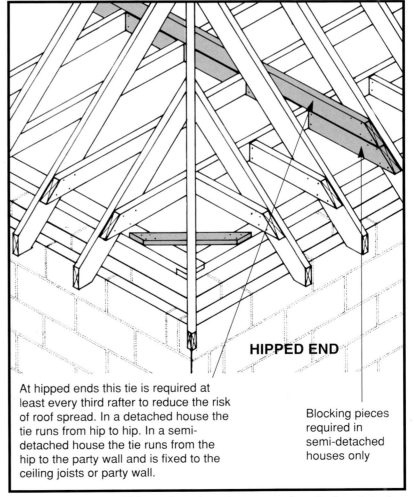

At hipped ends this tie is required at least every third rafter to reduce the risk of roof spread. In a detached house the tie runs from hip to hip. In a semi-detached house the tie runs from the hip to the party wall and is fixed to the ceiling joists or party wall.

Blocking pieces required in semi-detached houses only

HIPPED END

Typical junction of hipped roof and corner of wall. As stated earlier, the corner under the hip is subject to outward thrust from the roof load. Secure fixing and tying of the wall plate is necessary to satisfactorily resist this thrust.

VALLEY CONSTRUCTION

When constructing valley roofs, particular care should be exercised in the weathering and structural detailing. When a valley rafter supports jack rafters, significant deflection can occur in the valley rafter, together with horizontal thrust at eaves level. Where the roof rafters are supported by intermediate purlins, the valley rafter often bears on the junction of the two purlins. Consideration must be given to the support of the purlins at this location. Where any doubt exists about the structure of the valley, an engineer must be engaged. The engineer appointed must be qualified by examination, be in private practice and possess professional indemnity insurance.

For guidance on the weathering of valleys see pages 209 and 211.

WATER CISTERN SUPPORT IN CUT TIMBER ROOFS

As with prefabricated trussed roofs, the weight of the water cistern in cut timber roofs must be adequately supported.

Where possible, the cisterns should be located directly above and bear on a load bearing partition. Where this is not possible, the joists carrying the cistern(s) must be specifically designed to carry the additional load.

INTRODUCTION

The incorporation of accommodation within the roof space is a common feature in house design. A roof incorporating such accommodation is called a dormer roof and the term dormer bungalow similarly applies to a bungalow with rooms in the roof space.

In the construction of a dormer roof a number of other items require attention, in addition to the matters relevant to the conventional roof as outlined on the preceding pages.

Structure

In dormer roofs the need to provide clear space of adequate width and height to accommodate rooms means that the structural form of the roof differs significantly from a conventional roof space. The design of the roof structure must take this into account, and ensure that sizing and disposition of members is adequate. The design must take into account the additional loads imposed, particularly on joists. In some cases a satisfactory structure can be achieved by timber construction throughout. In other cases it may involve the incorporation of structural steel members such as RSJs or Universal Beams as part of the structural design of the roof.

Partially constructed dormer roof, incorporating steel sections as part of the roof structure.

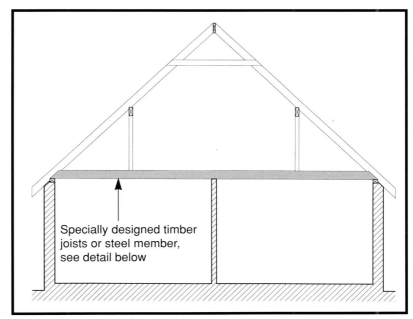

Dormer roof structure incorporating timber structural members. In this case the joists must be designed to take extra load from the roof or else an RSJ or U.B. must be provided under purlin support.

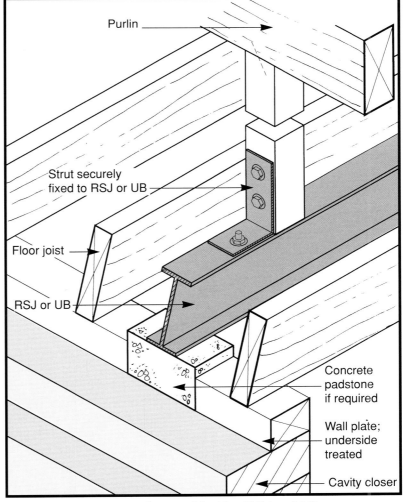

Typical support to purlin provided by RSJ or U.B.

STRUCTURE
continued

As a general rule the overall shape of a dormer roof should form a triangle: that is, the floor joists should be tied to the feet of the rafters to form a rigid frame. In some cases this may not occur – for example, where wall plate level is raised above floor level of the dormer accommodation to achieve a satisfactory ceiling height. In such cases, the absence of the usual triangulation must be compensated for by suitable alternative means in the design of the roof structure.
In all cases the structural design of a dormer roof should be carried out by an engineer. The engineer appointed must be qualified by examination, be in private practice and possess professional indemnity insurance.

As an alternative to an engineer designed cut roof, purpose-designed prefabricated dormer trusses can be used to form the roof structure.

Daylighting in dormer roofs

The provision of day light to rooms in dormer roofs is commonly achieved by the incorporation of dormer windows or rooflights. While there are no specific daylighting provisions in Building Regulations for window / rooflight sizes, it is recommended that the area of such openings be at least 10% of the floor area of the room served, to ensure a reasonable level of daylighting. Ventilation is required to ensure that dormer roofs are adequately ventilated to prevent condensation. A vapour barrier is also required on the warm side of the insulation, (see page 185).

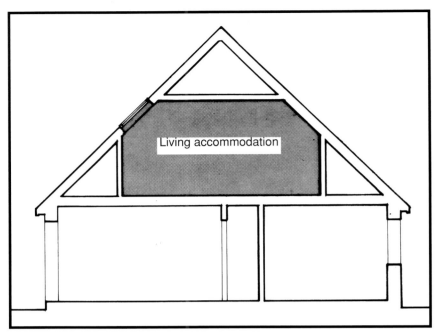

Dormer roof incorporating conventional triangulation at eaves.

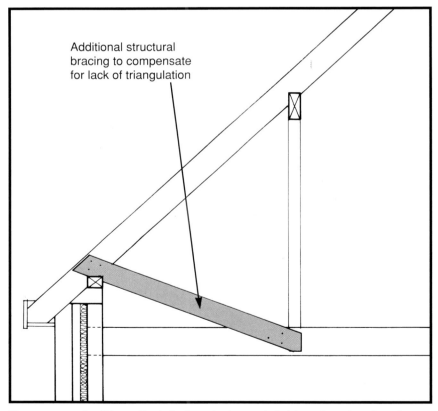

Dormer roof with wall plate level above joist level – structural bracing of the type illustrated or suitable alternative must be provided to compensate for absence of triangulation. Engineer's design is required in these situations. The engineer appointed must be qualified by examination, be in private practice and possess professional indemnity insurance.

DORMER WINDOWS

Ensure dormer windows of the type illustrated opposite are fully framed and jointed before roof finishes to dormer and main roof are laid.

Trimming members around dormers must be of adequate size to take the extra load from the cut main roof members.

The dormer window structure must be framed so that it is independent of the window frame, and incorporate a suitable lintel over the opening. Window frames are not intended to carry roof loads.

Weathering details

Where a flat roof adjoins a pitched roof, or where valleys or gutters occur, the water proof membrane should be carried up under the tiling to a height of 150 mm above the flat roof, valley or gutter, and be overlapped by the roofing underlay.

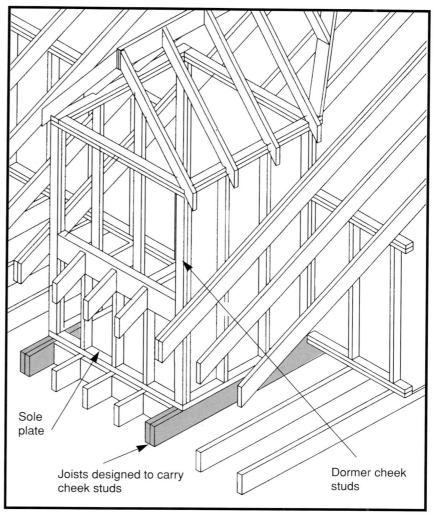

Sole plate

Joists designed to carry cheek studs

Dormer cheek studs

Typical dormer window construction. **Note:** The double joists which are designed to carry the dormer cheek studs.

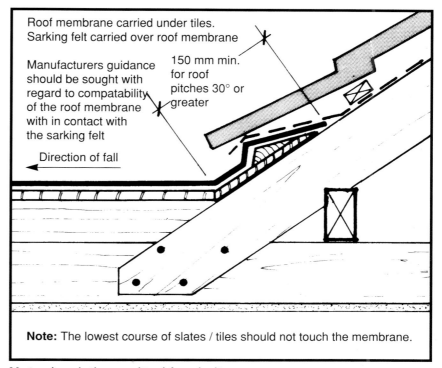

Roof membrane carried under tiles. Sarking felt carried over roof membrane

Manufacturers guidance should be sought with regard to compatability of the roof membrane with in contact with the sarking felt

150 mm min. for roof pitches 30° or greater

Direction of fall

Note: The lowest course of slates / tiles should not touch the membrane.

Note: Insulation omitted for clarity.

DORMER WINDOWS
continued

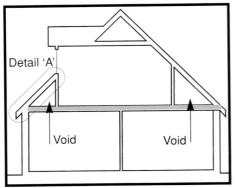

Typical dormer.

In addition to the floor of the dormer accommodation, the ceiling below the triangular voids must provide modified half hour fire resistance. In the case of dormer construction in a three-storey configuration, the appropriate level of fire resistance for all floors is a full half hour. For details of how modified and full half hour resistance can be achieved, see page 392.

Note:
Every effort should be made at design stage to ensure rafters and floor joists run in the same direction so that adequate triangulation can be achieved. If this is not possible due to the layout of the joists, then engineer's advice must be obtained to ensure that there is adequate tying back of rafters as indicated in the sketch. The horizontal thrust must be catered for to stop roof spread. The engineer appointed must be qualified by examination, be in private practice and possess professional indemnity insurance.

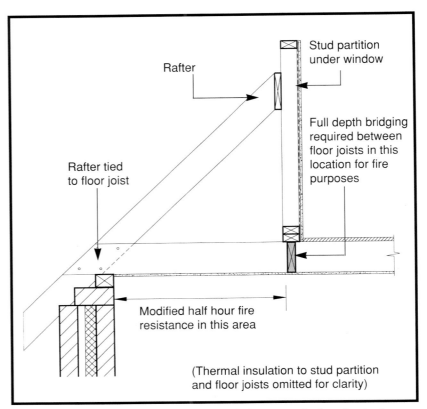

Detail A: Typical detail where floor joists are tied to feet of rafters. The floor joists must be designed to take the additional load from the dormer.

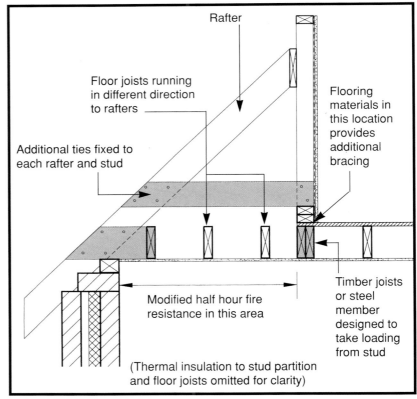

Alternative detail 'A': Where joists run parallel with wall plate, the partition should bear on timber joists or steel member designed to take the additional loading.

INTRODUCTION

Ventilation of roof spaces is necessary to remove water vapour and prevent harmful condensation. The need for ventilation is a consequence of higher standards of insulation, and an increase in activities generating water vapour within buildings.

Roof ventilation requirements

The sketches on pages 183 to 185 illustrate the dimensional requirements for continuous ventilation openings for various roof types, as set out in Technical Guidance Document F of the Building Regulations. These requirements should be complied with to avoid long-term condensation and associated problems.

The continuous openings or their equivalent* should have an area on opposite sides at least equal to a continuous ventilation strip running the full length of the eaves. The width of the strip depends on the roof type.

*The sketches on pages 183 to 185 illustrate the roof void being ventilated through the soffit. If, however, it is not possible to do this, alternative means of ventilation may be adopted. For example, the use of proprietary vent slates or vent tiles suitably located, provided that the number of vent slates/tiles used, gives the same equivalent area of ventilation as soffit ventilation for any given roof type. See page 187 for additional information and calculation methods for vent slates/tiles.

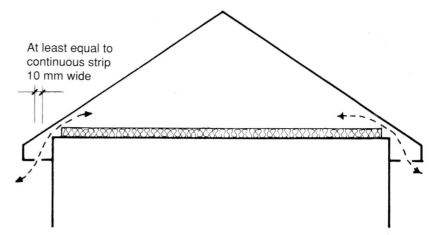

Pitched roof greater than 15°.

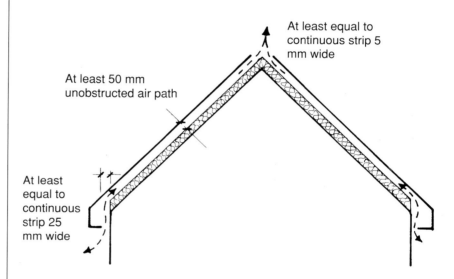

Ceiling following pitch of roof.

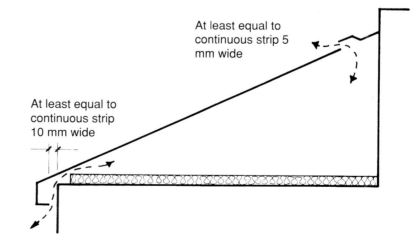

Lean-to roof.

Note: Dimensions for ventilation openings given in all the illustrations are for continuous openings. Alternatively, regularly spaced openings, suitably located and giving the same aggregate area, may be used.

ROOF VENTILATION REQUIREMENTS
continued

Means of ventilation

Continuous eaves ventilation using proprietary soffit vent incorporating fly screen to prevent birds, insects etc. entering the roof void.

At least equal to continuous strip 25 mm wide

At least 50 mm unobstructed air path

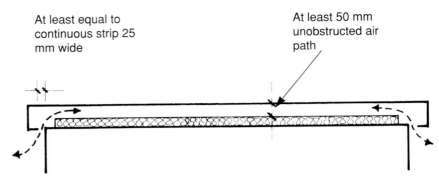

Flat roof (cold deck construction).

At least equal to continuous strip 25 mm wide

At least 50 mm unobstructed air path

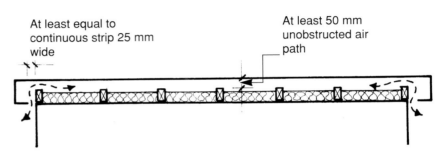

Flat roof (cold deck construction).

At least equal to continuous strip 25 mm wide

At least 50 mm unobstructed air path

At least equal to continuous strip 25 mm wide

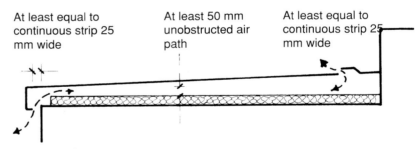

Flat roof abutment with wall (cold deck construction).

No ventilation required in this roof

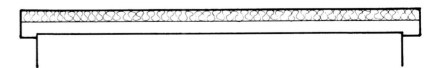

Flat roof (warm deck or inverted roof construction).

Note: Dimensions for ventilation openings given in all the illustrations are for continuous openings. Alternatively, regularly spaced openings suitably located and giving the same aggregate area, may be used.

ROOF VENTILATION REQUIREMENTS
continued

Vapour control layers

Vapour control layers can reduce the amount of moisture reaching the roof void, but cannot be relied on as an alternative to ventilation. In the case of dormer roofs where the ventilation is along the line of the rafters, it is necessary to install a vapour control layer on the warm side of the insulation, e.g., 500 gauge polythene with sealed laps or its equivalent.

Note: Any roofing underlay used must be appropriately certified, and installed in accordance with the requirements of the certificate. Certain types of roofing underlay may require a vapour control layer at ceiling level, and/or extra ventilation of the roof space. In such cases, manufactuer's guidance should be sought.

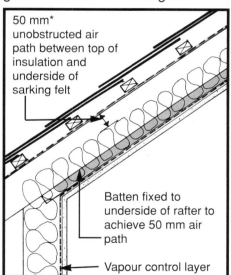

*To ensure the provision of the 50 mm unobstructed air path as illustrated on the sketches opposite, it may be necessary, because of the depth of insulation required and the depth of the rafter, to batten out the sloping portion of the roof. Alternatively, rafters deeper than actually required may be used.

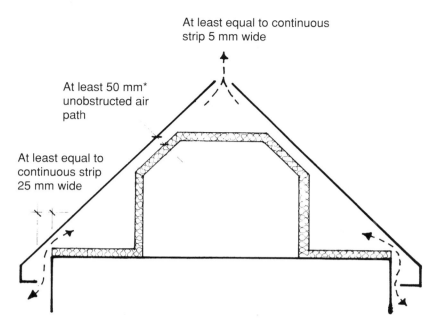

Dormer roof.

Note: If the roof above a dormer window is of pitched roof construction, provide at least 10 mm continuous strip along eaves on both sides.

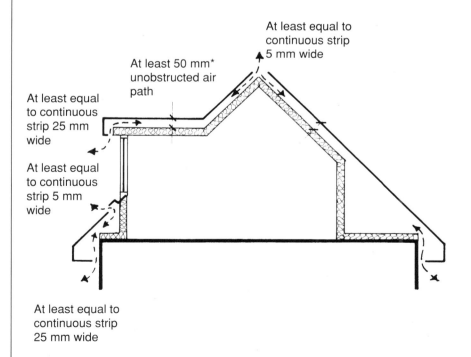

Dormer roof with flat roof dormer window.

Note: Dimensions for ventilation openings given in all the illustrations are for continuous openings. Alternatively, regularly spaced openings suitably located giving the same aggregate area may be used.

MEANS OF VENTILATION

Eaves ventilation

To ensure an unobstructed flow of air over the insulation at eaves level, the use of proprietary eaves ventilators is recommended.

Typical eaves ventilators.

Fixing of eaves ventilators.

Tile/slate ventilators.

Where it is not possible to ventilate the roof void through the soffit or at a lean-to roof abutment, proprietary tile/slate ventilators may be used. Page 187 outlines how to calculate the number of vent tiles/slates required. They should be installed in accordance with the manufacturer's instructions.

Ventilation to a lean-to roof abutment

Note:

In lean-to roof construction where the ceiling follows the slope of the roof, vent slates/tiles should not be used as the area between all the rafters will not be ventilated. For such construction, continuous abutment ventilation of the type illustrated on page 188 is required.

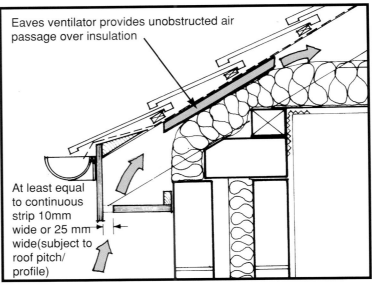

Eaves ventilator provides unobstructed air passage over insulation

At least equal to continuous strip 10mm wide or 25 mm wide(subject to roof pitch/profile)

Ventilation at eaves, the conventional method. (Provide mesh to obstruct insects etc.)

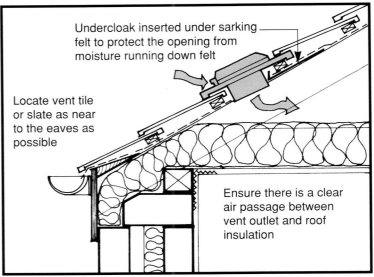

Undercloak inserted under sarking felt to protect the opening from moisture running down felt

Locate vent tile or slate as near to the eaves as possible

Ensure there is a clear air passage between vent outlet and roof insulation

Ventilation at eaves using vent tile.

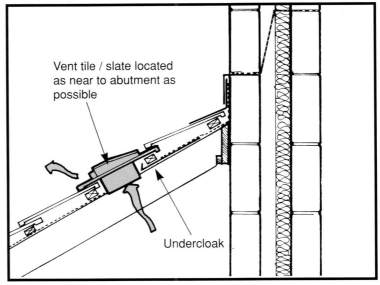

Vent tile / slate located as near to abutment as possible

Undercloak

Ventilation of lean-to roof at abutment.

SLATE AND TILE VENTILATORS

These can be used on slated or tiled roofs where the form of construction does not allow conventional ventilation at eaves level, and in certain circumstances at mid or high level, including: parapet walls, mansard roofs, and monopitched roof construction.

Vent slate.

Vent tile.

Calculating the number of tiles / slate ventilators required for a particular roof to achieve through ventilation at eaves level.

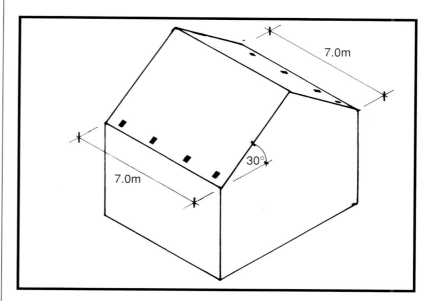

Example: The slated roof on the house has a total eaves length of 14 m and a roof pitch of 30°. The Building Regulations Technical Guidance Document F requires a 10mm continuous opening over the entire eaves length (or equivalent) for a roof with a pitch of 15° or more.

For this example, it is assumed the form of construction will not permit conventional ventilation at eaves, so proprietary slate or tile ventilators will have to be used.

Calculations

(Total eaves length) x (continuous opening size) ÷ (Capacity of vent slate/tile)=(No. of vent slates/tiles reqd.)

Note: The capacity of a vent slate / tile refers to the area it can adequately ventilate. This figure varies depending on the manufacturer. A typical figure would be 20,000 mm² (Manufacturer's guidance should be sought).

(14,000 mm) x (10 mm) = (140,000 mm²)
140,000 mm² ÷ 20,000 mm² = 7 no. vent slates required (minimum). Provide 8, i.e. 4 at each side of roof.

FLAT ROOF:
COLD DECK CONSTRUCTION

If this form of construction is used, the plasterboard in the ceiling should be foil backed, or a vapour control layer (e.g. 500 gauge polythene) should be tacked to the underside of the joists to control moisture build up in the insulation.

As advised on page 193 this form of roof construction should be avoided if at all possible due to the high risk of leaking, condensation and relatively low life expectancy of such construction.

Another means of ventilating flat roofs is the use of proprietary mushroom vents of the type illustrated. Manufacturers' brochures will advise on the required frequency of such vents in a roof. Such vents should be installed in conjunction with counter battens fixed above the tapered firring pieces, to achieve unobstructed airflow across the roof, as illustrated on page 194.

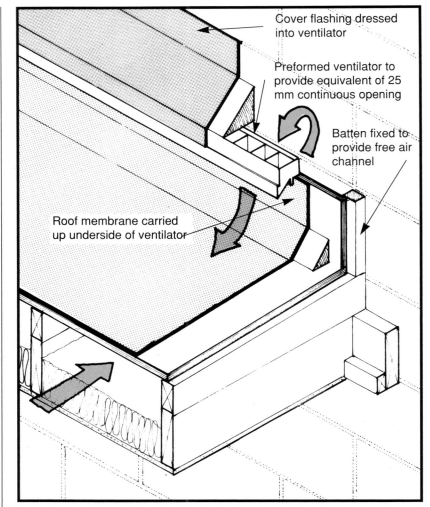

Cover flashing dressed into ventilator

Preformed ventilator to provide equivalent of 25 mm continuous opening

Batten fixed to provide free air channel

Roof membrane carried up underside of ventilator

Flat roof (cold deck construction) ventilation at abutments.

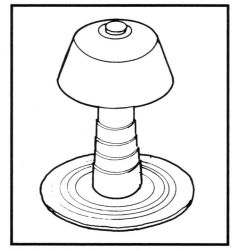

Typical "mushroom" ventilator.

DUO PITCHED ROOF WITH CENTRAL DIVISION WALL

This form of lean-to construction requires careful attention to the detail of the fixing of the head of the rafter to ensure rigidity, while maintaining the integrity of the party wall from the point of view of fire safety and sound insulation. The sketches on this page illustrate a recommended approach to such details. Supports to rafters and ceiling joists are omitted for clarity. All timber to be sized in accordance with IS 444.

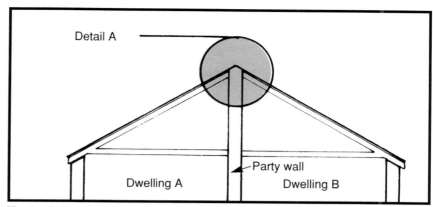

Typical "back-to-back" dwellings.

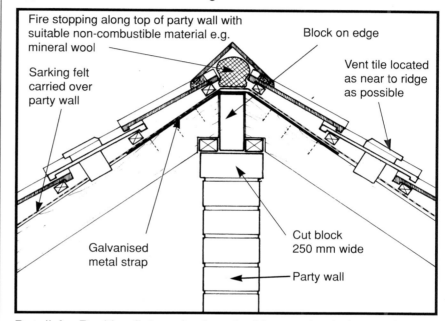

Detail A - Positive fixing of rafters in this area is vital to avoid horizontal thrust at eaves level.

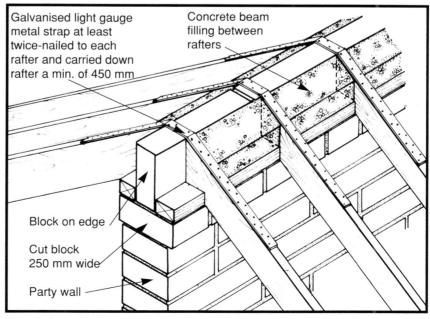

Detail A.

DUO PITCHED ROOF WITH CENTRAL DIVISION WALL

An alternative to the 'cut timber' back to back lean-to illustrated on the previous page is the use of prefabricated mono trusses as illustrated opposite.

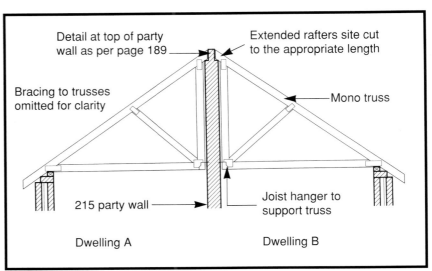

Typical 'back to back' detail using prefabricated mono trusses.

LEAN-TO ROOFS ABUTMENT DETAIL

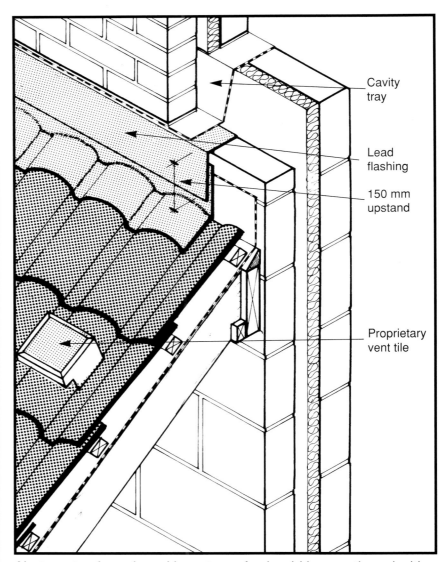

Abutments of porch and lean-to roofs should be weathered with flashings built into cavity tray as shown. Ventilation to the roof should be as described previously.

CANOPIES

Canopies over front doors are a regular feature in new houses. While the canopy itself is usually a relatively simple construction, detailed thought should be given to the support of the structure.

The photo below illustrates the consequences of inadequate support to a canopy. In this particular case the upper connection failed and the canopy collapsed.

Canopies can be built in a number of ways, including:

◆ Canopies supported on full height posts

◆ Canopies supported by struts

◆ Cantilever canopies.

The sketches on these pages illustrate typical fixing details for small canopies of traditional construction methods. For large or complicated canopies, fixing details should be obtained from an engineer. The engineer appointed must be qualified by examination, be in private practice and possess professional indemnity insurance.

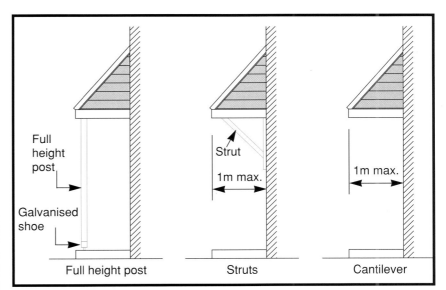

Typical canopy configurations.

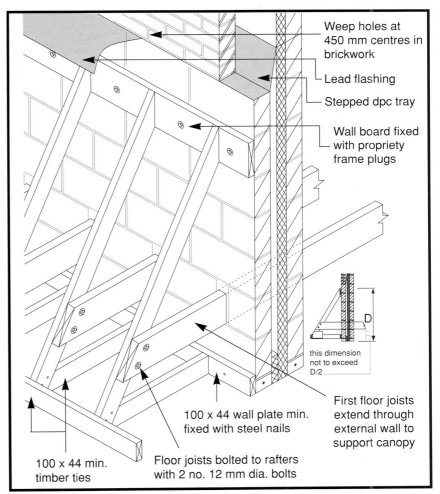

Cantilever canopy fixed to face of wall and supported by first floor joists. This method is suitable for both cavity and hollow blockwork construction but should only be used where the first floor joists are at right angles to the external wall containing the canopy.

CANOPIES
continued

Cantilever canopies can also be supported by means of rafters securely fixed to a wall plate with 30 mm x 2.5 mm x 800 mm min. long (600 mm min. measured on rafter slope) galvanised straps, at each rafter location. The wall plate is in turn fixed through the external wall by means of a minimum of 4 no. 12 mm min.dia. stainless steel bolts/threaded bar, which terminate at a back plate as illustrated opposite.

The method is suitable for both hollow blockwork and cavity wall construction.

Where brackets containing struts provide support to the canopy, the bracket should be securely fixed to the masonry by means of suitable stainless steel fixings.
Each of the fixings should terminate at a back plate, as illustrated opposite.

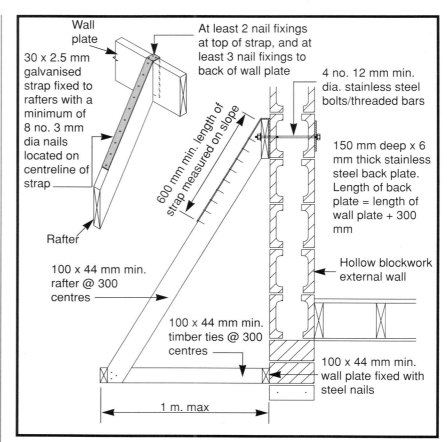

Typical fixing method for self-supporting canopy. When using this fixing method in cavity wall construction, the backplate may be located on the inside face of the outer leaf of masonry.

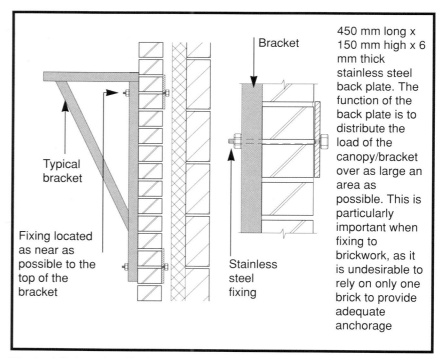

Typical fixing details for bracket support. These details can also be used in hollow blockwork construction.

INTRODUCTION

If at all possible, flat roof construction should be avoided due to the high risk of leaking, condensation and to the relatively low life expectancy of such construction.

Where flat roofs are used the following points must be taken into account:

◆ Concrete flat roofs without covering (to garages and outhouses for example) are prone to leaking. If a concrete flat roof is used provide a waterproof roof covering

◆ Chipboard, including prefelted chipboard, should not be used as the decking of a flat roof. Use weather and boil proof plywood (WBP) or moisture resistant oriented strand board (OSB). The roof designer should ensure that the appropriate decking for the purpose intended is used

◆ Use a good quality roof covering. Make sure it has an Agrément or other relevant certificate and is laid in accordance with manufacturer's instructions

◆ Lay flat roofs so that the design fall at no point is less than 1 in 40

◆ All water must drain away with no ponding.

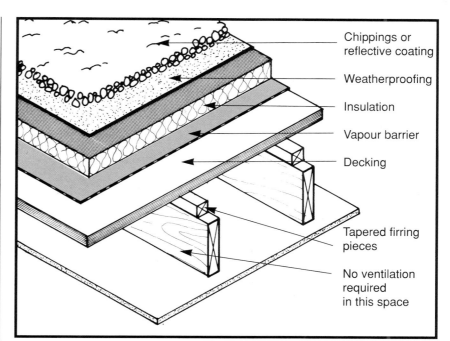

Warm deck roof: insulation above deck level.
Insulation must be rigid.

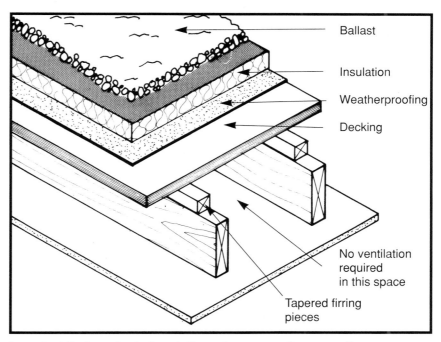

Inverted timber deck: insulation above weather proofing.
Insulation must be rigid and appropriate for use.

POINTS TO CONSIDER
continued

Pay particular attention to outlet points to ensure that ridges do not cause ponding.

◆ On balconies, ensure that there is a second rainwater outlet and a 150 mm upstand at any entrance doors

◆ Provide a layer of chippings to felt roofs as a fire prevention precaution and to reduce solar heat gain. Other finishes may be treated with proprietary reflective coating

◆ Where flat roof areas are contained by parapet and upstand walls, make provision for roof drainage overflow in the event of outlets becoming blocked.

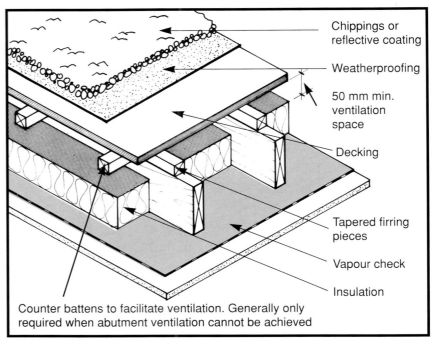

Chippings or reflective coating

Weatherproofing

50 mm min. ventilation space

Decking

Tapered firring pieces

Vapour check

Insulation

Counter battens to facilitate ventilation. Generally only required when abutment ventilation cannot be achieved

Cold deck construction: insulation between joists. Avoid this construction if possible.

COLD DECK CONSTRUCTION

Avoid using cold deck roof construction if at all possible. In the rare cases where it has to be used, it is necessary to ensure that the roof space is thoroughly ventilated to avoid build up of moisture and risk of timber decay.

A vapour barrier properly lapped and sealed is essential to control moisture build-up in insulation. Thorough ventilation of the roof void can be achieved by nailing counter battens on top of the firring pieces. If it is not possible to do this, an alternative means is to ventilate the roof at the abutment using preformed ventilators as illustrated on this page.

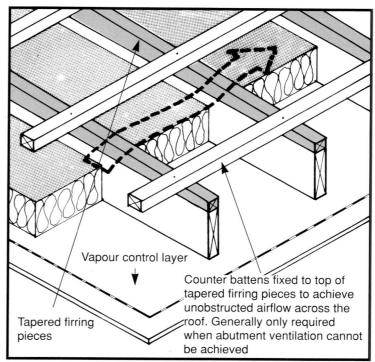

Vapour control layer

Counter battens fixed to top of tapered firring pieces to achieve unobstructed airflow across the roof. Generally only required when abutment ventilation cannot be achieved

Tapered firring pieces

Cold deck roof.
If this form of construction is used the plasterboard in the ceiling should be foil back and a vapour control layer (e.g. 500 gauge polythene) should be tacked to the underside of the joists, to control moisture build up in the insulation.

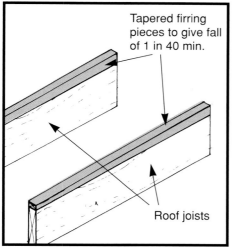

Tapered firring pieces to give fall of 1 in 40 min.

Roof joists

Use firring pieces to achieve fall in roof (or screed to falls on concrete decks).

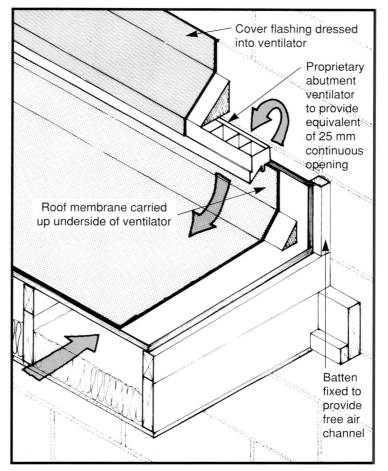

Cover flashing dressed into ventilator

Proprietary abutment ventilator to provide equivalent of 25 mm continuous opening

Roof membrane carried up underside of ventilator

Batten fixed to provide free air channel

Ventilation at abutment.

IMPORTANT NOTE

At the time of publication of this document, IS 444: 1998.
The use of structural timber in buildings had just superseded SR 11: Structural timber for domestic construction. SR 11 has been withdrawn and should no longer be used.
To aid the transition between these documents this publication reproduces extracts from both, see Appendix J.

INTRODUCTION

IS 444: 1998: The use of structural timber in buildings is the Irish standard for structural timber applications.

The standard provides span tables for various joist and rafter sizes across a range of strength classifications and spacings. Joist and rafter size is referred to as "target size", which is the desired size at 20% moisture content.

The average actual thickness and width of timber members should not be less than the target size, making allowance for changes in size due to changes in moisture content.

The moisture content at the time of construction should not normally exceed 20% with no value exceeding 24%.

For the design of timber outside the scope of IS 444 an engineer should be engaged. The engineer appointed must be qualified by examination, be in private practice and possess professional indemnity insurance.

IS 444 is available from: National Standards Authority of Ireland, Glasnevin, Dublin 9.

The following pages 196 to 205 explain IS 444, give worked examples and reproduce some of the tables.

STRENGTH CLASSIFICATION

IS 444 divides timber in ascending order of strength into six strength classes (C14, C16, C18, C22, C24, C27) depending on the species and grade of timber.

The common species and grades of Irish and imported timber that fall into these strength classes are set out below.

Combinations of species and visual strength grades.					
Softwood Species	Strength classes				
	C14	C16	C18	C22	C24
Irish Timber:					
Sitka Spruce	GS		SS		
Norway Spruce	GS		SS		
Lodgepole Pine	GS		SS		
Douglas Fir	GS		SS		
Larch		GS		SS	
Scots Pine		GS		SS	
Imported Timber:					
European Whitewood		GS			SS
European Redwood		GS			SS
Douglas Fir-Larch*		GS			SS
Spruce-Pine-Fir*		GS			SS
Hem-Fir*		GS			SS

*Source, Canada or USA

Note: NSAI/Enterprise Ireland should be contacted for the designation of other species and visual grades into an appropriate strength class. IS/EN 1912 lists visual strength grades, species and sources of timber and strength class from IS/EN 338 into which they are assigned.
All structural timber may be machine graded to the strength classes listed above, and in addition to strength class C27 as defined in table 2 of IS444.

TIMBER STRENGTH GRADES

The strength grade abbreviations in the above table are as follows:

GS - general structural grade visually graded.
SS - special structural grade visually graded.

Visual grading in accordance with IS/EN 519.

Visual grading in accordance with IS 127

Mechanical grading in accordance with IS/EN 519

TIMBER IDENTIFICATION MARKS

In order to comply with the requirements of IS 444, timber must be marked with the following information which will identify:

◆ Appropriate strength class and/or species grade

◆ Design standard (IS 444).

The grading and marking of timber by individual companies is subject to the supervisory control of The Timber Quality Bureau of Ireland, Enterprise Ireland, Glasnevin, Dublin 9.

Outlined opposite are typical examples of the visual and machine strength grading stamps which must occur on timber complying with the requirements of IS 444. Other combinations of species, grade and strength class are possible.

Species & Source Codes

Softwood Species	Source	Code
Species group 1 Sitka/Norway Spruce Lodgepole Pine Douglas Fir	Ireland	WE[1]/SGI
Species group 2 Larch Scots Pine	Ireland	WE[1]/SG2
Sitka/Norway Spruce	UK	B[2]/S
Douglas Fir	UK	B[2]/DF
Whitewood	NNE Europe[3]	EW
Redwood	NNE Europe[3]	ER
Whitewood & Redwood combined	NNE Europe[3]	EW/ER
Douglas Fir-Larch	North America	NA/DFL
Spruce-Pine-Fir	North America	NA/SPF
Hemlock Fir	North America	NA/HF

1 WE = Western Europe. This also includes timber grown in Britain.
2 B = British. A designation used in BS4978 which includes timber grown in Ireland.
3 Northern and North Eastern Europe, which includes the Scandinavian countries and Russia.

Visual Strength Grading Stamps

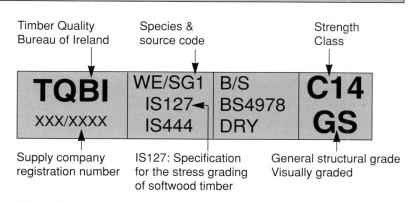

Timber Quality Bureau of Ireland — Species & source code — Strength Class

| TQBI XXX/XXXX | WE/SG1 IS127 IS444 | B/S BS4978 DRY | C14 GS |

Supply company registration number — IS127: Specification for the stress grading of softwood timber — General structural grade Visually graded

SG1 = Sitka Spruce, Norway Spruce, Douglas Fir, Lodgepole Pine

| TQBI XXX/XXXX | WE/SG1 IS127 IS444 | B/S BS4978 DRY | C18 SS |

SG1 = Sitka Spruce, Norway Spruce, Douglas Fir, Lodgepole Pine

| TQBI XXX/XXXX | EW/ER IS127 IS444 | EW/ER BS4978 DRY | C16 GS |

EW/ER = European Whitewood and Redwood

| TQBI XXX/XXXX | EW/ER IS127 IS444 | EW/ER BS4978 DRY | C24 SS |

EW/ER = European Whitewood and Redwood

Machine strength grading stamps

| TQBI XXX | WE/SG1 ISEN519 | B/S DRY BSEN519 | C16 IS444 |

Structural grading requirements for machine strength graded timber and grading machines

SG1 = Sitka Spruce, Norway Spruce, Douglas Fir, Lodgepole Pine

| TQBI XXX | WE/SG2 ISEN519 | B/S DRY BSEN519 | C18 IS444 |

SG2 = Scots Pine, Larch

CEILING JOISTS

The permissible clear span according to IS 444 is measured between the supports. However, traditional cut roof construction assumes that a hanger/binder connection supports the ceiling joists, the binders/ hangers being securely fixed to the ceiling joists. Based on this assumption, the span of the ceiling joist is from the support to the binder connection.

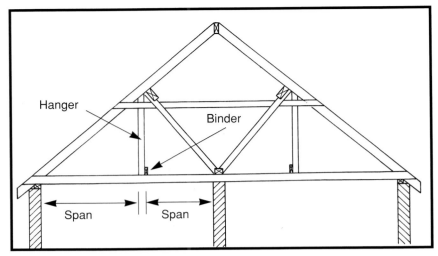

The permissible span is the clear span between supports.

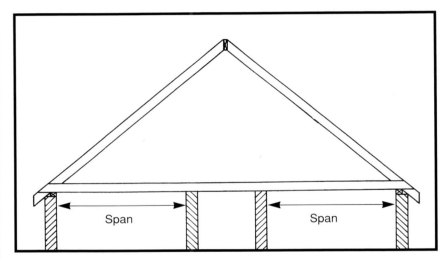

Ceiling joist span, measured between supports.

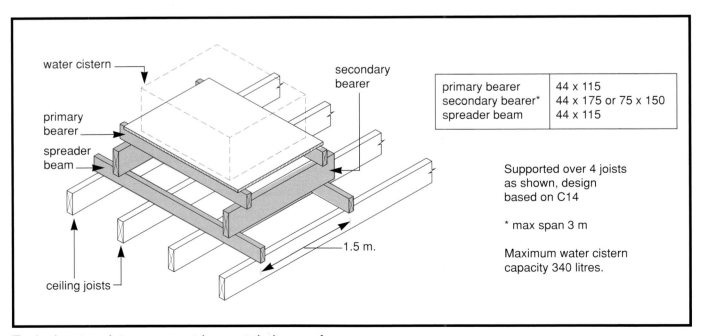

primary bearer	44 x 115
secondary bearer*	44 x 175 or 75 x 150
spreader beam	44 x 115

Supported over 4 joists as shown, design based on C14

* max span 3 m

Maximum water cistern capacity 340 litres.

Typical water cistern support in a cut timber roof

CEILING JOIST SPAN TABLES
(pitched roofs 20° to 40°)

Target size of joist (mm)	Class of timber / Spacing of rafters in mm / Span in metres																	
	C14			C16			C18			C22			C24			C27		
	300	400	600	300	400	600	300	400	600	300	400	600	300	400	600	300	400	600
36 x 100	1.58	1.53	1.43	1.99	1.91	1.78	2.16	2.07	1.92	2.48	2.37	2.19	2.70	2.57	2.36	3.45	3.25	2.96
36 x 115	2.01	1.93	1.79	2.52	2.40	2.21	2.72	2.59	2.38	3.11	2.95	2.69	3.38	3.19	2.90	4.27	3.95	3.44
36 x 125	2.31	2.21	2.04	2.88	2.74	2.51	3.11	2.94	2.69	3.55	3.35	3.04	3.85	3.62	3.27	4.73	4.29	3.74
36 x 150	3.10	2.94	2.69	3.84	3.61	3.27	4.13	3.87	3.49	4.69	4.38	3.92	5.06	4.71	4.21	5.69	5.16	4.50
36 x 175	3.95	3.71	3.35	4.84	4.52	4.04	5.20	4.84	4.31	5.87	5.44	4.83	6.32	5.77	5.03	6.65	6.03	5.26
36 x 200	4.83	4.50	4.03	5.88	5.45	4.84	6.30	5.82	5.15	7.02	6.37	5.55	7.28	6.60	5.75	7.61	6.90	6.01
36 x 225	5.73	5.32	4.72	6.95	6.40	5.64	7.42	6.82	5.99	7.90	7.17	6.25	8.19	7.43	6.48	8.56	7.77	6.77
44 x 100	1.90	1.82	1.70	2.38	2.27	2.10	2.58	2.45	2.26	2.95	2.80	2.56	3.20	3.03	2.77	4.04	3.67	3.19
44 x 115	2.40	2.29	2.11	2.99	2.83	2.59	3.22	3.05	2.78	3.68	3.46	3.14	3.98	3.74	3.38	4.66	4.23	3.68
44 x 125	2.75	2.61	2.40	3.41	3.22	2.93	3.67	3.46	3.14	4.18	3.92	3.53	4.52	4.23	3.79	5.07	4.60	4.01
44 x 150	3.67	3.45	3.13	4.51	4.22	3.79	4.84	4.52	4.04	5.48	5.09	4.44	5.83	5.29	4.61	6.09	5.53	4.82
44 x 175	4.63	4.33	3.88	5.66	5.25	4.66	6.06	5.61	4.97	6.57	5.96	5.19	6.81	6.18	5.38	7.12	6.46	5.63
44 x 200	5.64	5.23	4.65	6.84	6.30	5.55	7.30	6.67	5.81	7.51	6.82	5.94	7.79	7.07	6.16	8.14	7.39	6.44
44 x 225	6.67	6.15	5.43	8.04	7.37	6.45	8.28	7.51	6.54	8.46	7.67	6.69	8.77	7.96	6.94	9.16	8.31	7.25

Note:
Target size is the desired size at 20% moisture content.
Provide 50 mm min. end bearing at wall plate. Target dimensions of wall plate, 100 mm width x 75 mm deep.

Example:
Irish grown Sitka Spruce of general structural grade (GS) is required to span 1.9 m atspacings of 400 mm.
From the strength classification table on page 196, this type of timber is in strengthclass C14.
From the table above, a 36 x 115 mm joist would be suitable.

CEILING JOIST SPAN TABLES FOR PITCHED ROOFS 20° TO 40°, SUPPORTING DOMESTIC WATER CISTERN

Target size of joist (mm)	Class of timber / Spacing of joists in mm / Span in metres																	
	C14			C16			C18			C22			C24			C27		
	300	400	600	300	400	600	300	400	600	300	400	600	300	400	600	300	400	600
36 x 100	1.39	1.37	1.33	1.60	1.58	1.53	1.69	1.66	1.61	1.33	1.31	1.27	1.46	1.44	1.40	1.86	1.83	1.76
36 x 115	1.61	1.58	1.53	1.88	1.84	1.78	1.99	1.95	1.88	1.72	1.69	1.63	1.89	1.86	1.79	2.28	2.23	2.14
36 x 125	1.77	1.73	1.68	2.07	2.03	1.96	2.20	2.15	2.07	2.01	1.96	1.89	2.20	2.15	2.06	2.57	2.51	2.39
36 x 150	2.20	2.15	2.07	2.61	2.55	2.43	2.78	2.71	2.58	2.78	2.70	2.57	3.04	2.95	2.80	3.33	3.23	3.06
36 x 175	2.67	2.61	2.49	3.20	3.11	2.96	3.42	3.32	3.14	3.63	3.51	3.31	3.87	3.74	3.58	4.11	3.97	3.74
36 x 200	3.19	3.10	2.95	3.85	3.73	3.52	4.12	3.98	3.74	4.42	4.26	4.00	4.64	4.47	4.25	4.93	4.74	4.44
36 x 225	3.76	3.64	3.43	4.55	4.38	4.11	4.87	4.68	4.37	5.18	4.97	4.65	5.44	5.21	4.93	5.76	5.52	5.14
44 x 100	1.55	1.53	1.48	1.81	1.77	1.71	1.91	1.87	1.81	1.62	1.59	1.54	1.78	1.75	1.69	2.06	2.02	1.94
44 x 115	1.81	1.78	1.72	2.13	2.09	2.01	2.26	2.21	2.13	2.09	2.04	1.96	2.29	2.24	2.15	2.52	2.46	2.35
44 x 125	2.00	1.96	1.89	2.37	2.31	2.22	2.52	2.46	2.35	2.43	2.37	2.26	2.66	2.59	2.47	2.84	2.76	2.63
44 x 150	2.51	2.45	2.35	3.00	2.92	2.78	3.20	3.11	2.96	3.27	3.17	3.01	3.44	3.33	3.20	3.66	3.54	3.35
44 x 175	3.08	2.99	2.85	3.71	3.59	3.39	3.97	3.83	3.61	4.05	3.91	3.68	4.25	4.10	3.91	4.51	4.35	4.08
44 x 200	3.70	3.58	3.38	4.48	4.31	4.04	4.76	4.59	4.31	4.85	4.66	4.37	5.09	4.89	4.64	5.40	5.18	4.83
44 x 225	4.36	4.21	3.95	5.30	5.08	4.73	5.51	5.30	4.96	5.67	5.43	5.06	5.95	5.69	5.37	6.30	6.02	5.60

Note: Target size is the desired size at 20% moisture content. Provide 50 mm min. end bearing at wall plate.
Target dimensions of wall plate, 100 mm wide x 75 mm deep.

Example: From the above table a 44 x 115 mm ceiling joist of Strength Class C16 at 400 mm centres has a maximum span of 2.09m.

ROOF RAFTER SPAN TABLES FOR RAFTERS <u>WITHOUT</u> INTERMEDIATE PURLIN SUPPORT
(pitched roofs 20° to 40°)

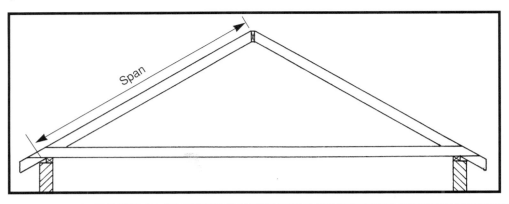

Target size of rafter (mm)	Class of timber / Spacing of rafters in mm / Span in metres																	
	C14			C16			C18			C22			C24			C27		
	300	400	600	300	400	600	300	400	600	300	400	600	300	400	600	300	400	600
36 x 100	2.47	2.17	1.76	2.70	2.44	2.01	2.73	2.47	2.10	2.79	2.53	2.20	2.89	2.62	2.28	3.02	2.74	2.39
36 x 115	2.85	2.49	2.02	3.11	2.82	2.30	3.14	2.85	2.40	3.21	2.91	2.54	3.33	3.02	2.63	3.48	3.16	2.75
36 x 125	3.10	2.70	2.19	3.38	3.07	2.50	3.42	3.10	2.61	3.50	3.17	2.76	3.62	3.29	2.87	3.79	3.44	3.00
36 x 150	3.72	3.22	2.61	4.07	3.67	2.98	4.11	3.73	3.11	4.20	3.82	3.33	4.36	3.96	3.45	4.55	4.13	3.60
36 x 175	4.32	3.74	3.04	4.76	4.25	3.46	4.81	4.36	3.61	4.91	4.46	3.89	5.09	4.62	4.03	5.32	4.83	4.21
36 x 200	4.92	4.25	3.45	5.44	4.84	3.94	5.50	5.00	4.11	5.62	5.10	4.42	5.83	5.29	4.62	6.09	5.53	4.82
36 x 225	5.51	4.76	3.87	6.13	5.42	4.41	6.20	5.63	4.60	6.33	5.75	4.95	6.56	5.96	5.19	6.86	6.23	5.43
44 x 100	2.64	2.40	1.95	2.89	2.62	2.23	2.92	2.65	2.31	2.98	2.71	2.36	3.09	2.81	2.44	3.23	2.93	2.56
44 x 115	3.05	2.76	2.24	3.33	3.02	2.55	3.36	3.05	2.66	3.44	3.12	2.72	3.56	3.23	2.82	3.72	3.38	2.95
44 x 125	3.32	2.99	2.43	3.62	3.28	2.77	3.66	3.32	2.89	3.74	3.39	2.96	3.88	3.52	3.07	4.05	3.68	3.21
44 x 150	3.99	3.56	2.90	4.35	3.95	3.30	4.40	4.00	3.44	4.50	4.08	3.56	4.66	4.23	3.69	4.87	4.42	3.86
44 x 175	4.66	4.14	3.36	5.09	4.62	3.83	5.15	4.67	4.00	5.26	4.77	4.16	5.45	4.95	4.32	5.69	5.17	4.51
44 x 200	5.34	4.70	3.83	5.82	5.28	4.36	5.89	5.34	4.55	6.01	5.46	4.76	6.24	5.66	4.94	6.51	5.91	5.16
44 x 225	6.01	5.27	4.29	6.56	5.95	4.89	6.63	6.02	5.09	6.77	6.15	5.37	7.02	6.38	5.56	7.34	6.66	5.81

Note:
Target size is the desired size at 20% moisture content.
Permissible span is measured on slope.
Provide 50 mm min. end bearing at wall plate.
Target dimensions of wall plate, 100 mm width x 75 mm deep.

Example:
European Whitewood of general strength grade (GS)
is required to span 4 m at spacings of 300 mm.
From the strength classification table on page 196,
this type of timber is in strength class C16.
From the table above, a 36 x 150 mm joist would be suitable.

ROOF RAFTER SPAN TABLES FOR RAFTERS WITH INTERMEDIATE PURLIN SUPPORT: LAPPED AT PURLIN SUPPORT (pitched roofs 20° to 40°)

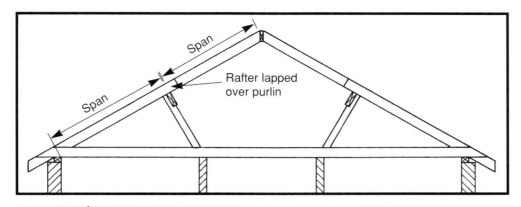

Target size of rafter (mm)	Class of timber / Spacing of rafters in mm / Span in metres																	
	C14			C16			C18			C22			C24			C27		
	300	400	600	300	400	600	300	400	600	300	400	600	300	400	600	300	400	600
36 x 100	2.47	2.15	1.74	2.70	2.44	1.99	2.73	2.47	2.08	2.79	2.53	2.20	2.89	2.62	2.28	3.02	2.74	2.39
36 x 115	2.83	2.47	2.00	3.11	2.81	2.28	3.14	2.85	2.38	3.21	2.91	2.54	3.33	3.02	2.63	3.48	3.16	2.75
36 x 125	3.07	2.67	2.17	3.38	3.05	2.48	3.42	3.10	2.58	3.50	3.17	2.76	3.62	3.29	2.87	3.79	3.44	3.00
36 x 150	3.66	3.19	2.59	4.07	3.63	2.96	4.11	3.73	3.08	4.20	3.82	3.32	4.36	3.96	3.45	4.55	4.13	3.60
36 x 175	4.25	3.70	3.01	4.76	4.22	3.43	4.81	4.36	3.58	4.91	4.46	3.85	5.09	4.62	4.03	5.32	4.83	4.21
36 x 200	4.84	4.21	3.42	5.44	4.80	3.91	5.50	5.00	4.07	5.62	5.10	4.38	5.83	5.29	4.59	6.09	5.53	4.82
36 x 225	5.42	4.72	3.83	6.13	5.37	4.38	6.20	5.60	4.56	6.33	5.75	4.91	6.56	5.96	5.14	6.86	6.23	5.43
44 x 100	2.64	2.38	1.94	2.89	2.62	2.21	2.92	2.65	2.30	2.98	2.71	2.36	3.09	2.81	2.44	3.23	2.93	2.56
44 x 115	3.05	2.73	2.22	3.33	3.02	2.53	3.36	3.05	2.64	3.44	3.12	2.72	3.56	3.23	2.82	3.72	3.38	2.95
44 x 125	3.32	2.96	2.41	3.62	3.28	2.74	3.66	3.32	2.86	3.74	3.39	2.96	3.88	3.52	3.07	4.05	3.68	3.21
44 x 150	3.99	3.53	2.87	4.35	3.95	3.27	4.40	4.00	3.41	4.50	4.08	3.56	4.66	4.23	3.69	4.87	4.42	3.86
44 x 175	4.66	4.10	3.33	5.09	4.62	3.80	5.15	4.67	3.96	5.26	4.77	4.16	5.45	4.95	4.32	5.69	5.17	4.51
44 x 200	5.34	4.66	3.79	5.82	5.28	4.32	5.89	5.34	4.51	6.02	5.46	4.76	6.24	5.66	4.94	6.51	5.91	5.16
44 x 225	5.99	5.22	4.25	6.56	5.94	4.84	6.63	6.02	5.05	6.77	6.15	5.37	7.02	6.38	5.56	7.34	6.66	5.81

Note:
Target size is the desired size at 20% moisture content.
Permissible span is measured on slope.
Provide 50 mm min. end bearing at wall plate.
Target dimensions of wall plate, 100 mm width x 75 mm deep.

Example:
European Whitewood of special structural grade (SS) is required to span 3m at spacings of 400 mm.
From the strength classification table on page 196, this type of timber is in strength class C24.
From the table above, a 36 x 115 mm joist would be suitable.

ROOF RAFTER SPAN TABLES FOR RAFTERS WITH INTERMEDIATE PURLIN SUPPORT: CONTINUOUS AT PURLIN SUPPORT (pitched roofs 20° to 40°)

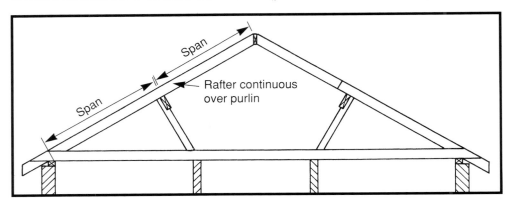

Target size of rafter (mm)	Class of timber / Spacing of rafters in mm / Span in metres																	
	C14			C16			C18			C22			C24			C27		
	300	400	600	300	400	600	300	400	600	300	400	600	300	400	600	300	400	600
36 x 100	2.51	2.16	1.75	2.85	2.47	2.00	2.97	2.57	2.09	3.19	2.76	2.25	3.34	2.90	2.36	3.77	3.28	2.68
36 x 115	2.87	2.48	2.01	3.26	2.82	2.30	3.40	2.94	2.40	3.65	3.16	2.58	3.83	3.32	2.70	4.32	3.75	3.07
36 x 125	3.11	2.69	2.18	3.54	3.06	2.49	3.69	3.19	2.60	3.96	3.43	2.80	4.15	3.60	2.93	4.68	4.07	3.32
36 x 150	3.70	3.20	2.60	4.21	3.64	2.97	4.38	3.79	3.09	4.70	4.08	3.33	4.92	4.27	3.49	5.55	4.83	3.95
36 x 175	4.23	3.67	2.98	4.80	4.16	3.40	4.99	4.33	3.54	5.34	4.65	3.80	5.59	4.87	3.98	6.28	5.48	4.49
36 x 200	4.74	4.11	3.36	5.36	4.66	3.82	5.57	4.85	3.97	5.96	5.19	4.26	6.23	5.43	4.46	6.97	6.09	5.01
36 x 225	5.42	4.69	3.82	6.15	5.33	4.35	6.40	5.55	4.53	6.86	5.96	4.87	7.18	6.24	5.10	8.08	7.03	5.77
44 x 100	2.77	2.40	1.95	3.15	2.73	2.22	3.38	2.84	2.32	3.52	3.05	2.49	3.69	3.20	2.61	4.15	3.61	2.96
44 x 115	3.18	2.75	2.23	3.61	3.12	2.55	3.75	3.25	2.65	4.03	3.50	2.85	4.22	3.66	2.99	4.76	4.14	3.39
44 x 125	3.44	2.98	2.42	3.91	3.39	2.76	4.07	3.53	2.88	4.37	3.79	3.09	4.58	3.97	3.24	5.16	4.49	3.67
44 x 150	4.11	3.55	2.89	4.66	4.04	3.29	4.85	4.21	3.43	5.21	4.52	3.69	5.46	4.74	3.87	6.15	5.35	4.38
44 x 175	4.76	4.12	3.35	5.41	4.69	3.82	5.63	4.88	3.98	6.04	5.25	4.29	6.33	5.50	4.49	7.14	6.21	5.09
44 x 200	5.35	4.64	3.78	6.07	5.27	4.30	6.31	5.48	4.48	6.76	5.88	4.81	7.08	6.16	5.05	7.96	6.94	5.70
44 x 225	5.92	5.14	4.19	6.70	5.82	4.77	6.96	6.06	4.96	7.44	6.48	5.32	7.79	6.79	5.57	8.73	7.62	6.27

Note:
Target size is the desired size at 20% moisture content.
Permissible span is measured on slope.
Provide 50 mm min. end bearing at wall plate.
Target dimensions of wall plate, 100 mm width x 75 mm deep.

Example:
Irish grown Sitka Spruce of special strength grade (SS) is required to span 4m at spacings of 300 mm.
From the strength classification table on page 196, this type of timber is in strength class C18.
From the table above, a 44 x 125 mm joist would be suitable.

PURLIN SPAN TABLES – STRENGTH CLASS C14-C16 (ROOF PITCH 20° - 40°)

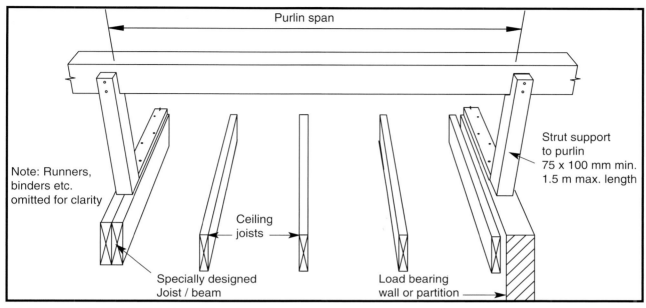

Note: Runners, binders etc. omitted for clarity

Specially designed Joist / beam

Ceiling joists

Load bearing wall or partition

Strut support to purlin 75 x 100 mm min. 1.5 m max. length

Purlin span

Target size of purlin (mm)	Span of roof rafters in metres									
	1.5	1.75	2	2.25	2.5	2.75	3	3.25	3.5	3.75
	Purlin span in metres, Class C14									
75 x 150	1.98	1.88	1.79	1.71	1.85	1.59	1.54	1.48	1.43	1.38
75 x 175	2.32	2.20	2.09	2.01	1.93	1.86	1.79	1.72	1.66	1.60
75 x 225	3.00	2.84	2.71	2.59	2.50	2.39	2.29	2.20	2.11	2.04

Target size of purlin (mm)	Span of roof rafters in metres									
	1.5	1.75	2	2.25	2.5	2.75	3	3.25	3.5	3.75
	Purlin span in metres, Class C16									
75 x 150	2.16	2.04	1.95	1.86	1.79	1.73	1.68	1.63	1.58	1.54
75 x 175	2.52	2.39	2.28	2.18	2.10	2.03	1.97	1.91	1.86	1.81
75 x 225	3.26	3.09	2.94	2.82	2.72	2.62	2.54	2.47	2.40	2.33

Note:
Target size is the desired size at 20% moisture content.
Rafter span is measured on slope.
Purlin span is the clear span between supports.

Example:
A purlin of strength class C14 is required to span 2.2 m
and is carrying roof rafters with a 1.75 m span.
A 75 x 175 mm member would be used.

The purlin span tables on the following pages do not take into account any additional loads, if any, from hangers.

PURLIN SPAN TABLES – STRENGTH CLASS C18-C22 (ROOF PITCH 20° - 40°)

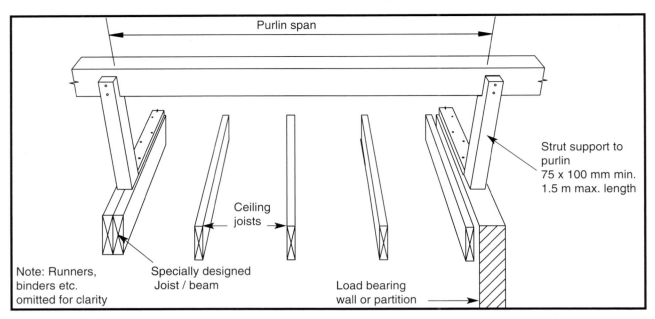

Note: Runners, binders etc. omitted for clarity

Specially designed Joist / beam

Ceiling joists

Load bearing wall or partition

Strut support to purlin 75 x 100 mm min. 1.5 m max. length

Target size of purlin (mm)	Span of roof rafters in metres									
	1.5	1.75	2	2.25	2.5	2.75	3	3.25	3.5	3.75
	Purlin span in metres, Class C18									
75 x 150	2.18	2.07	1.97	1.89	1.82	1.75	1.70	1.65	1.60	1.56
75 x 175	2.56	2.42	2.31	2.21	2.13	2.05	1.99	1.93	1.88	1.83
75 x 225	3.30	3.12	2.98	2.86	2.75	2.66	2.57	2.50	2.43	2.37

Target size of purlin (mm)	Span of roof rafters in metres									
	1.5	1.75	2	2.25	2.5	2.75	3	3.25	3.5	3.75
	Purlin span in metres, Class C22									
75 x 150	2.25	2.13	2.03	1.94	1.87	1.81	1.75	1.70	1.65	1.61
75 x 175	2.63	2.49	2.37	2.27	2.19	2.12	2.05	1.99	1.94	1.89
75 x 225	3.39	3.21	3.07	2.94	2.83	2.73	2.65	2.57	2.50	2.44

Note:
Target size is the desired size at 20% moisture content.
Rafter span is measured on slope.
Purlin span is the clear span between supports.

Example:
A purlin of strength class C22 is required to span 1.75 m
and is carrying roof rafters with a 3 m span.
A 75 x 150 mm member would be used.

PURLIN SPAN TABLES – STRENGTH CLASS C24-C27 (ROOF PITCH 20° - 40°)

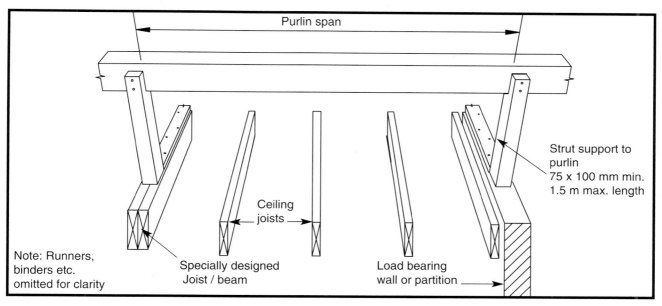

Purlin span

Strut support to purlin
75 x 100 mm min.
1.5 m max. length

Ceiling joists

Note: Runners, binders etc. omitted for clarity

Specially designed Joist / beam

Load bearing wall or partition

Target size of purlin (mm)	Span of roof rafters in metres									
	1.5	1.75	2	2.25	2.5	2.75	3	3.25	3.5	3.75
	Purlin span in metres, Class C24									
75 x 150	2.33	2.21	2.10	2.02	1.94	1.87	1.82	1.76	1.72	1.67
75 x 175	2.73	2.58	2.46	2.36	2.27	2.20	2.13	2.07	2.01	1.96
75 x 225	3.52	3.33	3.18	3.05	2.94	2.84	2.75	2.67	2.60	2.54

Target size of purlin (mm)	Span of roof rafters in metres									
	1.5	1.75	2	2.25	2.5	2.75	3	3.25	3.5	3.75
	Purlin span in metres, Class C27									
75 x 150	2.44	2.31	2.20	2.11	2.03	1.96	1.90	1.85	1.80	1.76
75 x 175	2.85	2.70	2.58	2.47	2.38	2.30	2.23	2.17	2.11	2.06
75 x 225	3.68	3.49	3.33	3.19	3.08	2.97	2.88	2.80	2.73	2.66

Note:
Target size is the desired size at 20% moisture content.
Rafter span is measured on slope.
Purlin span is the clear span between supports.

Example:
A purlin of strength class C27 is required to span 2.8 m
and is carrying roof rafters with a 3.25 m span.
A 75 x 225 mm member would be used.

INTRODUCTION

A number of factors such as cost, location aesthetics, etc., will influence whether tiles or slates are used to cover a roof. Whichever are used, the fixing recommendations of the manufacturer should be adhered to.

The details given on this and the following pages are for general guidance only and normal domestic roof construction.

Additional information on roof tiling and slating is available from:

◆ ICP 2: 1982: Code of Practice for Slating and Tiling (and any subsequent editions, revision due 2000)

◆ BS 5534: Part 1: 1997: Code of Practice for Slating and Tiling

◆ BS 5250: 1989: Control of Condensation in Buildings

◆ BS 8000: Workmanship on Building Sites. Part 6: 1990: Code of Practice for Slating and Tiling of Roofs and Claddings.

SARKING FELT

It must always be remembered that the sarking felt below tiles or slates is the second line of defence in excluding water from penetrating the roof. Care with the installation of sarking felt is important to ensure that this second line of defence is not breached.

The durability of the sarking felt should be compatible with the expected life span of the tiling or slating. The minimum grade of sarking felt to be used is Type 1F, to IS 36 or BS 747.

Type 1F sarking felt can degrade and therefore should not be used in the vicinity of the eaves. It is recommended that a sarking felt of a more durable material be used in this location, e.g. Type 5U, to IS 36 or BS 747 or equivalent.

Where different types of sarking felt are used in conjunction with each other, manufacturer's guidance with regard to compatibility should be sought.

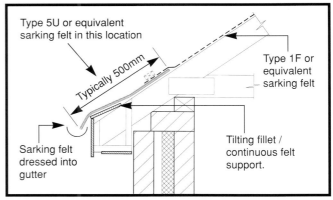

Sarking felt at eaves level.

Ensure sarking felt at eaves level is dressed 50 mm into the gutter, and provide a tilting fillet, continuous ply support or proprietary eaves ventilation tray to avoid a water trap behind the fascia board.

Some wood preservative treatments applied to timber and used in conjunction with some proprietary sarking felts may be harmful to the sarking felt. Manufacturer's guidance should be sought.

It is recommended that the sarking felt be tacked to the rafters at the head of the sheet with min. 3 mm dia. x 20 mm long extra large head felt nails of copper, aluminium alloy or galvanised steel. The nails should be covered by the overlap of the sarking felt above.

Where the length of the rafter slope measured on plan exceeds 6 m, careful consideration should be given to the selection of sarking felt. In such situations the use of high-performance underlay is recommended, e.g. Type 5U or equivalent.

All penetrations to the sarking felt, including any tears or punctures, should be suitably sealed or repaired to permanently prevent water ingress.

Note: Any roofing underlay used must be appropriately certified, and installed in accordance with the requirements of the certificate. Certain types of roofing underlay may require a vapour control layer at ceiling level, and/or extra ventilation of the roof space. In such cases, manufacturer's guidance should be sought.

SARKING FELT
continued

Typical laps in sarking felt.

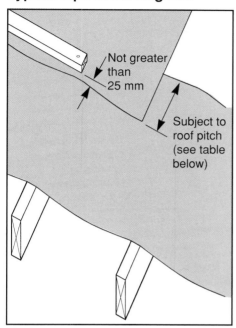

Horizontal/head lap in sarking felt.

Roof pitch	Minimum horizontal/head lap
less than 22^1/$_2$°	225 mm
22^1/$_2$° to 35°	150 mm
35° and over	100 mm

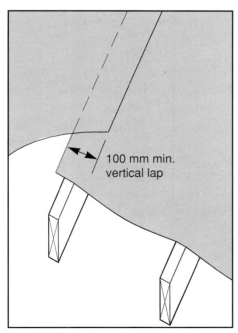

Vertical/side lap should occur over a rafter, so that fixings are at least 50 mm from the ends of the rolls being lapped.

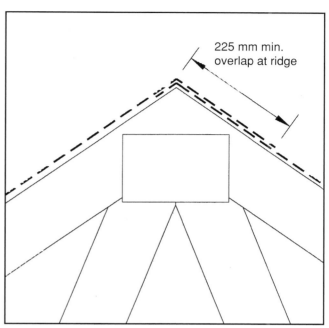

At ridge level, the sarking felt should be carried over the ridge by 225 mm min.

Proprietary ridge ventilators, where required, should be installed in accordance with manufacturer's recommendations.

At hips, an extra layer of sarking felt at least 600 mm wide should be provided. Lay the main felt around the hip and the extra layer up the hip.

BATTENS

The battens should be set out so that the spacing between all battens is equal, and does not exceed that recommended by the tile/slate manufacturer for the particular tile/slate being used, and the pitch of roof being covered. This will ensure that the minimum recommended headlap is achieved for the tile/slate being used. Minimum headlap can vary for different tile profiles and for slates, depending on the pitch of the roof, and the degree of its exposure to wind driven rain.

Batten length.
Battens should be at least 1.2 m long and long enough to be nailed at each end and at intermediate points to at least three rafters. Battens should not be cantilevered or spliced between supports.

Moisture content.
The moisture content of battens at the time of fixing should not exceed 22%. The dimensions of battens and counter battens are based on measurement at 20% moisture content. As timber swells on wetting and shrinks on drying, dimensions measured at other moisture contents may be adjusted to the 20% value by allowing 1% change in cross-sectional dimensions for every 4% change in moisture content.

Preservative treatment.
It is not essential to treat tiling or slating battens with a preservative. Impregnation with preservative should be considered where timber members are at risk from attack by wood-rotting fungi, i.e. where the moisture content of the battens is likely to remain above 20% for prolonged periods.

Attention is drawn to the risk of chemical attack by certain types of preservative treatments on certain roofing underlays, metal fittings and fasteners. Manufacturer's guidance should be sought in such situations.

BATTEN SIZES
(recommended nominal and minimum size, for battens graded in accordance with ICP 2)

Roofing material	Rafter spacing			
	400 mm and less		Greater than 400 mm and up to and including 600 mm	
	Nominal width x depth mm	Minimum width x depth mm	Nominal width x depth mm	Minimum width x depth mm
Single lap tiles	50 x 36	47 x 35	50 x 36	47 x 35
Fibre cement slates and natural slates	50 x 22	47 x 22	50 x 36	47 x 35

Where rafters are spaced at greater than 400 mm centres, the tiling batten size should be increased accordingly.

Note:
- Allowable tolerance of +3 mm/-1 mm are permitted in relation to batten target sizes
- Counterbattens should have the same width as the supporting rafter, and where fully supported should have a depth not less than 19 mm.

Batten fixing.
For duopitch roofs of not less than 17.5° with a ridge height not exceeding 7.2 m, and where the basic wind speed does not exceed 48 m/s, (such regions are generally represented by the shaded area of the map illustrated on page 213), battens should be nailed with 3.35 mm dia. nails, generally 65 mm long for 22 mm deep battens and 75 mm long for 35 mm deep battens. Nails should penetrate the rafter by a minimum of 40 mm. Typical nail types include round wire, annular ring shanks or helicat threaded shank nails.

Batten ends should be cut square and butt joints must occur over the rafters. Toe nail battens to rafters on either side of the joint. Not more than one batten in four should be joined over any truss or rafter.

Where thermal insulation is located on rafters, care should be taken to ensure that the required structural fixing for battens/counterbattens is achieved.

Tiling/slating battens

METAL LINED VALLEYS

A range of metals can be used to line valley gutters, including lead, copper, aluminium and zinc.

Lead lined valleys are more common in Irish house building practice and the guidance on the following pages reflects this. See page 226 for information on other suitable valley lining materials.

LEAD VALLEYS

◆ All leadwork should be fully supported along its length by valley support boards, min. 19 mm thick, e.g. WBP ply. Depending on the nature of the roof construction, i.e. prefabricated trusses or cut roof construction, typical methods of valley support are illustrated on pages 209 and 210.

◆ Code 5 lead should be used to form the valley lining, not less than 500 mm wide, and in lengths not greater than 1.5 m

◆ Never apply mortar directly to lead. There is a high risk of movement of the lead which could cause mortar to crack and fall away

◆ Apply mortar bedding to the undercloak (I cement: 3 sand) in a tiled valley

◆ Where possible, nail or clip all tiles and slates on either side of the valley. Bed small tile pieces firmly in mortar. However, the use of half tiles located one tile in from the valley edge, tile and a half or double tiles, will help limit the use of small tile pieces, thus allowing for mechanical fixing of all tiles on either side of the valley

◆ Take care to ensure that interlocks in tiles are not blocked by mortar

◆ Never lay bituminous roofing underlay directly below a lead valley. Heat from the sun may soften the bitumen and cause the lead to stick to the valley support boards. There is then a high risk of the lead splitting when it cools again after expanding.

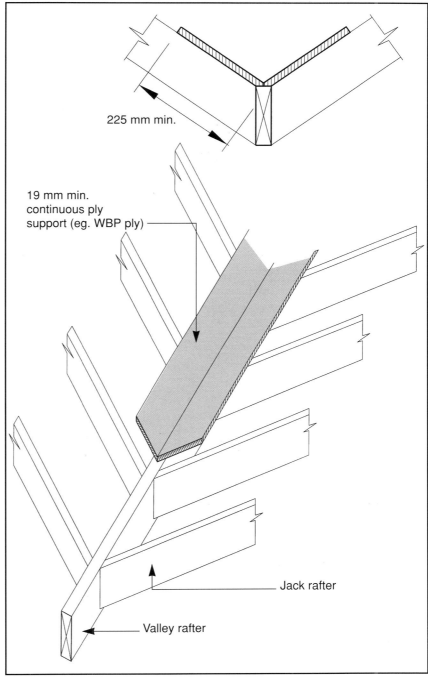

225 mm min.

19 mm min. continuous ply support (eg. WBP ply)

Jack rafter

Valley rafter

Typical method of installation of valley support boards where the valley does not exceed 6m in length measured along the valley board.

LEAD VALLEYS

Typical methods of installation of valley support boards, where the valley exceeds 6m in length measured along the valley board.

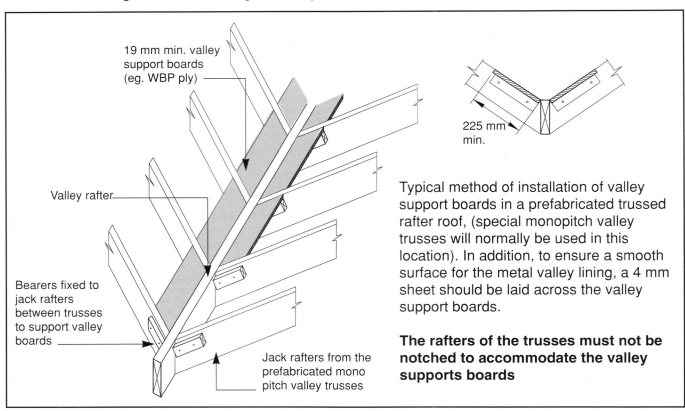

Typical method of installation of valley support boards in a prefabricated trussed rafter roof, (special monopitch valley trusses will normally be used in this location). In addition, to ensure a smooth surface for the metal valley lining, a 4 mm sheet should be laid across the valley support boards.

The rafters of the trusses must not be notched to accommodate the valley supports boards

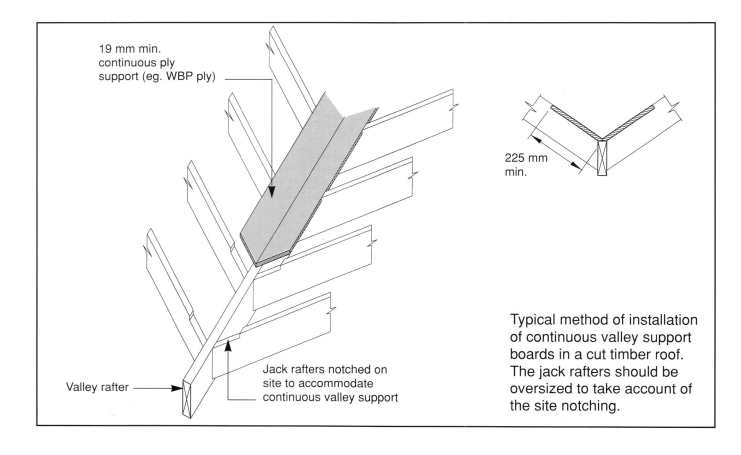

Typical method of installation of continuous valley support boards in a cut timber roof. The jack rafters should be oversized to take account of the site notching.

TYPICAL LEAD VALLEY DETAILS
SINGLE LAP TILES, CLAY AND CONCRETE (INTERLOCKING), TYPICAL VALLEY DETAIL

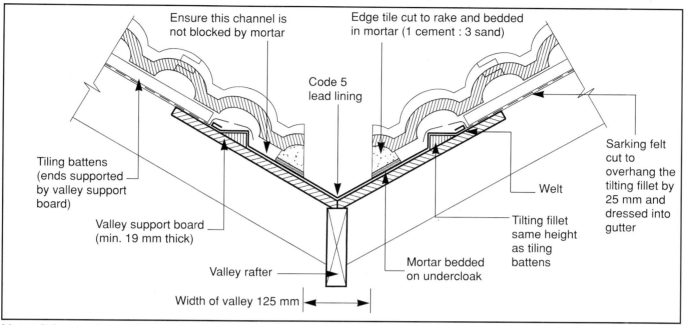

Note: It is good practice to dampen all products prior to bedding and ensure that all bedding surfaces are clean and free from harmful matter. Mortar bedding of roofing accessories should not be undertaken in wet or frosty weather or when such conditions are imminent.

FIBRE CEMENT AND NATURAL, SLATES TYPICAL VALLEY DETAIL

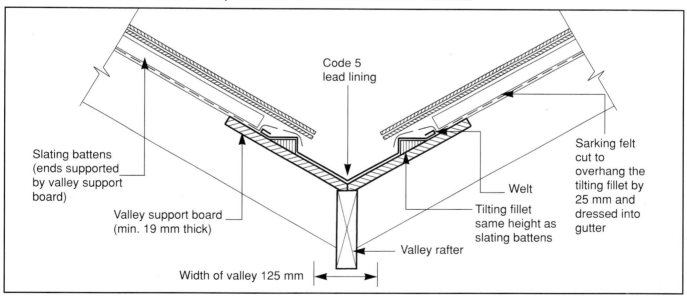

Laps in the lead lined valley vary, depending on the pitch of the roof rafters. See table opposite.
It should be noted that the pitch of the valley rafter is approx. 5° less than the pitch of the roof rafters.

Roof rafter pitch (degrees)	Lap required (mm)
20	220
30	150
40	115
50	100

RECOMMENDATIONS FOR MINIMUM ROOF PITCH, HEADLAPS AND SIDELAPS

The minimum recommendations, with regard to roof pitch, headlaps, sidelaps, etc., outlined on the following pages, 216, 219 & 223 are intended for use where the length of the rafter does not exceed 6 m, when measured on plan.

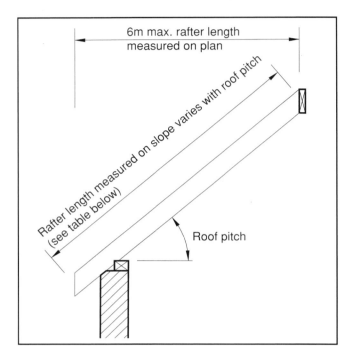

Roof pitch	Rafter length (m) measured on slope
45°	8.5
40°	7.8
35°	7.3
30°	6.9
25°	6.6

Where the rafter length exceeds 6 m, when measured on plan, manufacturers guidance should be sought with regard to roof pitch, headlaps, sidelaps, etc.

EXPOSURE TO LOCAL WIND DRIVEN RAIN

The minimum headlap, sidelap and roof pitch requirements outlined on pages 216, 219 and 223 vary depending on the category of exposure based on driving rain.

The map below details two simplified categories of exposure and may be used when designing buildings up to 12 m ridge height.

■ **Severe exposure:** always obtains in districts where the driving rain index is 5m²/sec/yr or more.

□ **Normal exposure:** generally, obtains in districts where the driving rain index is less than 5m²/sec/yr.
In districts of normal exposure, buildings which stand above their surroundings, or buildings of any height on hill slopes or hill tops, should be regarded as having severe exposure.

■ severe exposure
□ normal exposure

Map showing two simplified categories of exposure based on driving rain data from the Meteorological Service Climatological note no. 3 (1973))

Note: The information given in this map is current at the time of publication. It is recommended that the validity of the data be confirmed at the time of use. This map should be read in conjunction with pages 216 & 219.

MINIMUM RECOMMENDATIONS FOR MECHANICAL FIXING OF TILES AND SLATES

The requirements for mechanical fixing of tiles and slates are determined by the following factors:

◆ Roof pitch

◆ Type of tile/slate being used

◆ Location of roof (see map opposite)

◆ Height of building.

In all cases, the following criteria should be satisfied:

◆ Adequate resistance to wind uplift should be provided by the combined resistance of the self weight of the tiles/slates and their mechanical fixing

◆ At the perimeter of the roof all tiles or slates should be mechanically fixed. See page 225 for definition of perimeter areas

◆ Minimum fixing requirements in accordance with pages, 214, 215, 218 & 222

◆ Nails, hooks, etc., in accordance with the guidance on pages 215, 218 & 222.

Normal buildings
Generally, buildings located in the un-hatched area of the map opposite.

Exposed buildings.
For the purposes of selecting appropriate mechanical fixings, buildings in the following circumstances are considered to be exposed.

◆ Any building which stands above its surroundings, or has an eaves height in excess of 9 m above adjoining ground level

◆ Any building on hill slopes or hill tops

◆ Any building, e.g. in a built up area, which is subject to adverse wind effects, e.g. funnelling

◆ Any building which is located in the hatched area of the map opposite.

Severely exposed buildings.

For the purposes of selecting appropriate mechanical fixings, buildings in the following circumstances are considered to be severely exposed.

◆ Any building which is located in the hatched area of the map below,
and

◆ stands above its surroundings, or has an eaves height in excess of 9 m above adjoining ground level,
or

◆ is located on a hill slope or hill top,
or

◆ is subject to adverse wind effects e.g. funnelling in a built up area.

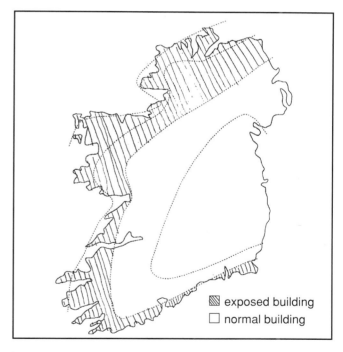

exposed building
normal building

Map showing Ireland divided into two zones on the basis of wind speeds. Data supplied by Met Eireann.

MINIMUM RECOMMENDATIONS FOR MECHANICAL FIXING OF TILES

SINGLE LAP TILES, CLAY OR CONCRETE. MINIMUM FIXING REQUIREMENTS FOR NORMAL BUILDING, (see Map, page 213). ROOF PITCH LESS THAN 45°

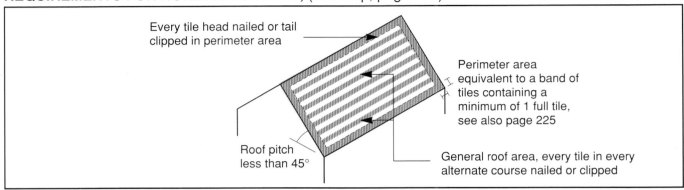

Every tile head nailed or tail clipped in perimeter area

Perimeter area equivalent to a band of tiles containing a minimum of 1 full tile, see also page 225

Roof pitch less than 45°

General roof area, every tile in every alternate course nailed or clipped

SINGLE LAP TILES, CLAY OR CONCRETE. MINIMUM FIXING REQUIREMENTS FOR EXPOSED BUILDING, (see Map, page 213). ROOF PITCH LESS THAN 45°

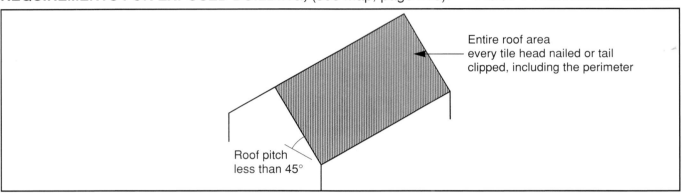

Entire roof area every tile head nailed or tail clipped, including the perimeter

Roof pitch less than 45°

SINGLE LAP TILES, CLAY OR CONCRETE. MINIMUM FIXING REQUIREMENTS FOR SEVERELY EXPOSED BUILDING, (see Map, page 213). ROOF PITCH LESS THAN 45°

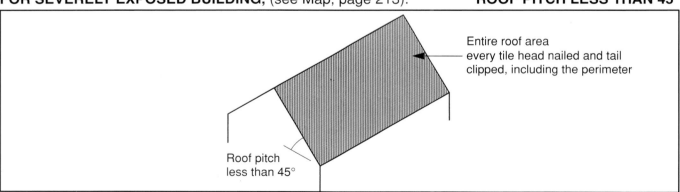

Entire roof area every tile head nailed and tail clipped, including the perimeter

Roof pitch less than 45°

SINGLE LAP TILES, CLAY OR CONCRETE. MINIMUM FIXING REQUIREMENTS FOR NORMAL BUILDING, (see Map, page 213). ROOF PITCH 45°-55°

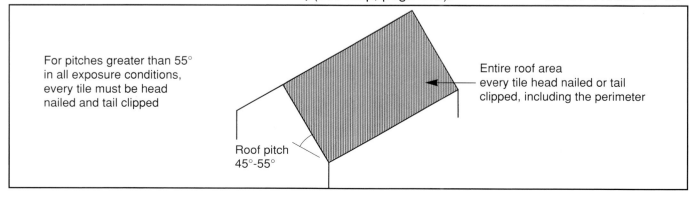

For pitches greater than 55° in all exposure conditions, every tile must be head nailed and tail clipped

Entire roof area every tile head nailed or tail clipped, including the perimeter

Roof pitch 45°-55°

MINIMUM RECOMMENDATIONS FOR MECHANICAL FIXING OF TILES

SINGLE LAP TILES, CLAY OR CONCRETE. MINIMUM FIXING REQUIREMENTS FOR EXPOSED AND SEVERELY EXPOSED BUILDING, (see Map, page 213). **ROOF PITCH 45°- 55°**

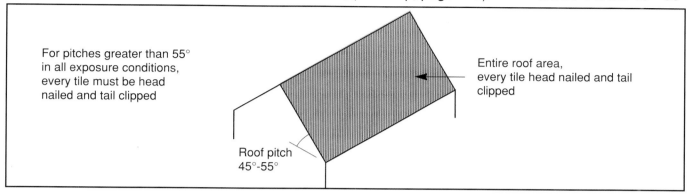

For pitches greater than 55° in all exposure conditions, every tile must be head nailed and tail clipped

Entire roof area, every tile head nailed and tail clipped

Roof pitch 45°-55°

Recommended nails for single lap tile fixing

Clay/conc. tiles	Nail dia. (mm)	Nail length (mm)	Nail type
Single lap tiles (flat or profiled)	3.35	for nails up to 65 mm in length, not less than 15 mm penetration into batten.	aluminium, copper or silicone bronze
	3.75	for nails greater than 65 mm in length, not less than 15 mm penetration into batten.	aluminium, copper or silicone bronze

Nails intended for use with clips should be aluminium or stainless steel. Type, shank dia. and length should be as recommended by the tile manufacturer.

Example of single lap tiles.

Typical lead lined valley with single lap tiles.

SINGLE LAP TILES, CLAY OR CONCRETE (INTERLOCKING)

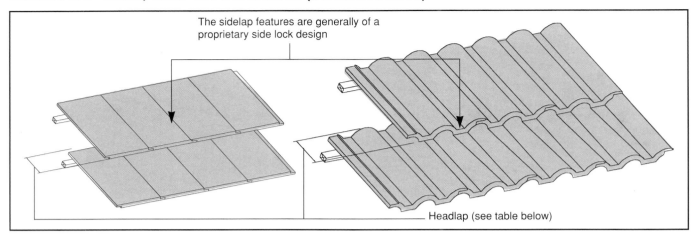

The sidelap features are generally of a proprietary side lock design

Headlap (see table below)

Minimum headlap requirements for single lap clay or concrete tiles (interlocking).

Roof pitch	Normal exposure (see page 212)		Severe exposure (see page 212)	
	profiled tiles	flat tiles	profiled tiles	flat tiles
greater than 30°	75	100	100	100
25.5° to 29.5°	100	100	100	100 *
22.5° to 24.5°	100	100	100*	100 *
17.5° to 22°	Manufacturer's guidance should be sought			

◆ *High performance underlay recommended. ◆ The design of some products requires a limit to the max. headlap.
◆ Some clay tiles have the headlap fixed by design features on the top surface at the head of the tile and features on the under surface at the tail of the tile. ◆ The sidelap features are generally of a proprietary side-lock design.

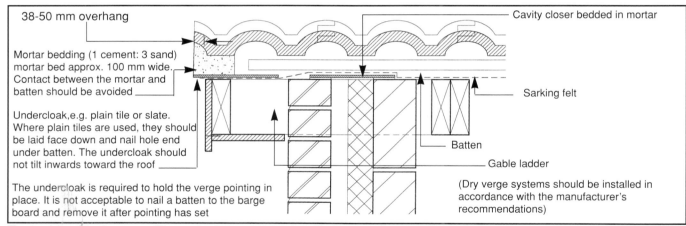

38-50 mm overhang

Mortar bedding (1 cement: 3 sand) mortar bed approx. 100 mm wide. Contact between the mortar and batten should be avoided

Undercloak,e.g. plain tile or slate. Where plain tiles are used, they should be laid face down and nail hole end under batten. The undercloak should not tilt inwards toward the roof

The undercloak is required to hold the verge pointing in place. It is not acceptable to nail a batten to the barge board and remove it after pointing has set

Cavity closer bedded in mortar

Sarking felt

Batten

Gable ladder

(Dry verge systems should be installed in accordance with the manufacturer's recommendations)

Typical bedded verge. The principle of this detail also applies to plain tiles.

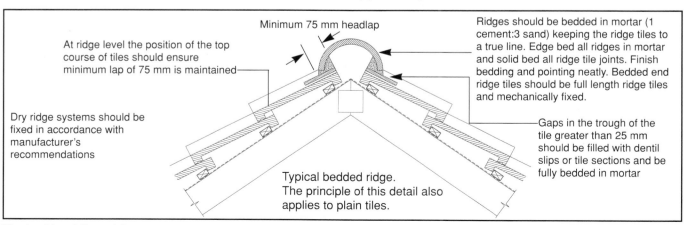

Minimum 75 mm headlap

At ridge level the position of the top course of tiles should ensure minimum lap of 75 mm is maintained

Dry ridge systems should be fixed in accordance with manufacturer's recommendations

Ridges should be bedded in mortar (1 cement:3 sand) keeping the ridge tiles to a true line. Edge bed all ridges in mortar and solid bed all ridge tile joints. Finish bedding and pointing neatly. Bedded end ridge tiles should be full length ridge tiles and mechanically fixed.

Gaps in the trough of the tile greater than 25 mm should be filled with dentil slips or tile sections and be fully bedded in mortar

Typical bedded ridge. The principle of this detail also applies to plain tiles.

Typical bedding ridge

Note : It is good practice to dampen all products prior to bedding and ensure that all bedding surfaces are clean and free from harmful matter. Mortar bedding of roofing accessories should not be undertaken in wet or frosty weather or when such conditions are imminent.

SINGLE LAP TILES, CLAY OR CONCRETE (INTERLOCKING)

HIP IRON

For rafter pitches greater than 35°, a hip iron should be mechanically fixed to the eaves end of the hip rafter.

The hip iron should conform to the requirements outlined on page 224.

It is not acceptable to nail a batten to the barge and remove it after the mortar bedding has set, as illustrated above. An undercloak must be provided in this location as detailed on the previous page.

Correct verge detail with undercloak.

HIP DETAILS

Single lap tiles, clay or concrete (interlocking), hip detail considerations.

For roofs laid with single lap clay or concrete interlocking tiles, the following should be considered:

◆ Where hip tiles are mechanically fixed, they should be fixed to conform to the manufacturer's recommendations

◆ The overlap of the adjacent course of tiles by the hip ridge tiles should be not less than 75mm

◆ Clay and concrete hip ridges e.g. half round, angular, segmental, etc. should be bedded with mortar or laid dry with a proprietary system

◆ It is desirable to use a slightly flatter shaped ridge tile on hips than on a main ridge, e.g. segmental or third round hip

◆ Close mitred hips are not recommended with interlocking tiles.

Example of single lap tiles.

MINIMUM RECOMMENDATIONS FOR MECHANICAL FIXING OF SLATES

DOUBLE LAP FIBRE CEMENT SLATES. MINIMUM FIXING REQUIREMENTS FOR ALL LOCATIONS AND EXPOSURE CONDITION,
(see Map, page 213).

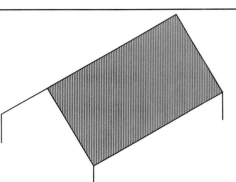

Nailing:
Double nail every slate. Generally slates larger than 400 mm x 200 mm are additionally restrained by a copper crampion/disc rivet connecting the tail on the centre line of the slate to the two slates below, through the gap between them.

DOUBLE LAP NATURAL SLATES. MINIMUM FIXING REQUIREMENTS FOR ALL LOCATIONS AND EXPOSURE CONDITIONS,
(see Map, page 213).

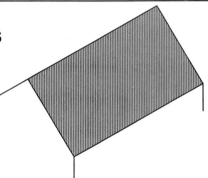

Nailing:
Double nail every slate. Slates should generally be centre nailed to eliminate the tendancy of head nailed slates to rattle in the wind, although very small slates, under eaves slates and ridge slates may be head nailed.

MINIMUM HOOK FIXING REQUIREMENTS FOR ALL DOUBLE LAP SLATES

The use of hook fixings, one to every slate, is an alternative to the nail fixing of slates. Slate manufacturer's recommendations should be followed.

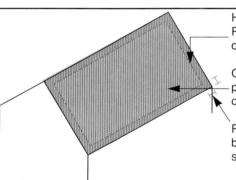

Hook fixing:
Perimeter area, hook fix and double nail every slate.

General roof area (excluding perimeter) for all exposure conditions, hook fix every slate .

Perimeter area equivalent to a band of slates, min. 600mm wide, see also page 225

Recommended nails for slate fixing

Slate type	Nail dia. (mm)	Nail length (mm)	Nail type
fibre cement slates	2.65	30	aluminium, copper or silicone bronze
natural slates	3.35	30	aluminium, copper or silicone bronze

◆ Where there is a gap between slate and batten, such as when tilt is provided at the eaves, longer nails are required unless thicker battens are used to take up the gap between slate and batten. Nail lengths in such cases should generally be equal to the sum of the calculated batten penetration, twice the slate thickness and any gap between slates and the batten.

FIBRE CEMENT AND NATURAL SLATES

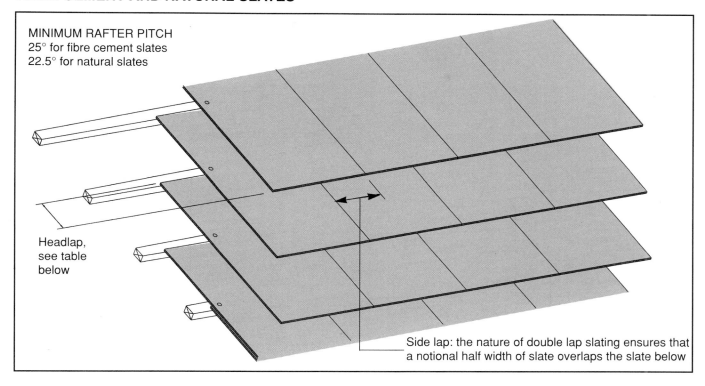

MINIMUM RAFTER PITCH
25° for fibre cement slates
22.5° for natural slates

Headlap,
see table
below

Side lap: the nature of double lap slating ensures that a notional half width of slate overlaps the slate below

Minimum headlap (mm) for double lap fibre cement slates (600 mm x 300 mm)

Roof pitch	Normal exposure (see page 212)	Severe exposure (see page 212)
greater than 35°	90	100
30° - 35°	100	110
25° - 30°	110	110*

* High performance underlay recommended.
- ◆ For other roof pitches and slates sizes manufacturer's recommendations should be sought.
- ◆ Sidelap: The nature of double lap slating ensures that a notional half width of slate overlaps the slate below.

Minimum headlap (mm) for double lap natural slates

Slate dimensions		Roof pitch Normal exposure area (see page212)			Roof pitch Severe exposure area (see page 212)		
Inches	mm	22.5°	25°	30°	22.5°	25°	30°
24 x 12	610 x 305	105	90	80	140	120	105
20 x 12	510 x 305	100	90	80	120	100	90
20 x 10	510 x 255	110	90	80	130	115	100

A satisfactory headlap should be a function of the length and width, and the length of the slate, exposure category, roof pitch and angle of creep. The table above gives general guidance.

FIBRE CEMENT AND NATURAL SLATES

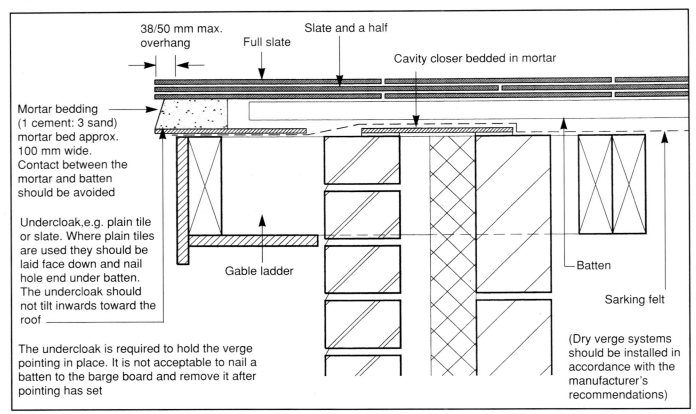

38/50 mm max. overhang

Full slate

Slate and a half

Cavity closer bedded in mortar

Mortar bedding (1 cement: 3 sand) mortar bed approx. 100 mm wide. Contact between the mortar and batten should be avoided

Undercloak,e.g. plain tile or slate. Where plain tiles are used they should be laid face down and nail hole end under batten. The undercloak should not tilt inwards toward the roof

The undercloak is required to hold the verge pointing in place. It is not acceptable to nail a batten to the barge board and remove it after pointing has set

Gable ladder

Batten

Sarking felt

(Dry verge systems should be installed in accordance with the manufacturer's recommendations)

Typical bedded verge (double lap fibre cement slates).

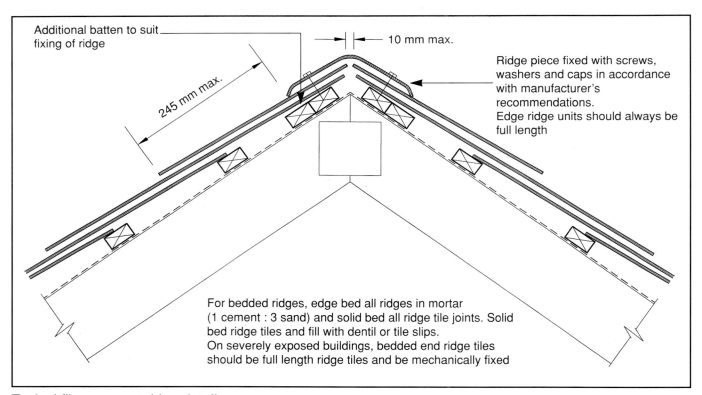

Additional batten to suit fixing of ridge

10 mm max.

245 mm max.

Ridge piece fixed with screws, washers and caps in accordance with manufacturer's recommendations.
Edge ridge units should always be full length

For bedded ridges, edge bed all ridges in mortar (1 cement : 3 sand) and solid bed all ridge tile joints. Solid bed ridge tiles and fill with dentil or tile slips.
On severely exposed buildings, bedded end ridge tiles should be full length ridge tiles and be mechanically fixed

Typical fibre cement ridge detail.

Note : It is good practice to dampen all products prior to bedding and ensure that all bedding surfaces are clean and free from harmful matter. Mortar bedding of roofing accessories should not be undertaken in wet or frosty weather or when such conditions are imminent.

FIBRE CEMENT SLATES, HIP DETAILS

Bedded hip cappings

Where hip cappings are bedded in mortar, the following should be considered:

◆ Where the main roof pitch is greater than 35°, a hip iron should be mechanically fixed to the eaves of the hip rafter. For hip iron specification, see page 224

◆ Cut the bottom hip capping to align with the eaves

◆ Edge bed all hip cappings in mortar and solid bed all hip tile joints

◆ Solid bed all end hip cappings

◆ On severely exposed buildings bedded end hip cappings should be full length and mechanically fixed.

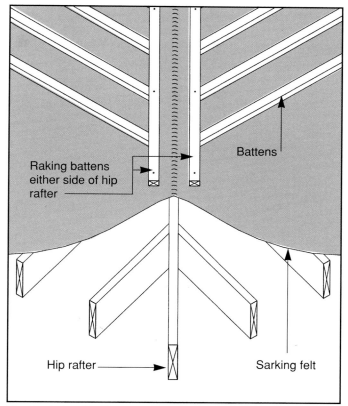

Typical dry-fix fibre cement slates hip detail.

(Diagram labels: Battens, Raking battens either side of hip rafter, Hip rafter, Sarking felt)

Typical fibre cement slate roofs.

MITRED HIPS

◆ Minimum roof pitch of 35° is recommended
◆ Mitred hips should be laid with soakers

DRY-FIX HIP CAPPINGS

Consideration should be given to the following:

◆ Position and fix a raking batten on either side of the hip rafter to suit fixing of hip capping

◆ Cut slates or wide slates to a close mitre to the hip line ensuring that the head of the slate is not less than 100 mm wide

◆ Rake cut slates to the hip line

◆ Cut the bottom hip capping to form a full length unit to align with the eaves

◆ Lay hip cappings with internal socket joints facing up-slope

◆ Fix hip cappings to a true line with screws, washers and caps in accordance with manufacturer's recommendations.

MINIMUM RECOMMENDATIONS FOR MECHANICAL FIXING OF TILES

DOUBLE LAP PLAIN TILES (NIBBED), CLAY OR CONCRETE. MINIMUM FIXING REQUIREMENTS FOR NORMAL BUILDING, (see Map, page 213).

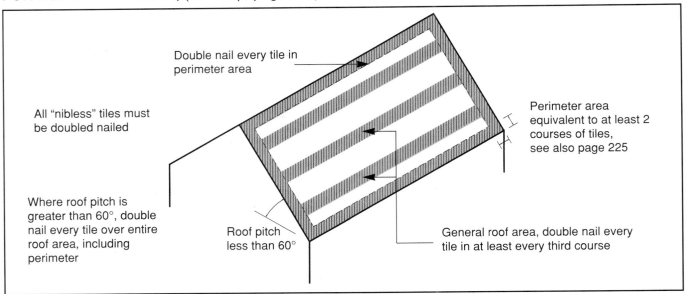

Double nail every tile in perimeter area

All "nibless" tiles must be doubled nailed

Where roof pitch is greater than 60°, double nail every tile over entire roof area, including perimeter

Roof pitch less than 60°

Perimeter area equivalent to at least 2 courses of tiles, see also page 225

General roof area, double nail every tile in at least every third course

DOUBLE LAP PLAIN TILES (NIBBED), CLAY OR CONCRETE. MINIMUM FIXING REQUIREMENTS FOR EXPOSED AND SEVERELY EXPOSED BUILDING, (see Map, page 213).

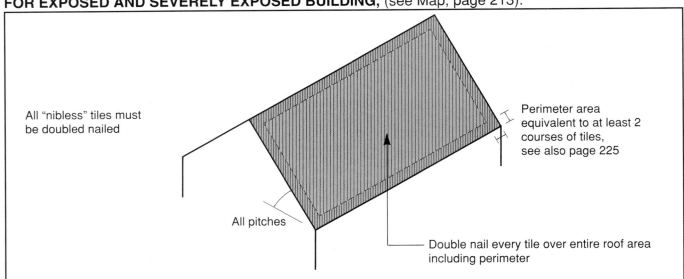

All "nibless" tiles must be doubled nailed

All pitches

Perimeter area equivalent to at least 2 courses of tiles, see also page 225

Double nail every tile over entire roof area including perimeter

Recommended nails for double lap tile fixing

Clay/conc. tiles	Nail dia. (mm)	Nail length (mm)	Nail type
plain tile	2.65	not less than 15 mm penetration into batten	aluminium, copper or silicone bronze

DOUBLE LAP PLAIN TILES, CLAY OR CONCRETE

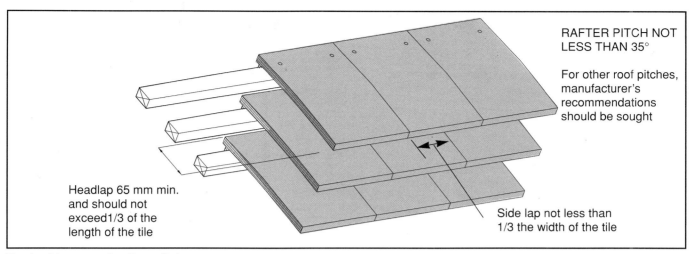

RAFTER PITCH NOT LESS THAN 35°

For other roof pitches, manufacturer's recommendations should be sought

Headlap 65 mm min. and should not exceed1/3 of the length of the tile

Side lap not less than 1/3 the width of the tile

Typical laps and rafter pitch.

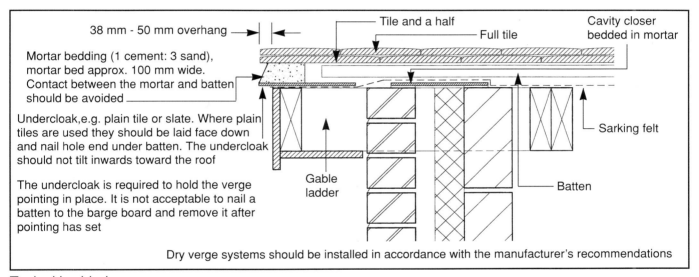

38 mm - 50 mm overhang

Tile and a half

Full tile

Cavity closer bedded in mortar

Mortar bedding (1 cement: 3 sand), mortar bed approx. 100 mm wide. Contact between the mortar and batten should be avoided

Undercloak,e.g. plain tile or slate. Where plain tiles are used they should be laid face down and nail hole end under batten. The undercloak should not tilt inwards toward the roof

The undercloak is required to hold the verge pointing in place. It is not acceptable to nail a batten to the barge board and remove it after pointing has set

Sarking felt

Gable ladder

Batten

Dry verge systems should be installed in accordance with the manufacturer's recommendations

Typical bedded verge.

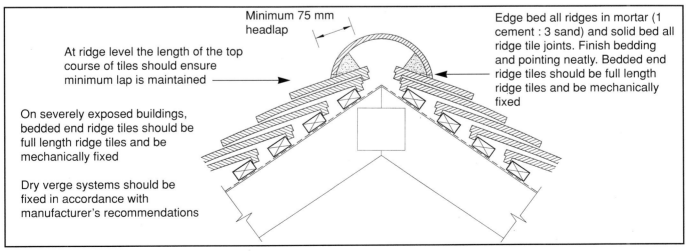

Minimum 75 mm headlap

Edge bed all ridges in mortar (1 cement : 3 sand) and solid bed all ridge tile joints. Finish bedding and pointing neatly. Bedded end ridge tiles should be full length ridge tiles and be mechanically fixed

At ridge level the length of the top course of tiles should ensure minimum lap is maintained

On severely exposed buildings, bedded end ridge tiles should be full length ridge tiles and be mechanically fixed

Dry verge systems should be fixed in accordance with manufacturer's recommendations

Typical bedded ridge.

Note : It is good practice to dampen all products prior to bedding and ensure that all bedding surfaces are clean and free from harmful matter. Mortar bedding of roofing accessories should not be undertaken in wet or frosty weather or when such conditions are imminent.

DOUBLE LAP PLAIN TILES, CLAY OR CONCRETE

HIP IRON

Where provided, a hip iron should be mechanically fixed to the eaves end of the hip rafter, to support mortar bedded hip ridge tiles. Note: Hip irons are not required where hip tiles are mechanically fixed.

Hip irons should be formed of steel complying with BS 1449, Part 1., hot dipped galvanised after cutting, forming and holing, or stainless steel complying with BS 1554.

Hip irons should not be less than 25 mm wide and 6 mm thick. The iron should be turned up at the lower end by an amount sufficient to support the hip covering. The straight length should extend up the rafter and should not be less than 300 mm long. Two holes should be provided and fixed with 2 no. 5.6 mm dia. screws made from the same material as the hip iron.

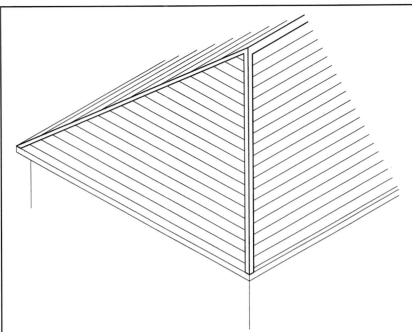

For roofs laid with double lap plain tiles the following should be considered:

◆ Where hip tiles are mechanically fixed, they should be fixed to conform to the manufacturer's recommendations

◆ The overlap of the adjacent course of tiles by the hip ridge tiles should not be less than 75 mm

◆ Clay and concrete hip ridges, e.g. half round, angular, segmental, etc. should be bedded with mortar or laid dry with a proprietary system

◆ Bonnet hip tiles should be nailed and bedded with mortar. Bonnets are only suitable on roof pitches not exceeding 60°

◆ Arris hip tiles (purpose made, angular) should be nailed and mortar bedded

◆ Mitred hips should be laid with soakers.

Double lap plain tiles, clay or concrete. Hip detail considerations.

DEFINITION OF PERIMETER AREAS
(see also pages 214, 218 and 222.)

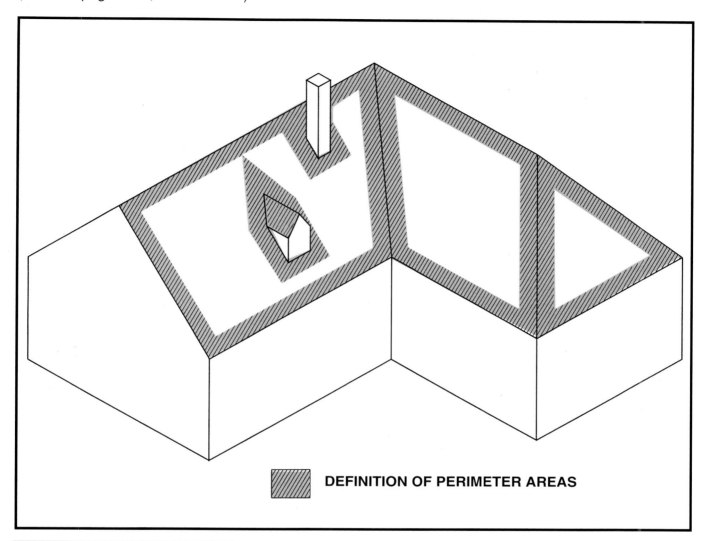

DEFINITION OF PERIMETER AREAS

Example of water ponding at eaves level, as a result of the absence of a tilting fillet/continuous felt support. This situation should never be allowed to happen.

FLASHINGS, SOAKERS ETC.

Sheet materials used for flashings, soakers etc. should conform to the recommendations below. Consideration should be given to the type of metal intended for use in flashings and junctions to ensure that any mechanical or chemical properties do not adversely affect the durability of the work.

It is recommended that there should be no contact between dissimilar metals. to reduce the likelihood of significant bi-metallic corrosion. Cover flashings, for example, should generally be of the same material as the soakers which they cover.

It should be noted that where lead and aluminium are used together in a marine environment, the chemical reaction between lead oxide on the surface of the lead sheet and the sodium chloride in salt water creates a caustic run-off which can attack aluminium.

Untreated lead and aluminium flashings may cause run off and staining of the roof covering, although durability is not impaired. A coating of patination oil on all lead surfaces, pre-coated or painted aluminium, is recommended to avoid unsightly stains on a newly completed roof. Patination oil must be applied in accordance with the manufacturer's recommendations to all surfaces and edges the same day and before any rain, snow, frost or dew. Wet or dusty conditions should be avoided during the application of patination oil.

Proprietary flashings, soakers, etc. should be detailed in accordance with manufacturer's recommendations.

Proprietary flashing and junction units, which have adequate strength, water resistance and durability and which do not adversely affect the laying performance of the roofing products may also be used. Such products should be installed in accordance with manufacturer's recommendations.

Lead sheet: should conform to BS 1178

Location	code	colour	thickness (mm)	weight kg/m²
soakers	3	green	1.32	14.97
flashings & saddles	4	blue	1.80	20.41
valleys	5	red	2.24	25.40

Copper sheet: should conform to the recommendations given in BS 2870

Location	type
flashings, soakers & saddles	type "Fully Annealed" 0.55 mm
gutters, self supporting	0.70 mm type $\frac{1}{2}$ H (depending on width & length)
valley, fully supported	0.45 mm-0.70 mm type $\frac{1}{4}$ to $\frac{1}{2}$ H (10 max length without expansion joint))

Aluminium & aluminium alloy: should conform to ISEN 485 and ISEN 573

Location	type
flashings, soakers, saddles & gutters, including valley gutters	grades 1080A, 1050A, 1200 and 3103 are suitable with the temper selected according to the strength and forming properties required, min. thickness 0.70 mm

Zinc and zinc alloy: should conform to the recommendations given in ISEN 988

Location	type
flashings, soakers, saddles & gutters, including valley gutters	0.80 mm min.

FLASHINGS

Proper flashings at junctions of roofs with other elements is vital if a sound, dry roof is to result.

The details illustrated on this and the following pages illustrate good flashing practice.

Note: Where the roof abuts a cavity wall with a brick or fairfaced block outer leaf, a cavity tray stepped dpc should be provided to discharge over the cover flashing.

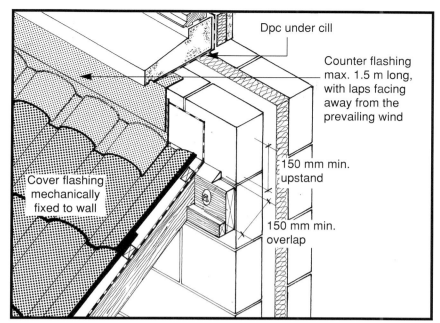

Detail of tiled roof at wall abutment. Ensure head course of tiles/slates at abutments is lapped adequately by flashing.

Abutment flashing detail. Note the weepholes at 450 mm centres.

BACK GUTTER

A gutter should be formed where the bottom edge of tiling or slating meets an abutment. The gutter should be formed before tiling/slating but after felting and battening is complete.

A treated timber layboard should be provided to give support to the lead lining. The layboard should be carried up as far as the first tiling batten.

Fix a treated tilting fillet, at least 150 mm wide, close to the abutment to flatten the pitch of the lead. Dress a sheet of code 4 lead into position on the timber supports. This lead should be the width of the abutment plus 450 mm. The vertical upstand should be at least 100 mm up the abutment. Dress the extra width of lead around the corner of the abutment after any side abutment weathering has been fitted. Dress the upper edge of the lead over the bottom tiling batten and turn it back to form a welt. Chase the abutment (25 mm deep chase. Insert a cover flashing of code 4 lead and dress it over the vertical upstand of the gutter.

Finish the roofing underlay with a 100 mm lap onto the lead. Lay the tiles/slates in the normal way, making sure that the bottom course is not kicked up by the flat section of gutter.

In brickwork abutments adequate cavity trays must be installed to discharge over flashing.

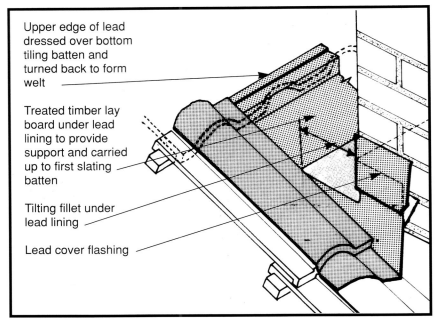

Upper edge of lead dressed over bottom tiling batten and turned back to form welt

Treated timber lay board under lead lining to provide support and carried up to first slating batten

Tilting fillet under lead lining

Lead cover flashing

Typical back gutter.

Abutment checklist– points to watch:

◆ Lead, particularly the heavier codes, can be difficult to work. In cold weather take care not to split or puncture it while working

◆ Always use proper lead working tools. Hammers are not recommended for dressing lead

◆ Nail and/or clip all tiles next to an abutment

◆ Fillets of mortar are not recommended at abutments because cracking of the mortar brings a high risk of failure.

SIDE ABUTMENTS

Abutment flashing with soakers.

The length of a soaker is determined by the length of the tile or slate onto which it is being fitted. It should be the gauge of the tile or slate (i.e. the length of the tile or slate minus the lap, divided by two) plus the lap (i.e. the distance one slate or tile overlaps the course next but one below it) plus 25 mm so that the soaker can be turned down over the top of the tile. This prevents the soaker slipping out of position. The width of a soaker should be a minimum of 175 mm to allow for a 75 mm upstand against the wall and 100 mm under the tiles or slates. A suitable thickness of lead sheet for soakers is code 3.

Chimney flashings.

Flashings to chimney stacks which penetrate pitched roofs consist of side flashings, front apron, back gutter and metal tray dpc (built into the stack in the case of brick chimneys) with integral lead flashing dressed down over the front apron.

The order of fixing to the completed stack is: first, front apron, then, side flashings and lastly, the back gutter. The metal tray dpc is incorporated into the stack as it is being built.

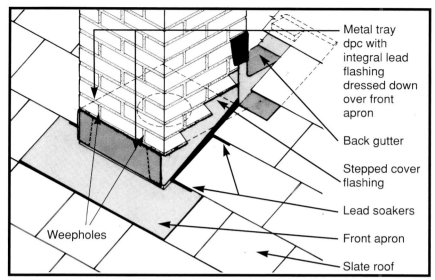

Metal tray dpc with integral lead flashing dressed down over front apron

Back gutter

Stepped cover flashing

Lead soakers

Front apron

Slate roof

Weepholes

Typical abutment details incorporating soakers.

Front apron.

A lead front apron should extend 150 to 200 mm beyond each edge of the stack, depending on the form of roof covering. In width the piece of lead will need to allow 150 mm for the upstand and 150 to 200 mm for the cover down the roof slope; the lower the pitch, the greater the cover. Where a front apron is to be fitted to a chimney stack that has small secret gutters at the sides, the extension beyond the corners will need to be increased; the extra length required depends on the width and depth of the gutter.

SIDE ABUTMENTS
continued

There are two common ways of weathering a side abutment with interlocking tiles:

1. Stepped cover flashings
2. Secret gutters

Stepped cover flashing

Turn the roofing underlay about 50 mm up the abutment. Finish the tiling battens as close to the abutment as possible. Lay the tiles to butt as close as possible to the wall. Usually this can be done without cutting any tiles, by adjusting the tile shunt across the roof. Half tiles may be useful. Cut a piece of code 4 lead as shown to form a combined step and cover flashing. The flashing should not be more than 1.5m long and should be wide enough to cover the abutting tile by 150 mm, or to cover the first roll, whichever gives the greatest cover. Chase out the brickwork mortar joints (25 mm deep chase). Push the folds of the flashing into the chase and wedge in with small pieces of lead. Dress the cover flashing as tightly as possible to the tile profile. Then repoint the brickwork.

Note:

If the abutment is rendered, the render should not be applied directly to the flashings, as this restricts movement and may cause splitting of the flashing or detachment of the rendering. Use proprietary expanded metal stop bead 75 mm above the finished roof line.

Note:

The lead flashing should be chased into the joints in the brickwork. It should not be nailed directly to the brickwork.

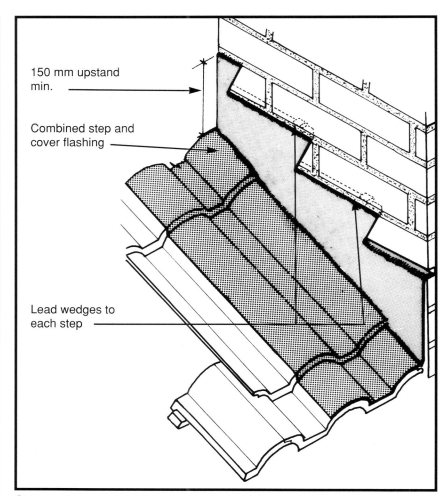

150 mm upstand min.

Combined step and cover flashing

Lead wedges to each step

Stepped cover flashing on contoured tiles.

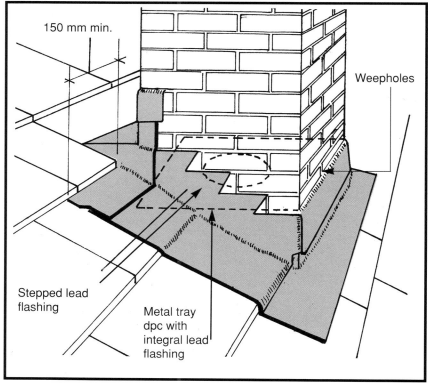

150 mm min.

Weepholes

Stepped lead flashing

Metal tray dpc with integral lead flashing

Stepped cover flashing on flat interlocking tiles.

SECRET GUTTER

The secret gutter should be formed before tiling commences.

A treated timber support should be fixed between the last rafter and the abutment. This should be at least 75 mm wide and run the full length of the abutment.

Fix a splayed timber fillet at the discharge point to raise the lead lining to the right height. Take care not to create a backward fall with this fillet.

Fix a treated counter batten along the outer edge of the rafter. This should be thinner than the main tiling battens by at least two thicknesses of lead.

Line the gutter with code 4 lead, in lengths of not more than 1.5 m. Lap each strip over the lower one and fix with copper nails at the head. For lap details, see page 211.

The lead welts should be turned up to exclude birds and vermin from entering the tile batten space.

The gutter should be about 50 mm deep and have a vertical upstand of at least 100 mm against the abutment.

At the discharge point, the lead lining should be splayed out across the timber fillet to avoid the risk of an overflow at the side.

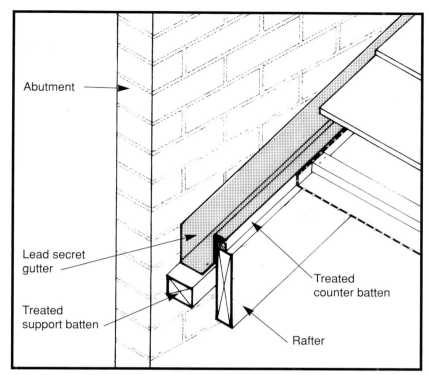

Typical section through lead secret gutter.

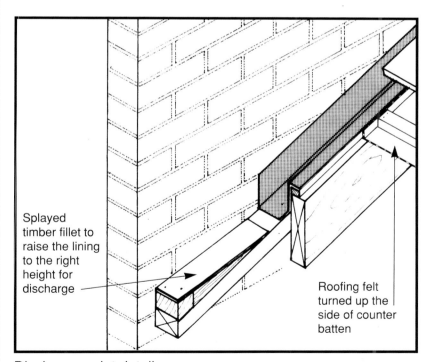

Discharge point detail.

SECRET GUTTER
continued

Turn the roofing underlay up the side of the counter batten. The tiling battens should butt up to the counter batten.

Lay tiles to leave a gap of 25 -38 mm by the abutment. This allows for future cleaning out of the gutter to avoid blockages.

A cover flashing above the secret gutter is advisable, particularly in areas of high exposure or on roofs under trees where the risk of blockages is high.

Fit a stepped flashing chased into the brickwork (25 mm deep chase) and dressed over the vertical upstand.

Note:

If the abutment is rendered the render should not be applied directly to the flashings as this restricts movement and may cause splitting of the flashing or detachment of the rendering. Use proprietary expanded metal stop bead 75 mm above the finished roof line, see detail on page 75.

Where the roof abuts a cavity wall with a brick or fairfaced block outer leaf, a cavity tray dpc should be provided. The cavity tray should discharge any moisture collected via an integral weephole, or via weepholes provided in perpend joints at 1 m centres, over the cover flashing.

In brick and fairfaced block chimneys, a metal tray dpc should be similarly incorporated. See pages 118 and 119.

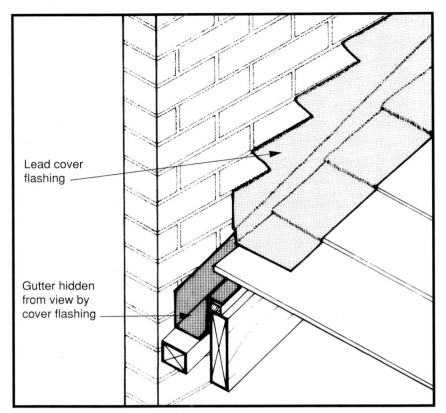

Lead cover flashing

Gutter hidden from view by cover flashing

Complete secret gutter with lead cover flashing.

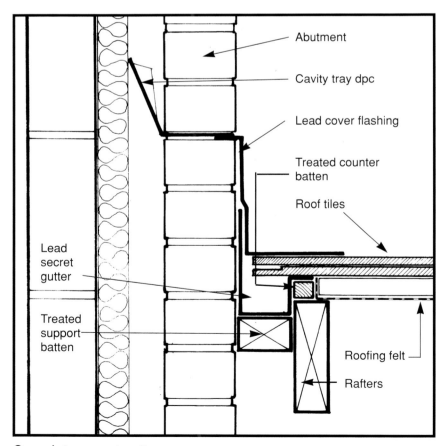

Abutment

Cavity tray dpc

Lead cover flashing

Treated counter batten

Roof tiles

Lead secret gutter

Treated support batten

Roofing felt

Rafters

Complete secret gutter.

FLAT-ROOFED DORMER WINDOW

Where pitched roofs incorporate dormer windows which have flat roofs the following recommendations apply:

◆ Where rainwater discharges from the flat roof of a dormer window onto a pitched roof a lead apron should be provided at the point of discharge as illustrated

◆ Where only narrow widths of pitched roof occur adjoining flat-roofed dormer windows, the rainwater run-off from the roof should be arranged so as not to discharge onto such areas

◆ The drainage fall on the flat roof should be towards the vertical face of the dormer and not inwards towards the junction of flat roof and pitched roof.

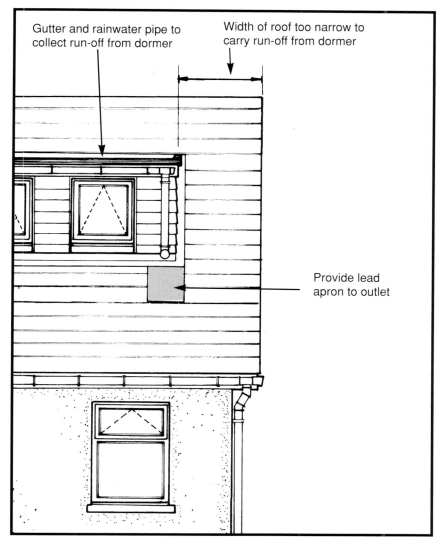

Gutter and rainwater pipe to collect run-off from dormer

Width of roof too narrow to carry run-off from dormer

Provide lead apron to outlet

Run-off from flat roof dormer window. Where possible, rainwater should not discharge over roof.

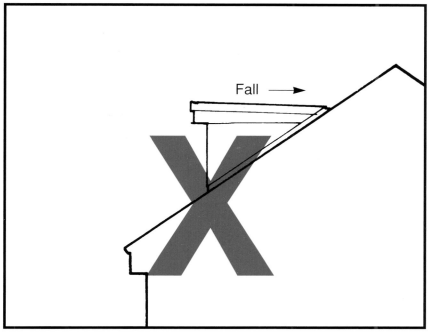

Fall

Never allow the dormer roof to fall backwards.

SIZING GUTTERS AND DOWNPIPES

To efficiently size gutters and downpipes the effective area of the roof being drained must first be established. This depends on the pitch of the roof, see Table 1 opposite. When the effective area of the roof has been calculated and the location of the downpipes determined, the size of the gutter and downpipe can be obtained from the graph below, (see examples on following page).

The information on these pages has been derived from Building Regulations Technical Guidance Document H and BS 6367: 1983: Drainage of Roofs and Paved Areas, and applies only to straight lengths of gutters. Where a gutter includes an angle, reference should be made to BS 6367 for guidance.

Table 1	
Roof type	Effective area
Flat 30° Pitch 45° Pitch 60° Pitch 70° Pitch or greater	Plan area Plan area x 1.15 Plan area x 1.40 Plan area x 2.0 Elevational area x 0.5

Gutter and outlet size graph. (half-round gutters).

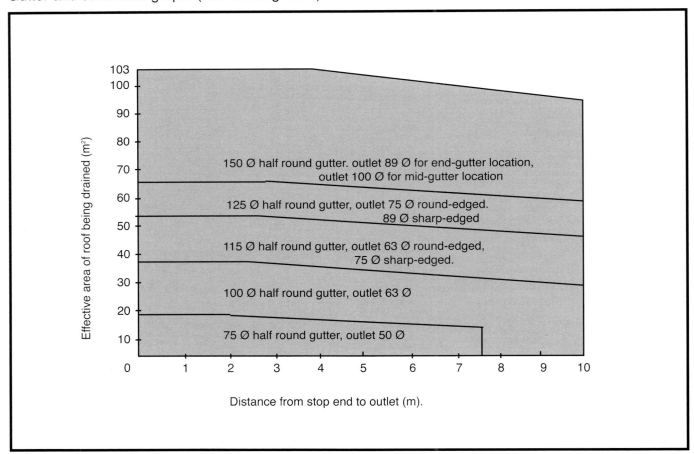

Notes:

1. Gutters and downpipes may be omitted from a roof at any height provided that it has an area of 6 m² or less and provided no other roof drains onto it.
2. Rainwater pipes for standard eaves gutters should have the same nominal bore as the gutter outlets to which they are connected.
3. Gutters should be laid with any fall towards the nearest outlet.
4. Gutters should be laid so that any overflow in excess of the design capacity will be discharged clear of the building.

SIZING GUTTERS AND DOWNPIPES

Example 1	Example 2
Detached house and garage	**Semi-detached houses**

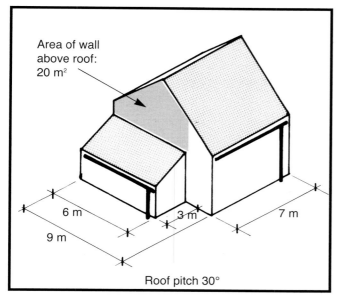

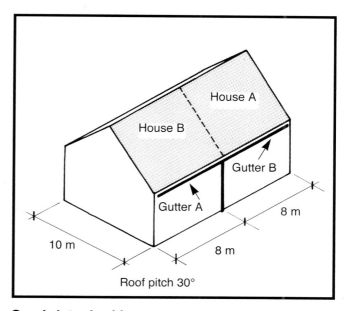

1. **Garage**: 3 m x 6 m (plan area of garage roof) x 1.15 (multiplying factor for 30° roof pitch from table 1) = 20.7 m²

   20 m² (area of wall above roof) x 0.5 (multiplying factor for surfaces of 70° pitch or greater from Table 1) = 1.0 m²
   Effective roof area:
   20.7 m² + 10 m² = 30.7 m²

   From the gutter sizing graph on the previous page, it can be seen that a 100 mm dia. half round gutter with 63 mm dia. outlet is sufficient for this area of roof.

2. **House**: 7 m x 4.5 m (plan area of house roof) x 1.15 (multiplying factor for 30° roof pitch from table 1) = 36.2 m² (effective roof area).

   From the gutter sizing graph on the previous page, it can be seen that a 115 mm dia. half round gutter with 63 mm dia. outlet is sufficient for this area of roof.

Semi-detached houses:
Note: Roof area of house A discharges to gutter A and roof area house B discharges to gutter B, both gutters discharge to a single downpipe, located centrally.

Calculation:
8 m x 5 m (plan area roof of one house x 1.15 (multiplying factor for 30° roof pitch from table 1) = 46 m² (effective roof area of 1 house)

From the gutter sizing graph on the previous page, it can be seen that a 115 mm diameter half round gutter with a 63 mm. diameter round edged outlet or 75 mm diameter sharp-edged outlet is adequate for the area of roof in question.

INTRODUCTION

See the detailed guidance on pages 234 and 235 in relation to the procedures for the correct sizing of gutters and downpipes to ensure adequate capacity for the area of roof being drained.

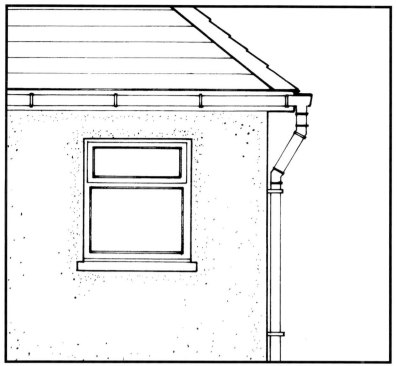

Ensure that gutters are of adequate size and laid to a proper fall. Ensure adequate number of downpipes. Provide sufficient clips to gutters and drainpipes.

DRYING OUT

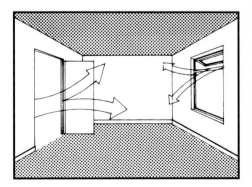

Allow adequate ventilation to speed up drying of wet finishes. It is also important to allow adequate time for drying out. Drying out of wet finishes can cause twisting / warping of doors if hung too early.

Ensure that building is closed to the weather before commencing finishing trades, thus avoiding damage to finishes by exposure to the effects of the weather.

LETTER PLATES

The Department of the Environment and Local Government has published amendments to the Building Regulations 1997 and a revised edition of the associated Technical Guidance Document to Part D of the Regulations (Materials and Workmanship).

The revised requirements of Part D ban the use of low-level letter plates in the construction of new dwellings with effect from 1st. of January 2001.

Regulation D2 now requires that: *A letter plate aperture shall be so positioned at a reasonable height above ground level so as not to endanger the health and safety of persons using such apertures.*

The sketch opposite outlines the positioning requirements for letter plates.

The length of the aperture of a letter plate should be 250 mm (±10 mm) and the height should be 38 mm (±1.5 mm).

In addition, letter plates should be designed, manufactured and installed in accordance with **IS 195: 1976 Letter Plates.**

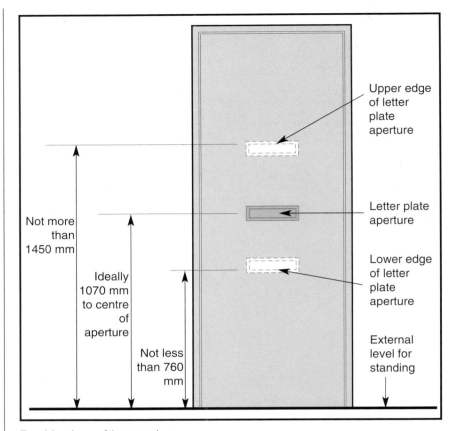

Positioning of letter plate

ALL STAGES

PROTECTION GUIDELINES

To avoid costly repair work, every effort should be made to protect completed work from damage and carelessness.

The following guidelines should be applied:.

◆ Avoid heavy construction traffic over external door thresholds as waterbars get damaged thus decreasing watertightness in the building

◆ Protect doors with polythene or original wrapping

◆ Protect door frames and linings with timber strips or plywood to at least 1 m above floor level

◆ Flooring should be protected with suitable temporary covering (e.g. building paper) towithstand damp caused by plaster droppings and the like

◆ Protect stair treads and handrails with timber strips, plywood or building paper. Avoid the use of polythene

◆ Protect installed kitchen worktops and unit faces. Do not use worktops as work benches or cupboards for temporary storage of tools and site materials.

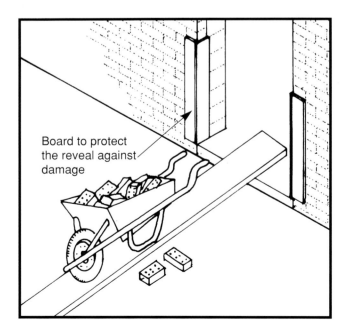

Board to protect the reveal against damage

◆ Protect reveals

TIMBER PRESERVATION

All external softwood timber components such as windows, external doors and frames, fascia boards, barge boards, etc., should receive a double vacuum preservative treatment prior to delivery to the site. A certificate of treatment should be obtained from the timber supplier. The cut ends of pretreated timber should receive a liberal brush treatment with preservative on site.

Surface coating of external joinery timbers

Paint finish
Where joinery timbers are intended to receive a paint finish they should first be primed on all surfaces including concealed areas. This reduces moisture uptake, expansion and shrinkage in service. Ideally, joinery should be shop primed. Where this is not possible, ensure all joinery components are primed promptly upon delivery to the site.

Clear finish
Where joinery timbers are intended to receive a clear surface finish, they should be sealed as early as possible on all exposed and concealed surfaces, with a sealing coat compatible with the intended finish.

SITE STORAGE

In the interest of cost saving and site safety, appropriate measures should be taken for the protection and storage of materials on site.

The following guidelines should be applied.

Joinery

Ensure that joinery on site is kept dry at all times. If stored in the open, cover top and sides allowing ventilation to the stack, and also keep the stack well clear of the ground.

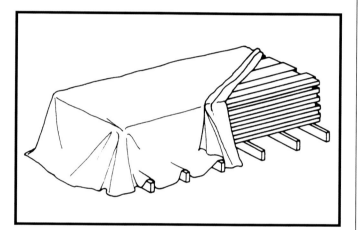

Bagged materials

Hydrated lime, cement and premixed dry bagged materials should be stored off the ground, under cover and away from damp surfaces, in such a manner as to allow the bags to be used in rotation in the order of delivery.

Ready-mixed sand-lime mix for mortar should be tipped onto a cleaned sealed banker board with a sealed base and should be covered when not in use.

Covering over is particularly important when coloured mortars are being used, because rain and weathering may wash out some of the pigment or other fine materials and lead to a variation in colour.

Plasterboard

Plasterboard should be stored off the ground and horizontally on a level base consisting of a timber platform or bearers at least 100 mm wide laid across the width of the boards at centres not exceeding 400 mm.

If plasterboard is not stored in a weatherproof building, completely cover the stack with a waterproof sheet secured all round. Protect from damp rising from below the stack. Unless special provisions are made, do not stack boards to a height of more than 1 m.

Storage of plasterboard

Insulation

Insulation products should be delivered to site suitably wrapped in polythene or similar material. They should be stored under cover and protected from direct sunlight. Contact with solvents and organic based materials such as coal tar, pitch or creosote should be avoided.

Additional advice on handling and storage and health and safety requirements is available from manufacturers.

SITE STORAGE
continued

Trussed rafters

Trussed rafters should be:

◆ Stored and handled to prevent distortion and sagging or bending

◆ Stored on level bearers at wall plate position, vertically for long term storage. (Horizontal stacking is acceptable for short term storage)

◆ Cover to protect from rain and sun, whilst ensuring good ventilation

◆ Stored in a secure manner.

Prolonged dampness may cause rot in timber and corrosion of connector plates.

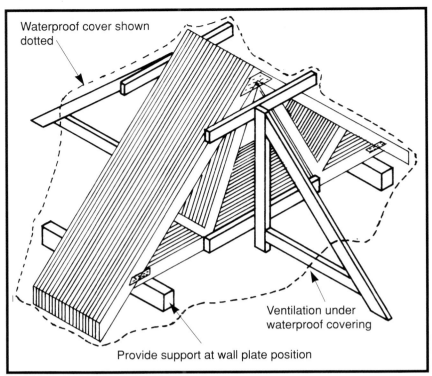

Long term storage.

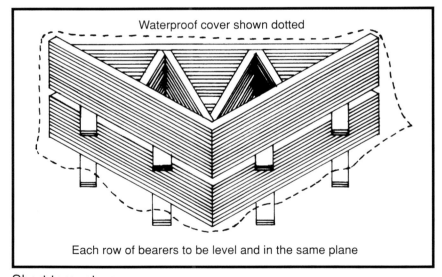

Short term storage.

CONSTRUCTION DETAILS - RADON MEMBRANE
continued

Membranes used for radon protection will normally be provided instead of damp proof membranes incorporated in ground floor construction. Membranes used for radon protection should be non-biodegradable and of suitable strength and durability. The performance requirements for radon membranes to ensure compliance with Building Regulations are outlined on page 262. Sand blinding of the hardcore is essential to reduce the risk of damaging the membrane.

Any material or product used must have the relevant Agrément, or other appropriate certificate, confirming suitability for use and should be installed in accordance with the requirements of that certificate.

In addition, particular care should be taken in installing the membrane as all joints and service penetrations must be fully sealed. In view of the difficulty in achieving gas tight seals under site conditions, it is recommended that the membranes be prefabricated and installed by appropriately trained personnel. Alternatively proprietary products can be used in these locations as illustrated opposite.

Manufacturers' guidance should be sought to establish if the radon membrane can be used instead of a dpc, or if a dpc is required in conjunction with the membrane in rising walls.

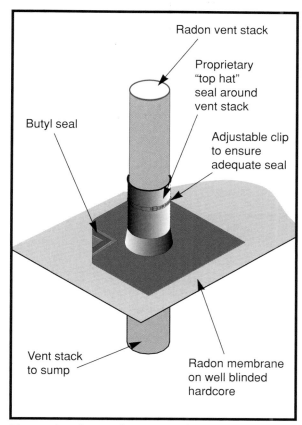

Example of proprietary top hat seal around radon vent stack.

RAFT FOUNDATIONS

Some publications indicate that it may be possible to rely on a properly reinforced concrete ground floor raft to provide a membrane. However, it is strongly recommended that a raft foundation should be treated as a normal floor slab and a radon membrane and/or sump be incorporated where necessary. The membrane will normally be placed on top of the raft and under the insulation and floor screed. A typical example of this detail is illustrated on page 264.

PERFORMANCE REQUIREMENTS OF RADON MEMBRANES

Technical Guidance Document C of the Building Regulations, outlines the minimum performance requirements for Low Density Polyethylene (LDPE) radon membranes.

Unreinforced LDPE radon membrane:

◆ Tear resistance $\geq$ 100 N when tested in accordance with MOAT 27 (5.4.1)

◆ Moisture Vapour Transmission Rate $\leq$ 0.40 g/m^2/24 hours, and

◆ Elongation (at break) $\geq$ 100% when tested in accordance with BS 2782 (320A).

Reinforced LDPE radon membrane:

◆ Tear resistance $\geq$ 100 N when tested in accordance with MOAT 27 (5.4.1)

◆ Moisture Vapour Transmission Rate $\leq$ 0.40 g/m^2/24 hours, and

◆ Elongation (at max. load) $\geq$ 12% when tested in accordance with ISO 1421.

Sub floors prepared for installation of radon barrier.

Radon barrier being installed.

TYPICAL RADON MEMBRANE DETAILS

Note: Other arrangement details, including those by radon membrane and dpc manufacturers may be equally applicable.

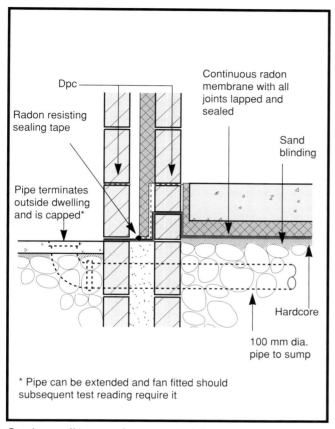

Dpc

Continuous radon membrane with all joints lapped and sealed

Radon resisting sealing tape

Sand blinding

Pipe terminates outside dwelling and is capped*

Hardcore

100 mm dia. pipe to sump

* Pipe can be extended and fan fitted should subsequent test reading require it

Cavity wall/ground supported floor.

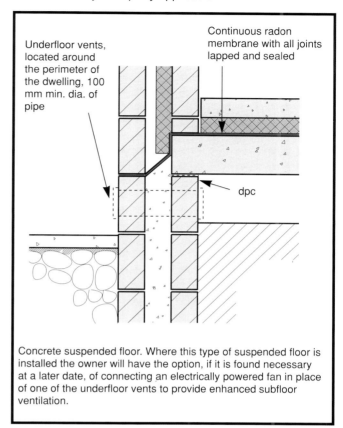

Underfloor vents, located around the perimeter of the dwelling, 100 mm min. dia. of pipe

Continuous radon membrane with all joints lapped and sealed

dpc

Concrete suspended floor. Where this type of suspended floor is installed the owner will have the option, if it is found necessary at a later date, of connecting an electrically powered fan in place of one of the underfloor vents to provide enhanced subfloor ventilation.

Suspended concrete floor.

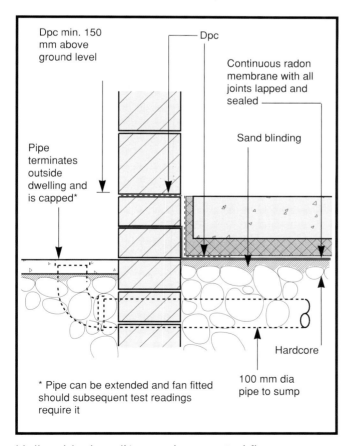

Dpc min. 150 mm above ground level

Dpc

Continuous radon membrane with all joints lapped and sealed

Sand blinding

Pipe terminates outside dwelling and is capped*

Hardcore

100 mm dia pipe to sump

* Pipe can be extended and fan fitted should subsequent test readings require it

Hollow block wall/ground supported floor.

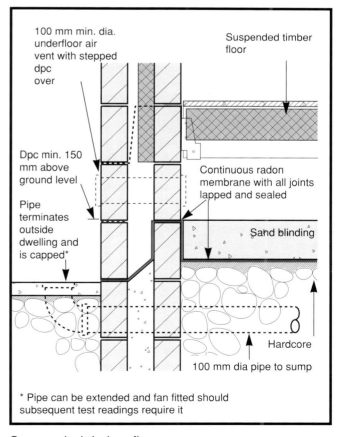

100 mm min. dia. underfloor air vent with stepped dpc over

Suspended timber floor

Dpc min. 150 mm above ground level

Pipe terminates outside dwelling and is capped*

Continuous radon membrane with all joints lapped and sealed

Sand blinding

Hardcore

100 mm dia pipe to sump

* Pipe can be extended and fan fitted should subsequent test readings require it

Suspended timber floor.

TYPICAL RADON MEMBRANE DETAILS

Note: Other arrangement details, including those by radon membrane and dpc manufacturers may be equally applicable.

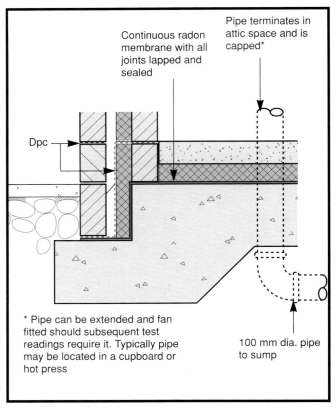

Continuous radon membrane with all joints lapped and sealed

Pipe terminates in attic space and is capped*

Dpc

* Pipe can be extended and fan fitted should subsequent test readings require it. Typically pipe may be located in a cupboard or hot press

100 mm dia. pipe to sump

Raft foundation.

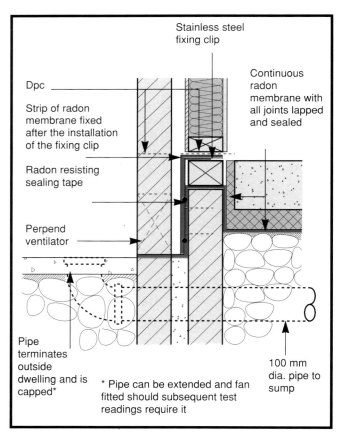

Stainless steel fixing clip

Dpc

Strip of radon membrane fixed after the installation of the fixing clip

Continuous radon membrane with all joints lapped and sealed

Radon resisting sealing tape

Perpend ventilator

Pipe terminates outside dwelling and is capped*

* Pipe can be extended and fan fitted should subsequent test readings require it

100 mm dia. pipe to sump

Timber frame construction, (sole plate held in position with fixing clip).

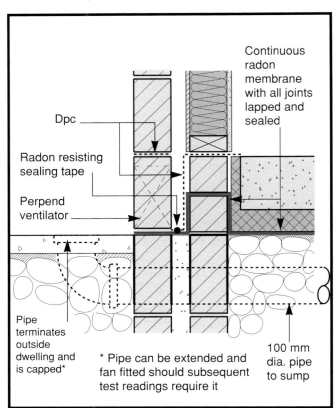

Continuous radon membrane with all joints lapped and sealed

Dpc

Radon resisting sealing tape

Perpend ventilator

Pipe terminates outside dwelling and is capped*

* Pipe can be extended and fan fitted should subsequent test readings require it

100 mm dia. pipe to sump

Timber frame construction, (timber frame fixed directly to rising wall).

RADON SUMP

As advised earlier, dwellings in high radon areas require the installation of a radon membrane and a sump/collection chamber. Dwellings outside high radon areas will require the installation of a sump/collection chamber.

In a building with concrete floating ground floor (i.e. ground supported), this will usually mean providing a sump/collection chamber in the permeable hardcore layer under the slab.

Where clean permeable hardcore is used, a single sump is likely to have an influence over an area of approximately 250 m² and for a distance of up to 15 m from the sump. Obstructions below the floor slab may reduce the effect of the sump system and it may be necessary to provide free airways in the rising walls or provide separate sumps in each compartment. To create free airways it is suggested that a gap equivalent to 12,500 mm² per metre run of wall (a gap of a quarter of a block in length in each four blocks) should be adequate.

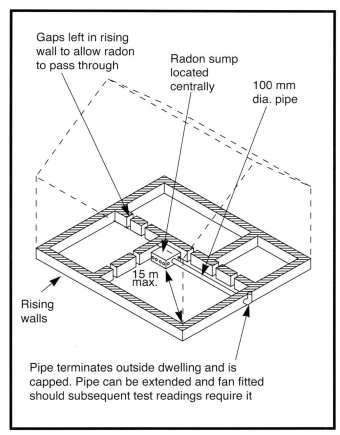

Typical sump location in a single dwelling. Each dwelling should have a separate sump and associated means of extraction.

The recommended underfloor sump consists of either a proprietary collection box or a site constructed void incorporating a 600 x 600 x 50 mm paving slab supported on bricks or blocks.

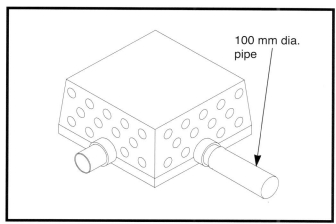

Typical proprietary sump.

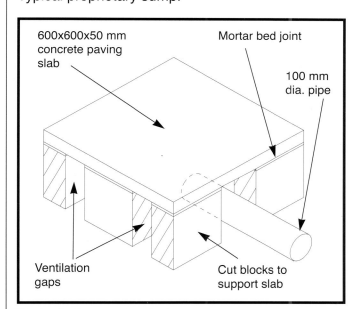

Typical site constructed sump.

Care must be taken (for example, by bedding the slab on the bricks or blocks with mortar and allowing it to cure) to reduce the likelihood of collapse. Care should be exercised when placing hardcore around this type of sump to ensure that hardcore does not enter the chamber. For this reason, the use of a proprietary system is recommended.

RADON SUMP
continued

A 100 mm diameter pipe is inserted into the sump and extended horizontally (details as shown on pages 263 and 264) to the outside of the dwelling. All joints in the pipework and where it passes through the external wall must be sealed, to avoid drawing in air from the outside. The pipe should be capped off at ground level (or at a level where it will not cause obstruction), to prevent vermin and rain penetration. Alternatively the pipe may extend vertically into the attic space where it is capped, see sketch opposite. The pipe can be extended and a fan fitted should a subsequent test reading require it. Any pipe passing through the radon membrane must have an airtight seal and prefabricated "top hat" sections, as illustrated on page 261.

To reduce the risk of accidental connection to drainage systems, the capped radon sump outlet should be clearly marked to identify its function.

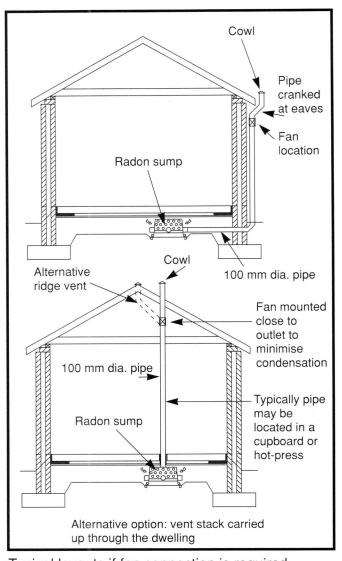

Alternative option: vent stack carried up through the dwelling

Typical layouts if fan connection is required.

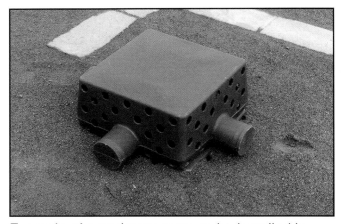

Example of proprietary sump to be installed in hardcore, 100 mm dia. pipe to be connected to sump outlet.

Proprietary sump installed in hardcore.

Proprietary radon sump with extract pipe attached.

CONCLUSION

- RADON IS A GAS WHICH IS ASSOCIATED WITH AN INCREASED RISK OF DEVELOPING LUNG CANCER.

- THE BUILDING REGULATIONS REQUIRE THAT CERTAIN PRECAUTIONS BE TAKEN, WHEN CONSTRUCTING NEW HOUSES, TO REDUCE LEVELS OF RADON WHERE NECESSARY.

- DESIGNERS AND BUILDERS MUST MAKE THEMSELVES AWARE OF THE REQUIREMENTS FOR RADON PRECAUTIONS TO BE INCORPORATED IN HOUSES BEING DESIGNED AND BUILT BY THEM.

REFERENCES

The information contained in this Appendix is an introduction to the topic and the following publications will be of assistance and should be consulted.

Radiological Protection Institute of Ireland Map,
"Radon in Irish Dwellings".

There are five RPII reports entitled **"Radon in Dwellings - The National Survey"** giving results of the survey.

- The 1st. report gives the results for: Cavan, Dublin, Louth, Monaghan and Wicklow.
- The 2nd. report gives the results for: Carlow, Donegal, Kildare, Kilkenny, Laois, Leitrim, Longford, Meath, Offaly, Roscommon, Sligo, Waterford, Westmeath, and Wexford.
- The 3rd. report gives results for: Cork and Kerry.
- The 4th. report gives results for: Clare, Limerick and Tipperary.
- The 5th. report gives results for: Galway and Mayo.

The above publications are available from the Government Publications Sales Office, Molesworth Street, Dublin 2.
Tel: 01 661 311.
Fax. 01 475 2760.

ENFO - The Environmental Information Service, 17 St. Andrew St., Dublin 2.
Tel: 01 6793144.
"Radon".

Building Research Establishment, Report BR 211 available from C.R.C. Ltd., 151 Rosebery Avenue, London EC1 R 4QX.

TIMBER FRAME CONSTRUCTION

INTRODUCTION

Timber frame construction is an established building technique that has been used for many years. This Appendix describes, for builders, the fundamentals of timber frame buildings to ensure that they are constructed properly, that the construction details are the best possible and that the dwelling is structurally sound.

Timber is easily worked and its low self-weight facilitates handling and erection operations and reduces the weight of the structure. A timber framed building can be carried out in wholly dry construction and the building completed more quickly than an equivalent building involving the 'wet' trades.

Timbers vary considerably in their properties and appearances between species, and even between parts of one tree. Accordingly, the choice of timber for use in a timber frame building requires careful control. For this reason HomeBond will only register timber frame construction which comprises a system supplied by a HomeBond approved timber frame manufacturer.

This appendix gives detailed construction guidance for two storey detached, semi-detached and terraced timber frame houses, with particular emphasis on:

◆ Setting out

◆ Rising walls and foundations

◆ Ground floor construction

◆ External walls

◆ Party (separating) walls

◆ First floor construction

◆ Site fixing

◆ Fire safety

◆ Site supervision generally.

TIMBER FRAME CONSTRUCTION GUIDELINES

◆ Use a system from a HomeBond approved timber frame manufacturer. "Stick-built" timber frame construction is not acceptable to HomeBond

◆ Obtain a certificate from the timber frame manufacturer that the design has been checked for compliance with all relevant technical requirements

◆ Obtain drawings for on site use. These should include assembly drawings showing timber frame connections, weathering and damp proofing details and, where critical, erection sequence for use by site personnel. It is recommended that 1: 5 scale be used for details and 1: 50 be used for general arrangement drawings.

Site control:

◆ Clear instructions must be provided at all times. This is particularly important in relation to ordering materials and work on the site. Failure to issue correct and clear instructions can lead to problems at a later stage

◆ Make sure you are using the correct materials, documentation and drawings. Make sure that the person carrying out the work has the correct and necessary information to do the work properly

◆ Refer always to the drawings and work schedules provided. If in doubt about any aspect of the work, refer back to the timber frame supplier

◆ The fixing schedule, issued by the timber frame manufacturer, must be adhered to. Components should always be completely fixed in accordance with the fixing schedule

◆ Keep a record of drawings, instructions and documents issued. Keep a record of the sequence of site work carried out.

WHAT BUILDERS OF TIMBER FRAME HOUSES MUST DO

◆ Site supervision is a key factor in timber frame construction. The timber frame manufacturer will issue a checklist for all stages of the project. Each item on the list should be ticked off on completion. Keep the completed checklist safe

◆ Make sure you have all the necessary documentation, instructions and knowledge before you commence work. Instructions should include the sequence of erection of the various elements relevant to the proper execution of the work, including the provision of temporary bracing or support

◆ Do not alter panels or other structural members without the written notification or permission of the timber frame manufacturer. Notching and drilling of elements must be in accordance with the recommendations set out elsewhere in this manual, unless specifically covered by the designer. Record any changes made on site

◆ Check materials and components on a continuous basis. Repair or replace damaged or unsuitable materials or components

◆ Party wall construction is a key aspect in timber frame construction, to prevent the spread of fire and the transmission of sound. HomeBond does not permit the construction of conventional masonry chimneys in timber frame party walls

◆ The timber frame is only suitable for short term exposure to the elements. After erection of the timber frame, the roof should be promptly felted and openings protected by polythene or similar material, to protect against weather penetration

◆ Ensure foundations and rising walls are set out accurately.

Typical timber frame houses under construction

ACCURACY OF SETTING OUT

Because of the precise tolerances to which the factory manufactured timber frame components are manufactured, the accurate setting out of the substructure on which it sits is vital to ensure that the structural integrity of the frame is not compromised.

◆ Ensure all dimensions are rigidly adhered to

◆ Check the diagonal measurements of the base/substructure

◆ Check that corners are square

◆ If packing such as mortar or slate is used under the sole plate, it should not exceed 15 mm in thickness and be of a suitable material that will not deform under load and will fully support studs so that no deformation of the frame will occur.

Certain timber frame systems do not incorporate a sole plate. Where it is used ensure that it is:

◆ Undamaged

◆ Adequately fixed to the sub structure, see page 276

◆ Laid level, +/- 6 mm

◆ Pressure treated with the proper preservative, see page 281

◆ Provided with a dpc to the underside which extends the full width of the wall.

The above criteria also apply where the bottom rail of the wall panel acts as the sole plate

◆ The bottom rail of the wall panels, at the junction with sole plate or rising walls, should be bedded in a suitable sealant to prevent undue draughts.

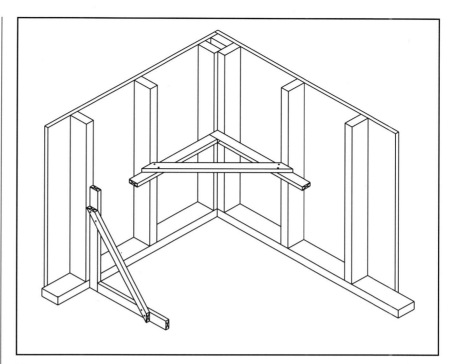

Ensure corners are set out accurately.

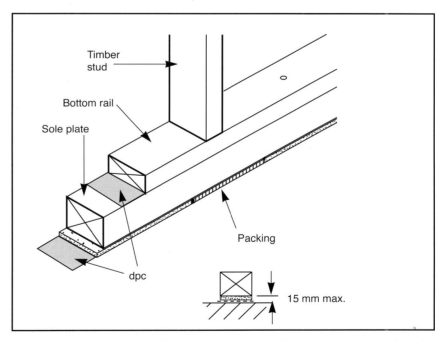

Level sole plate before fixing wall frame. If sole plate is not level it may be supported by a mortar bed (and slate if necessary). The bed should not be more than 15 mm thick and should extend the full width of the sole plate.

ACCURACY OF SETTING OUT
continued

In suspended timber floor construction, the subfloor must be level with or above external ground level to avoid the sump effect, see page 40.

The dpm should be adequately lapped under the dpc, see page 276.

The dpc must extend the full width of the wall.

All ground floor sole plates/bottom rails must have a dpc under.

Ledges should be avoided. Where they occur they should be protected by the breather membrane.

Securely anchor the timber frame structure to the substructure/rising wall, see page 277.

INACCURACIES IN SETTING OUT, WHICH MAY AFFECT THE WAY LOADS FROM THE STRUCTURE ARE TRANSFERRED TO THE SUBSTRUCTURE/RISING WALL, WILL NOT BE ACCEPTED.

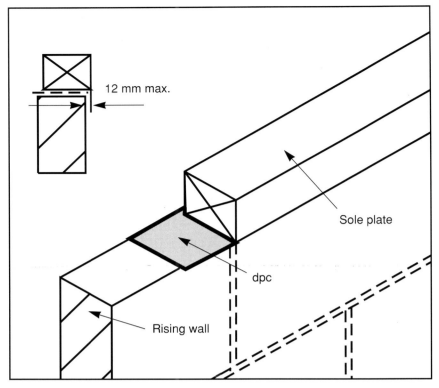

Sole plate or bottom rail should not overhang or form a ledge with the substructure to which it is fixed by more than 12 mm.

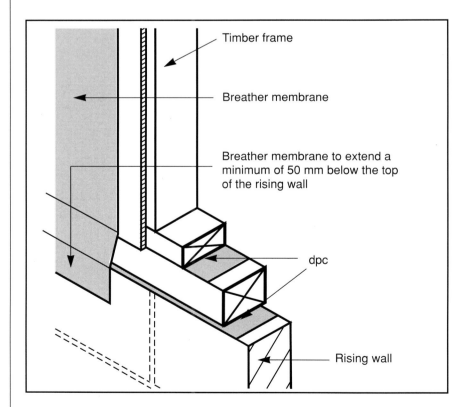

Ledges where moisture can gather should be avoided. Where they occur they should be protected by the breather membrane, which should be long enough to extend at least 50 mm below the top surface of the rising wall. No ledge should be larger than 12 mm.

RISING WALLS AND FOUNDATIONS

The appropriate foundations and rising walls should be completed prior to the delivery of the timber frame kit. This will ensure that the timber components can be placed in their final position with the minimum of handling and site storage.

Requirements for the construction of rising walls and foundations are detailed in Stage A of this Manual, (pages 14-34).

The cavity void in timber frame construction must be ventilated. This is usually achieved by proprietary ventilators, fitted in the perpends (vertical joints) of the masonry outer leaf, at 1500 mm horizontal centres, below dpc level. These ventilators also act as weepholes and must be kept free of obstruction.

Radon
Note that the details in this section do not deal with the practices to protect homes from radon. See Appendix A of this Manual.

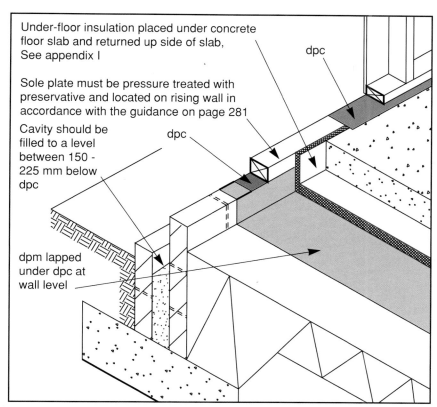

Under-floor insulation placed under concrete floor slab and returned up side of slab, See appendix I

Sole plate must be pressure treated with preservative and located on rising wall in accordance with the guidance on page 281

Cavity should be filled to a level between 150 - 225 mm below dpc

dpc

dpc

dpm lapped under dpc at wall level

Typical rising wall detail with sole plate.

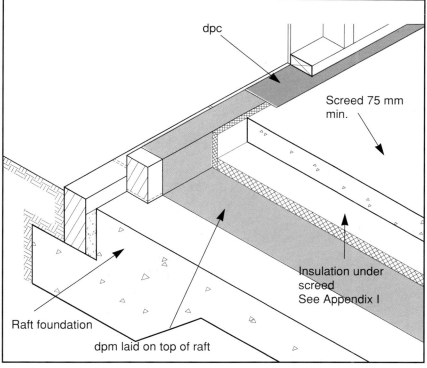

dpc

Screed 75 mm min.

Insulation under screed See Appendix I

Raft foundation

dpm laid on top of raft

Typical raft foundation detail. Reinforcement to raft not shown.

Proprietary perpend ventilators, below dpc level. Note, ventilators also required at eaves level, see page 296.

RISING WALLS & FOUNDATIONS

Sole plate

When using a sole plate on which the timber frame sits, it should be located on the rising wall by means of 4 mm dia. stainless steel masonry nails. The nails must be long enough to provide a minimum embedment of 50 mm into the substructure/rising wall and be located at 300 mm centres. Alternatively stainless steel anchor clips may be used, as illustrated opposite, fixed at 1200 mm centres.

NOTE: The methods described on this page provide alternative means of locating the sole plate on the substructure. Details of how the timber frame is anchored to the substructure are provided on page 277.

The function of the sole plate is to:

◆ Provide an accurately positioned base on which the timber frame and suspended ground floor is fixed

◆ Provide an accurate setting out template for wall panels

◆ Provide a nailing plate for the timber panels or ground floor joists

◆ Secure and protect dpc.

Sole plates must be pressure impregnated with preservative, see page 281.
Where a sole plate is not provided, all its functions must then be performed by the bottom rail of the wall panels.

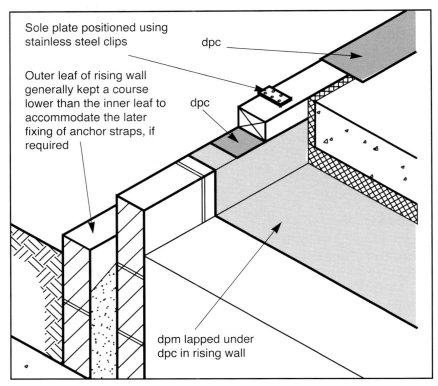

Sole plate positioned using stainless steel clips

dpc

Outer leaf of rising wall generally kept a course lower than the inner leaf to accommodate the later fixing of anchor straps, if required

dpc

dpm lapped under dpc in rising wall

Sole plate fixed in position on the rising wall with stainless steel clips at 1200 mm centres.

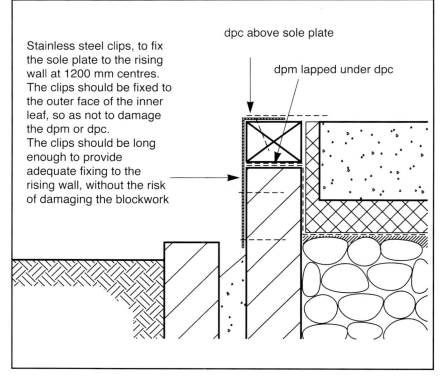

dpc above sole plate

dpm lapped under dpc

Stainless steel clips, to fix the sole plate to the rising wall at 1200 mm centres. The clips should be fixed to the outer face of the inner leaf, so as not to damage the dpm or dpc. The clips should be long enough to provide adequate fixing to the rising wall, without the risk of damaging the blockwork

Typical sole plate fixing detail.

RISING WALLS AND FOUNDATIONS

Anchor straps

Where required by the manufacturer, the timber frame inner leaf should be anchored into the external masonry leaf by means of stainless steel anchor straps fixed to full height studs.

The bend at the bottom of the strap bridges the cavity and is embedded into a horizontal bed joint, generally in the course below dpc level. The self weight of the masonry outer leaf will generally be sufficient to resist uplift of the lighter timber frame.

Straps are generally located at 1800 mm centres, either side of openings and as close to external corners as possible.

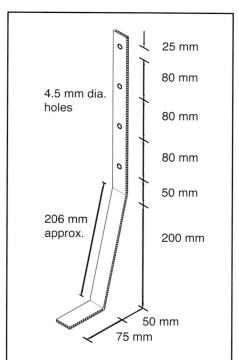

Typical stainless steel holding down strap. Cross section 30 x 2 mm, overall length 600 mm approx.

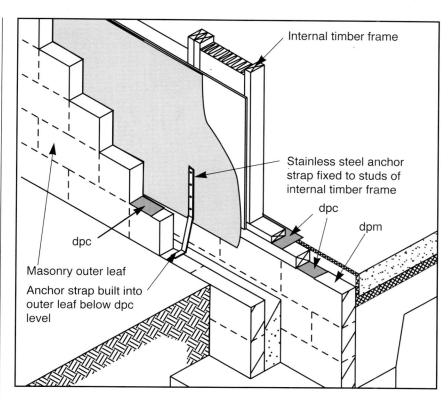

Timber frame anchored to the external masonry leaf, with 30 x 2 mm stainless steel straps, 600 mm long at 1800 mm centres, fixed to full height studs with 4 no. 4 mm dia. stainless steel nails 50 mm long.

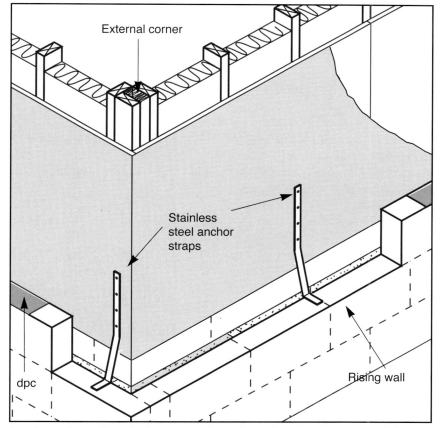

Anchor straps located as near to external corners as possible.

RISING WALLS AND FOUNDATIONS

A rising wall and appropriate foundation must be provided to ground floor internal load bearing partitions.

Provide dpc to the underside of all ground floor partitions.

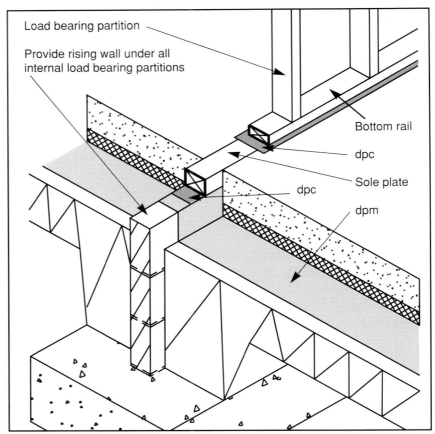

Load bearing partition

Provide rising wall under all internal load bearing partitions

Bottom rail

dpc

Sole plate

dpc

dpm

Typical internal rising wall detail under load bearing partition.

Where steel portal frames are included in the design of a timber frame dwelling, they must be fixed to the substructure in accordance with the structural design details, which must be supplied by the timber frame manufacturer.

Rising walls to all ground floor load bearing partitions.

GROUND FLOOR CONSTRUCTION

Floor types

Timber frame dwellings can be built with all the common types of ground floor. The selection of the appropriate floor type will depend on a number of factors including end-user requirements, site conditions, insulation standards, contractor's preference, availability and cost.

Guidance on concrete floors can be found in Stage A, and guidance on thermal insulation in Appendix I of this Manual.

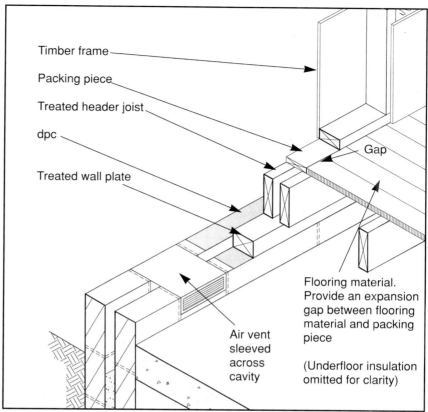

Timber frame

Packing piece

Treated header joist

dpc

Treated wall plate

Gap

Flooring material. Provide an expansion gap between flooring material and packing piece

(Underfloor insulation omitted for clarity)

Air vent sleeved across cavity

Typical suspended floor at external wall, with floor joists parallel to external wall. Insulation omitted for clarity.

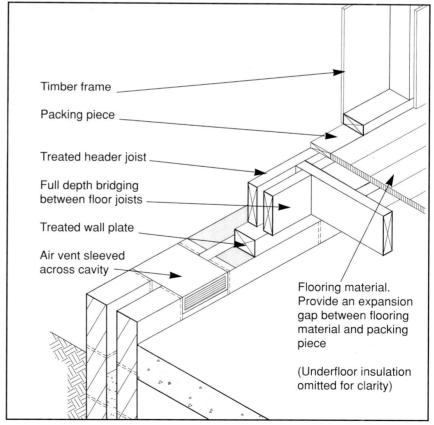

Timber frame

Packing piece

Treated header joist

Full depth bridging between floor joists

Treated wall plate

Air vent sleeved across cavity

Flooring material. Provide an expansion gap between flooring material and packing piece

(Underfloor insulation omitted for clarity)

Typical suspended timber floor, with joists at right angles to external wall. Insulation omitted for clarity.

GROUND FLOOR CONSTRUCTION

Floor types continued

Timber floors may be supplied by the manufacturer as prefabricated floor panel components, or formed using site cut joists. Prefabricated floor panels are the more common type.

With all suspended timber floor types, ventilation must be provided in accordance with the guidance on pages 38 and 39. The ventilating air must have an unobstructed path across the floor void.

Insulating materials for suspended timber floors include mineral wool, expanded polystyrene and polyurethane. Care should be taken during installation to ensure insulation is adequately supported and cold bridges are avoided. Insulation support details can be found on page 238.

In suspended floor construction, the surface of the oversite concrete must not be below the highest level of the ground or paving adjacent to the external walls, to avoid the sump effect. See page 40.

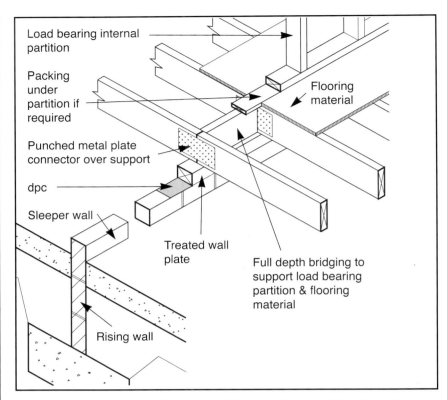

Typical suspended timber ground floor at internal load bearing wall, with joists at right angles to wall. Gaps should be left in the sleeper wall to allow ventilation of the underfloor void.

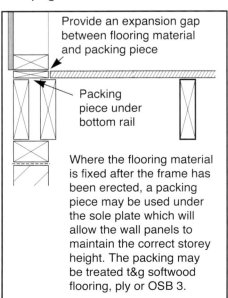

Provide an expansion gap between flooring material and packing piece

Packing piece under bottom rail

Where the flooring material is fixed after the frame has been erected, a packing piece may be used under the sole plate which will allow the wall panels to maintain the correct storey height. The packing may be treated t&g softwood flooring, ply or OSB 3.

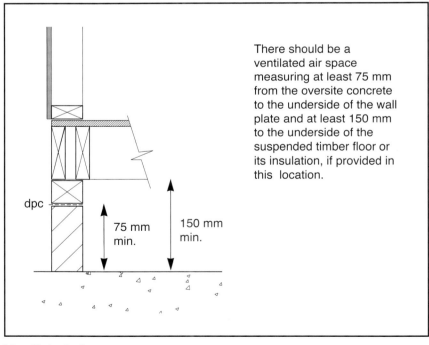

There should be a ventilated air space measuring at least 75 mm from the oversite concrete to the underside of the wall plate and at least 150 mm to the underside of the suspended timber floor or its insulation, if provided in this location.

Ventilated air space

PRESERVATIVE TREATMENT

Timber frame components are treated prior to assembly with an appropriate wood preservative solution as outlined opposite.

Any timber treated with preservative to meet these requirements, and cut after treatment, should be given two liberal applications of a suitable colour tinted preservative to the cut surfaces. Ensure that the dpc/dpm/radon membrane is compatible with such treatment.

ALL TIMBER CAVITY BARRIERS MUST BE PRESERVATIVE TREATED IN THE SAME MANNER AS THE EXTERNAL WALL COMPONENTS.

MINIMUM PRESERVATIVE TREATMENTS			
Timber components	TREATMENT SCHEDULES		
	CCA[1]	OS[2]	BORON[3]
Sole plate (or wall plate to suspended timber ground floor) above dpc level[4]	P7 3%	V/3	Applicable
External wall timbers[5]	P3 3%	V/3	Applicable
External joinery	P3 3%	V/2[6]	Not normally used

[1] CCA - Copper Chrome Arsenic. Percentage figures refer to solution strength.
[2] OS - Organic Solvents.
[3] BORON - Boron salts. Treatment must be carried out in accordance with the BWPA manual.
[4] This also applies to the bottom rail of panels where there is no sole plate.
[5] Studs, top and bottom rails, header joists, cavity barriers, noggings etc., but excluding panel sheathing.
[6] This treatment schedule is for pine, including European Redwood.

Note: The schedules for external joinery are based on European Redwood (permeable / moderately resistant to treatment). The other schedules are based on Irish Sitka Spruce / European Whitewood (resistant / moderately resistant to treatment).

The data above has been taken from BS 5268: Part 5. This standard should be referred to for further information on preservative treatment.

EXTERNAL WALLS

Components
The external wall typically consists of three parts, the load bearing timber frame inner leaf, ventilated cavity and external masonry leaf.

Sole plate:
The function and requirements for the sole plate, when incorporated, are detailed on page 273.

Stud framing:
The function of the stud framework is to act as the vertical load bearing skeleton of the external wall, to resist lateral wind loads and to provide a framework for the fixing of sheathing, internal linings, wall ties, etc.

Vertical loads on the wall panel should occur over the studs or be offset from the centreline of the stud by no more than the stud thickness. Otherwise the use of a head binder is recommended. A double rail allows normal loads from floor joists, rafters, etc., to occur between studs. Heavier loads from trimmers, purlins, beams, etc., cannot always be supported in this manner. Additional studs or posts under these members may be required. See pages 301 and 302 for support details in these locations.

Where a head binder forms part of the panel system, it should be installed in accordance with the system manufacturer's details.

Typical timber frame external wall panel. Note the head binder above the top rail.

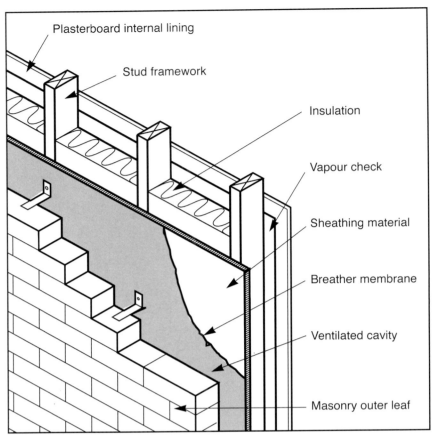

External wall components.

Labels: Plasterboard internal lining; Stud framework; Insulation; Vapour check; Sheathing material; Breather membrane; Ventilated cavity; Masonry outer leaf

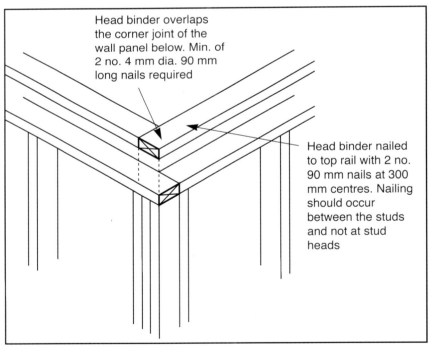

Head binder overlaps the corner joint of the wall panel below. Min. of 2 no. 4 mm dia. 90 mm long nails required

Head binder nailed to top rail with 2 no. 90 mm nails at 300 mm centres. Nailing should occur between the studs and not at stud heads

Head binder at corner of two panel junction, sheathing omitted for clarity.

EXTERNAL WALLS

Wall components continued

Noggings:
Generally not required for structural purposes in external walls, as the sheathing material fulfils the same function. Where they are used, their function is to:

◆ Provide support for partitions and/or plasterboard sheet edges

◆ Provide the support for fixings and fittings

◆ Resist buckling of studs

◆ Assist in providing the required fire resistance, where necessary.

Noggings may be site cut or factory fixed.

Sheathing:
The function of sheathing is to:

◆ Provide the necessary stiffness to resist lateral loads (racking)

◆ Reduce wind penetration of the structure

◆ Provide rapid enclosure of the building during construction

◆ Enclose and support wall insulation

◆ Reduce the risk of damage/distortion of the panels prior to fixing

◆ Provide solid background onto which the breather membrane is fixed

◆ Stiffen panel for handling.

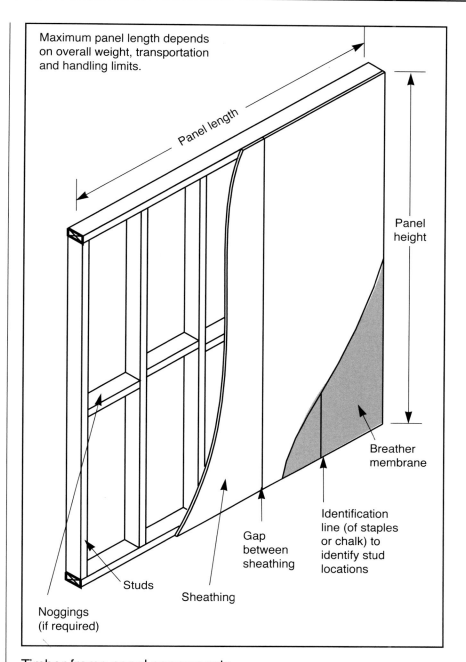

Timber frame panel components.

Sheathing materials include exterior grade ply and oriented stand board (OSB3). Sheathing materials are factory fitted by the timber frame manufacturer and should be of adequate durability and moisture resistance.

The following performance criteria for sheathing material should be considered:

◆ Racking resistance evidence, derived by test
◆ Durability in use
◆ Moisture resistance.

Any sheathing material used must have an appropriate certificate of approval.

EXTERNAL WALLS

Wall components continued

Vapour check:

To avoid condensation within the wall, a vapour check membrane must be fitted between the internal wall lining and the warm side of the insulation material. The function of the vapour check is to reduce the amount of moisture vapour entering and passing through the wall due to different internal and external temperatures and pressure levels.

Acceptable vapour checks include 500 gauge polythene and vapour check plasterboard, neither of which should be damaged in transport or erection.

Sheet membranes should be stapled to studs at 300 mm centres and overlap on the studs with horizontal joints taped and sealed, horizontal laps to be 100 mm minimum and vertical laps 150 mm minimum. Small tears must be repaired and holes formed tightly around service connections. Services passing through the vapour check should be sealed with tape. If the vapour check is seriously damaged, it should be removed and replaced. Vapour checks must be carefully cut and dressed into window and door reveals, and be folded and extended into ceilings by a minimum of 75 mm.

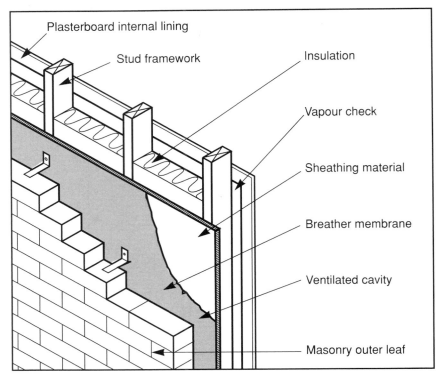

External wall components.

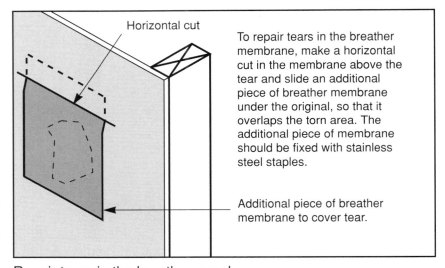

To repair tears in the breather membrane, make a horizontal cut in the membrane above the tear and slide an additional piece of breather membrane under the original, so that it overlaps the torn area. The additional piece of membrane should be fixed with stainless steel staples.

Additional piece of breather membrane to cover tear.

Repair tears in the breather membrane.

Vapour check on warm side of insulation.

EXTERNAL WALLS

Wall components continued

Breather membrane: The external face of the sheathing material must be covered with a breather membrane. This is usually factory installed with the necessary laps to cover the joints incorporated. Its function is to protect the frame until the cladding is complete and to provide a second line of defence against wind driven rain or moisture which might penetrate the cladding during the life of the building.

The breather membrane must be waterproof but permeable to allow moisture vapour passing out through the inner leaf to enter the ventilated cavity.

The breather membrane is generally fixed to the sheathing with austenitic stainless steel staples at 300 mm centres.

The bottom edge of the membrane should be long enough to overlap the dpc at sole plate level.

Breather membranes must comply with the requirements of BS 4016: 1997: Specification for flexible building membranes (breather type).

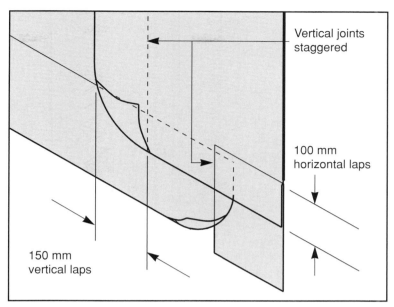

Vertical joints staggered

100 mm horizontal laps

150 mm vertical laps

Horizontal and vertical joints in breather membrane should be staggered.

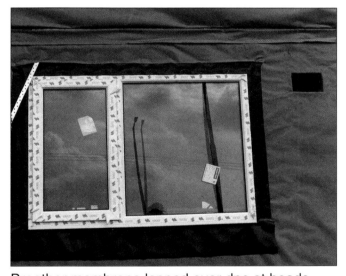

Breather membrane lapped over dpc at heads.

Breather membrane long enough to lap over dpc at sole plate level.

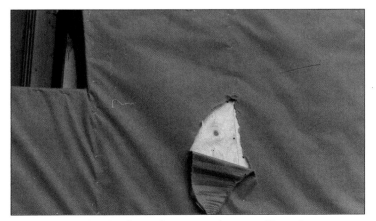

Avoid tears in the breather membrane. Repair or replace, if necessary.

EXTERNAL WALLS

Wall components continued

Thermal insulation:

The most common type of thermal insulation used in timber frame construction is mineral wool fitted in the void between studs. It is available as rolled quilts or semi-rigid batts in a range of thicknesses. The rolled type is normally stapled to the studs to hold it in place and sufficient staples must be used to prevent it from sagging, particularly near the top of the studs. Semi rigid batts can be tightly wedged between studs. An additional feature of the insulation is its contribution to sound insulation and fire resistance.

Gaps in the external wall insulation must be avoided. At the junction of external and internal walls, any additional stud provided to support the plasterboard edges, should have insulation fitted between it and the wall stud to prevent potential cold bridges.

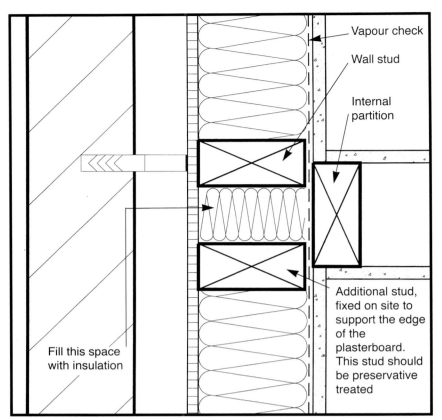

In addition to ensuring continuity of thermal insulation in the external walls, consideration should be given to the sequence of construction of the panels, to ensure that a continuous vapour check is provided to the external walls.

The "blue" identification lines on the breather membrane mark the location of the stud positions. The identification line ensures that the wall ties can be positioned and fixed at the stud locations.

EXTERNAL WALLS

Wall ties:

Flexible stainless steel wall ties complying with an appropriate Irish or British Agrément Certificate, should be nailed to the timber frame at stud locations which are generally marked by a line or row of staples. Wall ties must not be nailed to the sheathing material only. Each tie should be long enough to provide a minimum embedment of 50 mm into the masonry leaf. The appropriate wall ties and fixings are usually supplied by the timber frame manufacturer.

The top row of wall ties should be located no more than 225 mm from the top of the masonry leaf and the bottom row should be located approximately 225 mm above dpc level.

Unless specified otherwise, wall ties should be spaced at 450 mm vertical centres generally, 600 mm horizontal centres and at 225 mm vertical centres around opes and movement joints.

Mortar droppings must be removed from wall ties.

A 40 mm min. clear ventilated cavity must be maintained between the external masonry leaf and the timber frame.

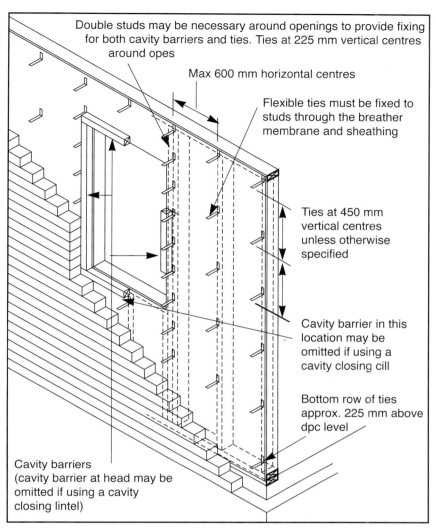

Double studs may be necessary around openings to provide fixing for both cavity barriers and ties. Ties at 225 mm vertical centres around opes

Max 600 mm horizontal centres

Flexible ties must be fixed to studs through the breather membrane and sheathing

Ties at 450 mm vertical centres unless otherwise specified

Cavity barrier in this location may be omitted if using a cavity closing cill

Bottom row of ties approx. 225 mm above dpc level

Cavity barriers (cavity barrier at head may be omitted if using a cavity closing lintel)

Location of wall ties.

Typical wall ties.

Wall ties in position.

EXTERNAL WALLS

Damp-proof courses

The proper location and installation of damp-proof courses in timber frame construction is particularly important.

Damp-proof courses should be provided at all external openings and to all cavity barriers in accordance with the guidance detailed on the following pages.

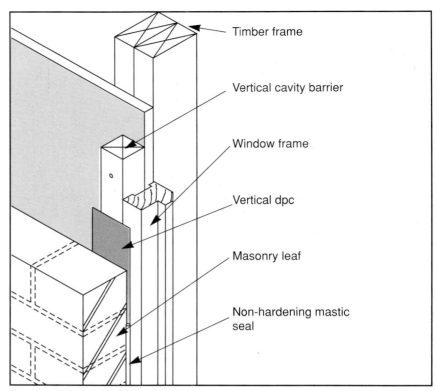

- Timber frame
- Vertical cavity barrier
- Window frame
- Vertical dpc
- Masonry leaf
- Non-hardening mastic seal

At jambs, ensure that vertical cavity barriers and dpc's are installed. The window frame should be fixed only to the timber frame and should be installed behind the masonry outer leaf.

Location of treated cavity barriers around ope. Damp-proof courses must also be fitted in such locations.

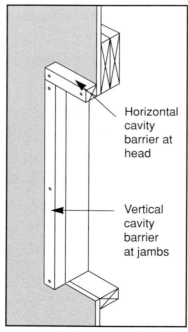

- Horizontal cavity barrier at head
- Vertical cavity barrier at jambs

Location of cavity barriers around openings.

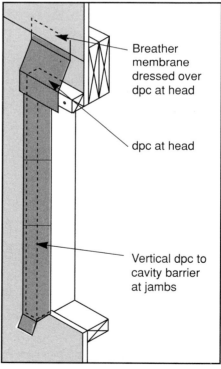

- Breather membrane dressed over dpc at head
- dpc at head
- Vertical dpc to cavity barrier at jambs

Ensure dpc's around openings are installed correctly, with breather membrane dressed over dpc at head, which in turn is dressed over the vertical dpc.

EXTERNAL WALLS

Damp-proof courses continued

Provide dpc's to the bottom, back and sides of all window cills, see page 69.

To accommodate natural shrinkage of the timber frame, a gap should be left between the underside of the window frame and the top of the cill. The dimensional requirements for this gap, depending on its location, are outlined on page 295.

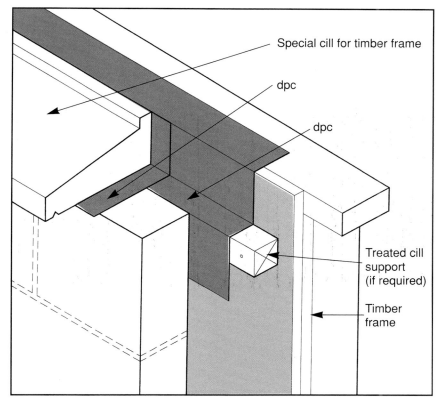

A special, "forward cill" is required for timber frame construction. The cill is carried by the outer masonry leaf, and to allow for differential movement it should not be fixed to the inner leaf. Provide dpc to bottom, back and sides of cill. Provide dpc to cavity barrier.

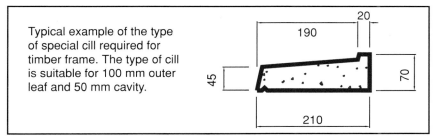

Typical example of the type of special cill required for timber frame. The type of cill is suitable for 100 mm outer leaf and 50 mm cavity.

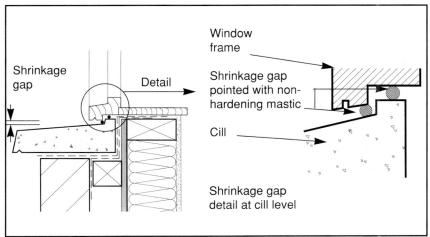

Shrinkage gap detail at cill level

To allow for natural shrinkage of the timber frame, provide a gap between the underside of the window frame and the top of the cill. Point this gap with a non-hardening mastic. Gap dimensions are given on page 295.

EXTERNAL WALLS

Damp-proof courses continued

Damp-proof courses must be provided to all steel lintels and lintel angles. The breather membrane must be dressed over the damp-proof courses provided to the lintel.

Typical proprietary steel lintel, shown prior to the fixing of dpc.

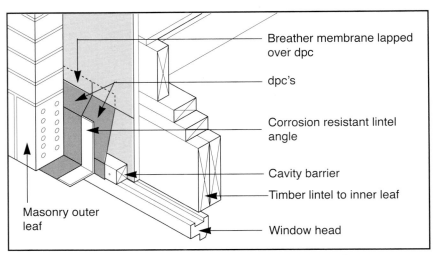

- Breather membrane lapped over dpc
- dpc's
- Corrosion resistant lintel angle
- Cavity barrier
- Timber lintel to inner leaf
- Window head
- Masonry outer leaf

Where a lintel angle is used to support the outer leaf masonry and it does not close the cavity, a cavity barrier must be installed. Where the outer masonry leaf is unrendered, provide weepholes at 450 mm centres.

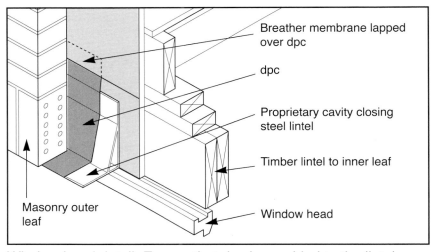

- Breather membrane lapped over dpc
- dpc
- Proprietary cavity closing steel lintel
- Timber lintel to inner leaf
- Window head
- Masonry outer leaf

Window head detail. Ensure that dpc is provided to the lintel. Where the outer masonry leaf is unrendered, provide weepholes at 450 mm centres.

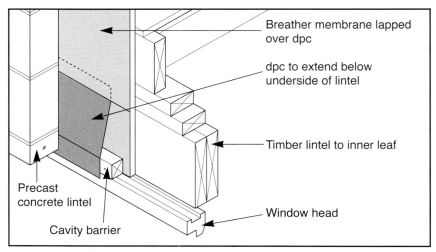

- Breather membrane lapped over dpc
- dpc to extend below underside of lintel
- Timber lintel to inner leaf
- Window head
- Precast concrete lintel
- Cavity barrier

Where a precast lintel is used, the dpc should extend below its underside, to allow any moisture entering the cavity to be directed to the outside.

EXTERNAL WALLS

Eaves detail

At eaves level the soffit board must not be carried over the masonry outer leaf.

To accommodate natural shrinkage of the timber frame, a gap must be left between the roof timbers and the top of the masonry outer leaf. The dimensional requirements for this gap are outlined on page 295.

Eaves/roof space ventilation requirements are detailed on pages 183 to 187.

Continuous felt support at eaves, to prevent ponding of water on the sarking felt behind the fascia board.

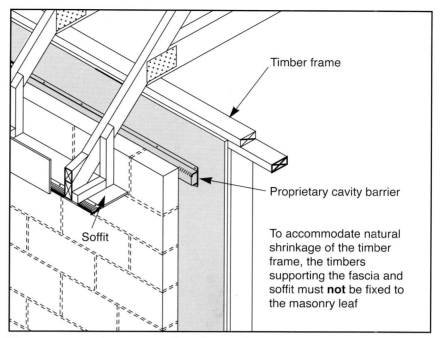

To prevent moisture entering the cavity, the soffit board should not be carried over the masonry outer leaf.

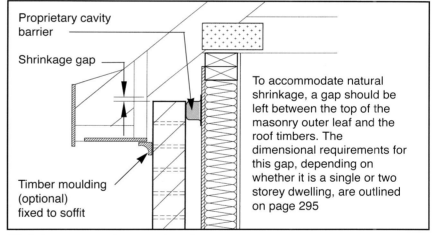

Shrinkage gap at eaves level.

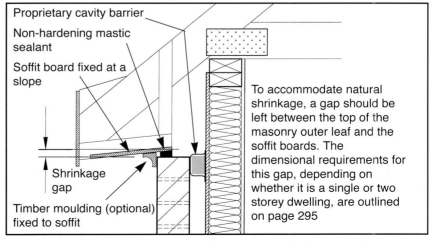

Alternative eaves detail with soffit board partially carried over the masonry outer leaf. Soffit board fixed at a slope to allow any water that enters to drain out through the soffit vents.

EXTERNAL WALLS

Spandrel panels to gable and party walls

The spandrel panel should be nailed directly to the top rail of the gable or party wall panel. The bottom rail of the spandrel panel may double as the head binder to the wall panel. The sketches opposite are based on this arrangement.

Sheathing should be provided to the external face of gable spandrel panels to provide strength and stability.

In dwellings which have a party and gable wall spandrel panel, the detailing of both should be considered to ensure that, when the roof trusses are fully loaded, the resulting truss deflection does not induce distortion in the roof at gable ends and over the party wall.

At gable walls, lateral restraint may be required to stabilise the gable, in accordance with the details opposite.

Spandrel panels and roof bracing

Where roof bracing members abut spandrel panels at gable or party walls, the roof bracing members should be fixed as detailed on page 293. The details given here illustrate prefabricated trussed rafter roofs only.

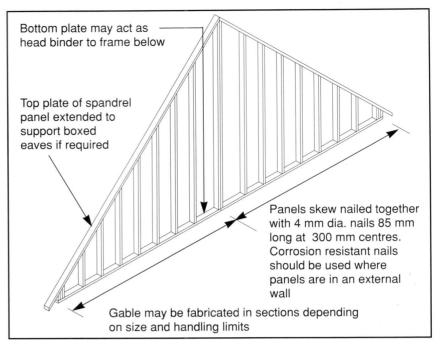

Bottom plate may act as head binder to frame below

Top plate of spandrel panel extended to support boxed eaves if required

Panels skew nailed together with 4 mm dia. nails 85 mm long at 300 mm centres. Corrosion resistant nails should be used where panels are in an external wall

Gable may be fabricated in sections depending on size and handling limits

Typical roof gable spandrel panel sheathed externally with plywood or other sheet material.

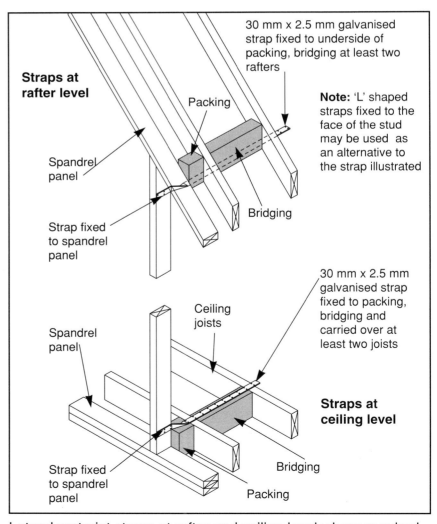

Straps at rafter level

30 mm x 2.5 mm galvanised strap fixed to underside of packing, bridging at least two rafters

Note: 'L' shaped straps fixed to the face of the stud may be used as an alternative to the strap illustrated

Packing

Spandrel panel

Bridging

Strap fixed to spandrel panel

30 mm x 2.5 mm galvanised strap fixed to packing, bridging and carried over at least two joists

Ceiling joists

Spandrel panel

Straps at ceiling level

Bridging

Strap fixed to spandrel panel

Packing

Lateral restraint straps at rafter and ceiling level where required.

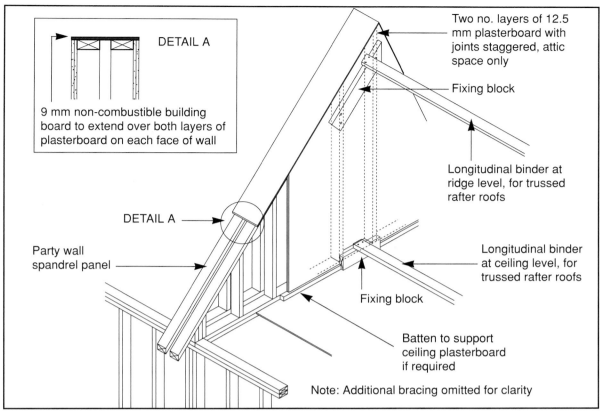

In a spandrel panel that forms part of the party wall in an attic space, the roof bracing members should be fixed to fixing blocks which themselves should be fixed to at least two stud members, after the two layers of plasterboard have been fixed.

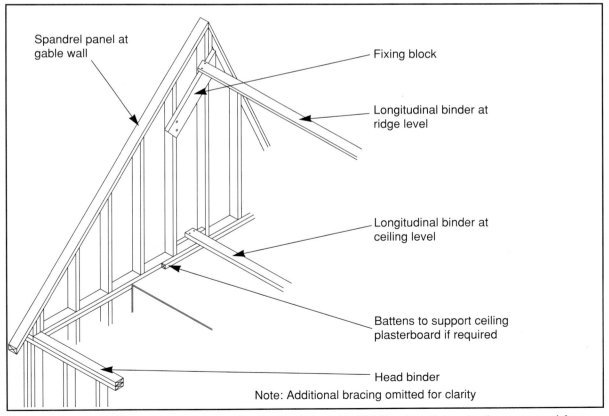

Bracing members fixed to gable wall spandrel panel. NOTE: sheathing to the external face of the spandrel panel omitted for clarity.

EXTERNAL WALLS

Verge details

Typical verge details are formed with gable ladders.

To accommodate natural shrinkage of the timber frame, a gap should be left between the top of the masonry outer leaf and the underside of the gable ladder. The dimensional requirements for this gap are outlined on page 295.

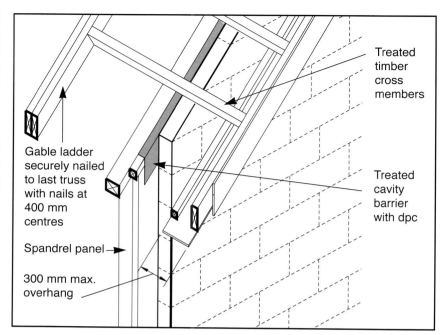

Gable ladder securely nailed to last truss with nails at 400 mm centres

Spandrel panel

300 mm max. overhang

Treated timber cross members

Treated cavity barrier with dpc

Typical gable ladder detail. To accommodate shrinkage a gap should be left between the top of the masonry outer leaf and the underside of the gable ladder unit. The dimensional requirements for this gap can be found on page 295. The gap should be sealed with a non-hardening mastic.

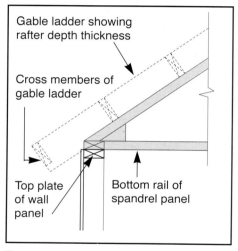

Gable ladder showing rafter depth thickness

Cross members of gable ladder

Top plate of wall panel

Bottom rail of spandrel panel

Typical gable ladder cross section

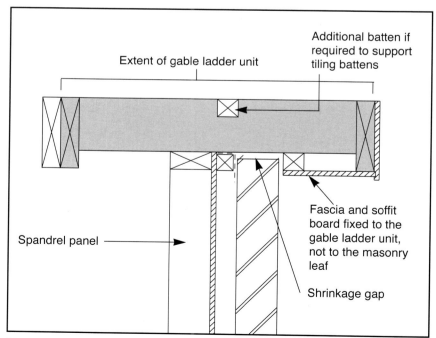

Extent of gable ladder unit

Additional batten if required to support tiling battens

Spandrel panel

Fascia and soffit board fixed to the gable ladder unit, not to the masonry leaf

Shrinkage gap

Typical verge detail formed with gable ladder.

EXTERNAL WALLS

Shrinkage

To accommodate natural shrinkage of the timber frame, provide a gap at the locations indicated, the dimensions of which should be taken from the table opposite.

Unless otherwise stated, the joinery should generally be fixed to the timber frame.

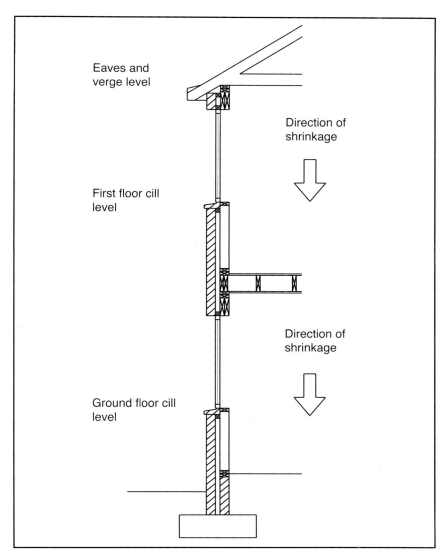

Location of shrinkage gaps.

	TYPES OF FLOOR CONSTRUCTION	
	Suspended timber ground floor where panels are supported on ground floor joists or perimeter joists	Other ground floor construction
Allowances, ground floor openings	5 mm	3 mm
Allowances, first floor openings	12 mm	9 mm
Eaves & verge for a single storey house	8 mm	6 mm
Eaves and verge for a two storey house	15 mm	12 mm

Dimensional requirements for shrinkage gaps.

EXTERNAL WALLS

Cavity ventilation

The cavity in timber frame construction must be ventilated to dissipate any moisture vapour that may collect. Ventilation is generally provided by proprietary ventilators, fitted in the perpends (vertical joints) of the masonry outer leaf, at 1500 mm centres, in the locations indicated opposite.

Typical example of proprietary perpend ventilations installed below dpc level.

Cavity trays

Where cavity trays are used it is preferable to use a proprietary tray that extends the full width of the cavity. Dress the breather membrane over the cavity tray. This will allow any moisture to drain into the tray.

Provide weep holes in perpends to allow the cavity to drain over the lead flashing.

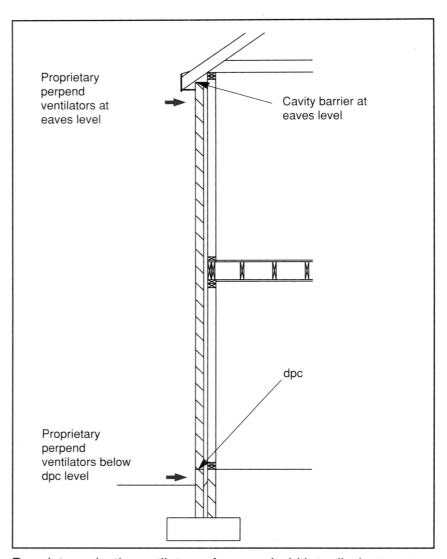

Proprietary perpend ventilators at eaves level

Cavity barrier at eaves level

dpc

Proprietary perpend ventilators below dpc level

Proprietary plastic ventilators of perpend width to dissipate water vapour in the cavity, located in positions shown and spaced at 1500 mm maximum horizontal centres.

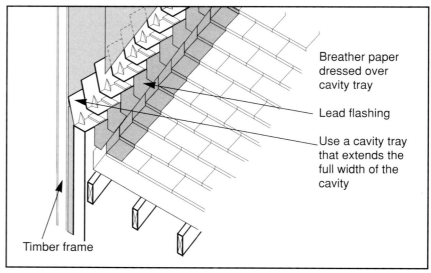

Breather paper dressed over cavity tray

Lead flashing

Use a cavity tray that extends the full width of the cavity

Timber frame

Where cavity trays are used, the breather membrane should be dressed over the tray. Where possible use a proprietary tray that extends the full width of the cavity. Detailed guidance on the installation of cavity trays is provided on pages 73 to 76.

FIREPLACES AND CHIMNEYS IN EXTERNAL WALLS

There are two main methods for constructing chimneys in external walls.

The fireplace and chimney can be built inside the room after the internal linings have been fixed, as illustrated opposite. This type of construction requires that floor and roof members be trimmed around the chimney stack.

Care should be taken at roof level when detailing flashings around the chimney to allow for movement of the timber frame.

Where metal ties are required between the chimney stack and the floor and roof timbers, these ties should be designed and supplied by the timber frame manufacturer and installed in accordance with the manufacturer's guidance.

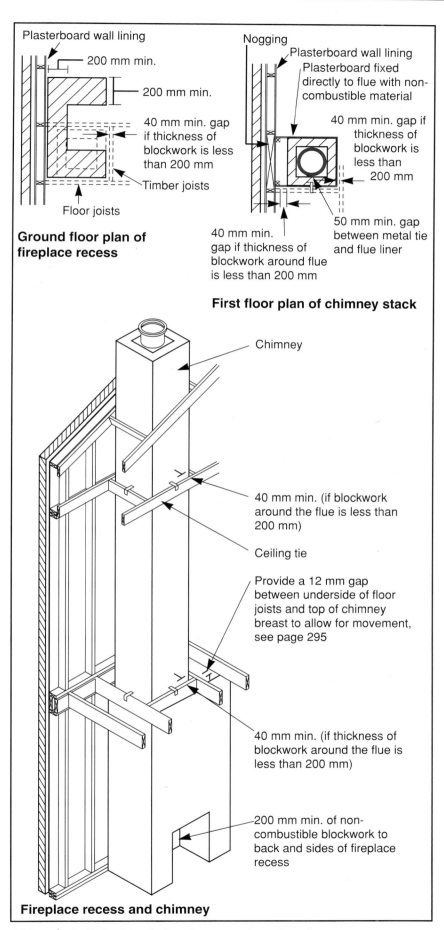

Ground floor plan of fireplace recess

First floor plan of chimney stack

Fireplace recess and chimney

Chimney built inside timber frame external wall.

FIREPLACES AND CHIMNEYS IN EXTERNAL WALLS

As an alternative to the method illustrated on the previous page, the fireplace and chimney stack can be located on the outside of the timber frame external wall panel as illustrated opposite.

The fireplace is formed in a preformed aperture in the timber frame wall panel. The structural integrity of the timber frame is maintained and specially trimmed openings are avoided.

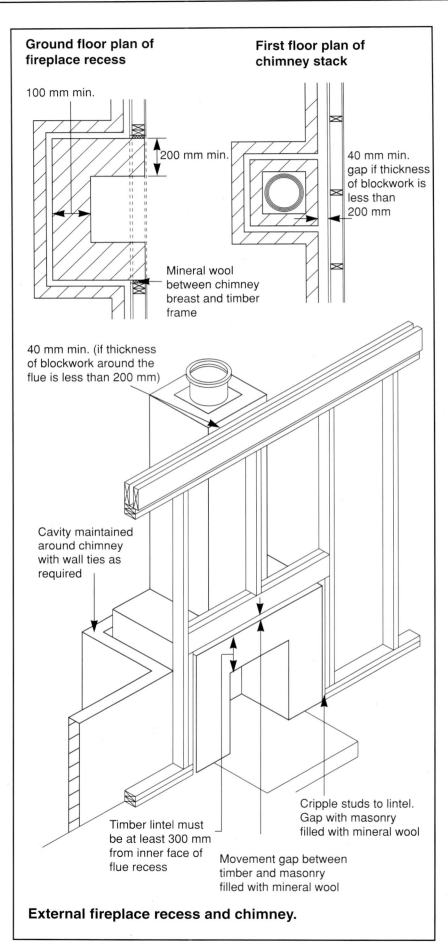

Ground floor plan of fireplace recess

100 mm min.

200 mm min.

Mineral wool between chimney breast and timber frame

First floor plan of chimney stack

40 mm min. gap if thickness of blockwork is less than 200 mm

40 mm min. (if thickness of blockwork around the flue is less than 200 mm)

Cavity maintained around chimney with wall ties as required

Timber lintel must be at least 300 mm from inner face of flue recess

Cripple studs to lintel. Gap with masonry filled with mineral wool

Movement gap between timber and masonry filled with mineral wool

External fireplace recess and chimney.

Chimney built outside timber frame

FIREPLACES AND CHIMNEYS IN EXTERNAL WALLS
continued

When constructing chimneys in external walls the dimensional requirements illustrated opposite must be adhered to.

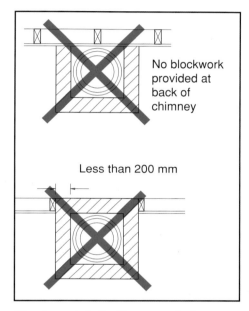

The two details illustrated above are not acceptable.

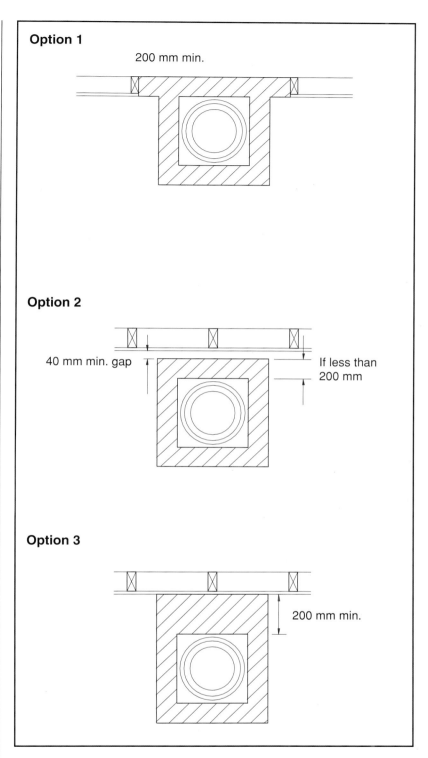

Dimensional requirements for chimneys in external walls.

EXTERNAL WALLS

Lintels within timber frame panels

Openings in load bearing wall panels will include a lintel at the head of the opening to transmit loads to the flanking studs and cripple studs. The number of cripple studs required depends on the size of the opening and the load being carried by the lintel.

Any modification to the timber frame can only be carried out with the agreement of the timber frame manufacturer.

Cripple studs should extend to the underside of the lintel members.

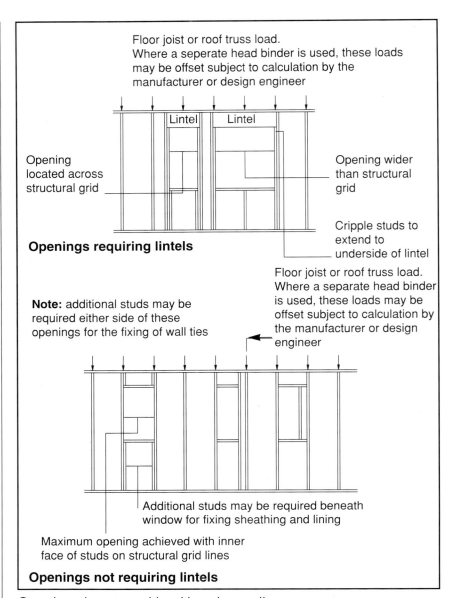

Floor joist or roof truss load.
Where a seperate head binder is used, these loads may be offset subject to calculation by the manufacturer or design engineer

Lintel   Lintel

Opening located across structural grid

Openings requiring lintels

Opening wider than structural grid

Cripple studs to extend to underside of lintel

Note: additional studs may be required either side of these openings for the fixing of wall ties

Floor joist or roof truss load. Where a separate head binder is used, these loads may be offset subject to calculation by the manufacturer or design engineer

Additional studs may be required beneath window for fixing sheathing and lining

Maximum opening achieved with inner face of studs on structural grid lines

Openings not requiring lintels

Openings in external load bearing walls.

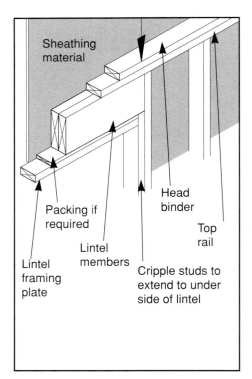

Sheathing material

Packing if required

Head binder

Top rail

Lintel members

Lintel framing plate

Cripple studs to extend to under side of lintel

Load bearing lintel in an external wall.

Additional studs under multiple truss.

EXTERNAL WALLS

Support for point loads

Heavy point loads from trimmer joists, multiple trusses, beams etc. are transmitted to the foundations by means of additional studs, the number of studs required being determined by calculation.

Where steel members are used to support roof or floor timbers, a wall plate should be bolted or shot fired to the steel to provide a suitable fixing for these timbers. The steel should be provided with suitable bearing at its support.

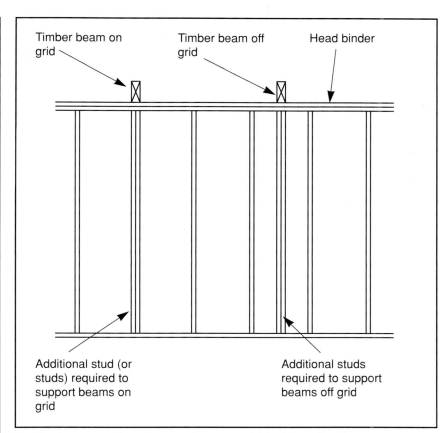

Timber beam on grid

Timber beam off grid

Head binder

Additional stud (or studs) required to support beams on grid

Additional studs required to support beams off grid

Typical support for trimmer beams within floor depth.

Typical lintel detail in a load bearing partition.

Typical external wall panel lintel detail

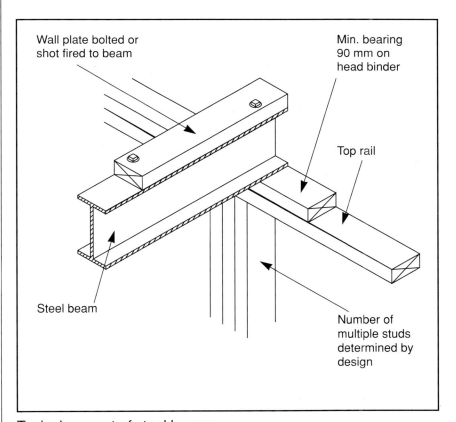

Wall plate bolted or shot fired to beam

Min. bearing 90 mm on head binder

Top rail

Steel beam

Number of multiple studs determined by design

Typical support of steel beams.

Multiple studs under trimmer joist.

Typical internal load bearing partition lintel detail. Note, the cripple studs extending to the underside of the lintel.

Multiple studs between external wall panels to accommodate downstand beam.

PARTY WALLS

The function of the party wall is to provide an effective barrier against the spread of fire and sound transmission. Party walls in timber frame construction may also be constructed in masonry.

- The party wall should be completely imperforate

- The two leaves of the party wall must be unconnected for their full height. (Apart from optional light gauge metal ties, located at 1.2 m centres, which provide temporary stability during construction)

- Electrical sockets, switches, services etc., must not penetrate or be fixed to the party wall linings- see page 305

- Services, including cables, ducting etc., must not be located in the party wall cavity

- Provide adequate fire stopping at roof level, in accordance with the guidance on page 104

- HomeBond does not permit the construction of conventional masonry chimneys in timber frame party walls

- Sound insulation quilt should be fixed to one of the party wall frames to prevent sagging.

Timber frame party walls are normally formed by two independent wall frames. The following pages illustrate in detail the various party wall junctions in a two storey semi-detached or terraced house.

Any masonry party wall in timber frame construction must be provided with additional support during construction.

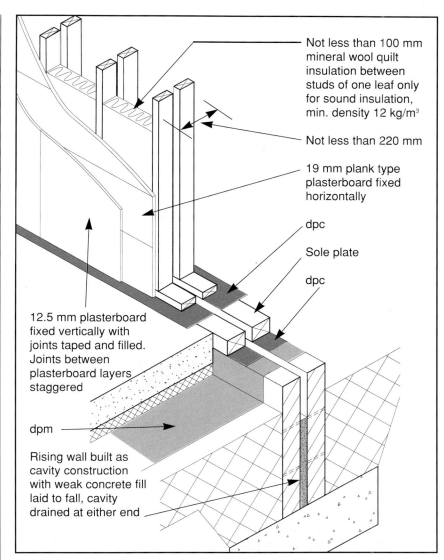

Not less than 100 mm mineral wool quilt insulation between studs of one leaf only for sound insulation, min. density 12 kg/m³

Not less than 220 mm

19 mm plank type plasterboard fixed horizontally

dpc

Sole plate

dpc

12.5 mm plasterboard fixed vertically with joints taped and filled. Joints between plasterboard layers staggered

dpm

Rising wall built as cavity construction with weak concrete fill laid to fall, cavity drained at either end

Typical party wall detail at ground floor level.

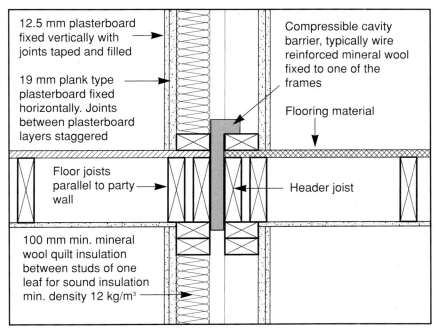

12.5 mm plasterboard fixed vertically with joints taped and filled

19 mm plank type plasterboard fixed horizontally. Joints between plasterboard layers staggered

Floor joists parallel to party wall

100 mm min. mineral wool quilt insulation between studs of one leaf for sound insulation min. density 12 kg/m³

Compressible cavity barrier, typically wire reinforced mineral wool fixed to one of the frames

Flooring material

Header joist

Typical party wall detail at first floor level.
Floor joists parallel to party wall.

PARTY WALLS
continued

The combined width of the two frames should not be less 220 mm (i.e. face of stud to face of stud), but a width of 250 mm will provide improved sound insulation.

In all cases a clear minimum cavity width of 40 mm min. must be maintained.

The two leaves of the party wall should provide a complete barrier against fire, including between the roof spaces. This is achieved with a minimum of two layers of plasterboard each side, to provide one hour fire resistance, as required by Technical Guidance Document B to the Building Regulations.

Fire stopping must also be provided at eaves level, see page 307.

Several types of cavity barrier can be used. The most common is wire reinforced mineral wool. Solid timber cavity barriers are generally not recommended in the party wall, as they may transmit sound across the cavity.

Rising wall built in cavity construction with weak concrete fill laid to fall, cavity drained at either end.

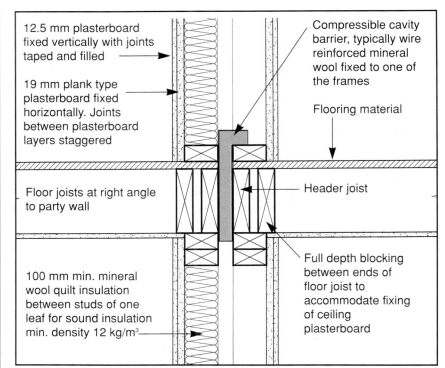

12.5 mm plasterboard fixed vertically with joints taped and filled

19 mm plank type plasterboard fixed horizontally. Joints between plasterboard layers staggered

Compressible cavity barrier, typically wire reinforced mineral wool fixed to one of the frames

Flooring material

Floor joists at right angle to party wall

Header joist

100 mm min. mineral wool quilt insulation between studs of one leaf for sound insulation min. density 12 kg/m³

Full depth blocking between ends of floor joist to accommodate fixing of ceiling plasterboard

Typical party wall detail at first floor level. Floor joists at right angles to party wall.

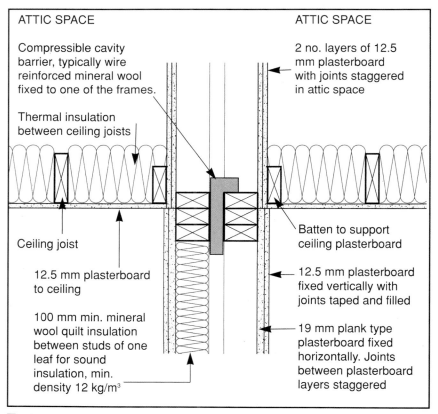

ATTIC SPACE

ATTIC SPACE

Compressible cavity barrier, typically wire reinforced mineral wool fixed to one of the frames.

Thermal insulation between ceiling joists

2 no. layers of 12.5 mm plasterboard with joints staggered in attic space

Ceiling joist

Batten to support ceiling plasterboard

12.5 mm plasterboard to ceiling

100 mm min. mineral wool quilt insulation between studs of one leaf for sound insulation, min. density 12 kg/m³

12.5 mm plasterboard fixed vertically with joints taped and filled

19 mm plank type plasterboard fixed horizontally. Joints between plasterboard layers staggered

Typical party wall detail at attic level. The sound insulation quilt is generally omitted from the party wall in the attic space. However, in the attic space of a dormer roof, the party wall must contain the sound insulation quilt. In addition the party wall between dormer roofs must be lined with two layers of plasterboard each side (19mm plank type fixed horizontally and 12.5 mm fixed vertically).

PARTY WALLS
continued

The cavity at the top of the party wall must be closed and the wall/roof junction fire stopped. This is usually achieved by covering the top rail of the party wall spandrel with a 9 mm non combustible building board cavity barrier, which should extend over and tightly butt the layers of plasterboard on both faces of the party wall.

The roofing felt is carried over the top of the party wall and the spaces between the tiling/slating battens filled with mortar bedding or mineral wool.

SERVICES

Electrical sockets, switches, services etc. should not be fixed to the party wall plasterboard lining.

Services may be located on the party wall, provided that an additional layer of lining board is fitted, separated from the party wall by battens as illustrated opposite. Services may then be recessed into this zone.

Timber frame party walls in a terrace of houses. Note the non-combustible building board cavity barrier at the top of the party walls.

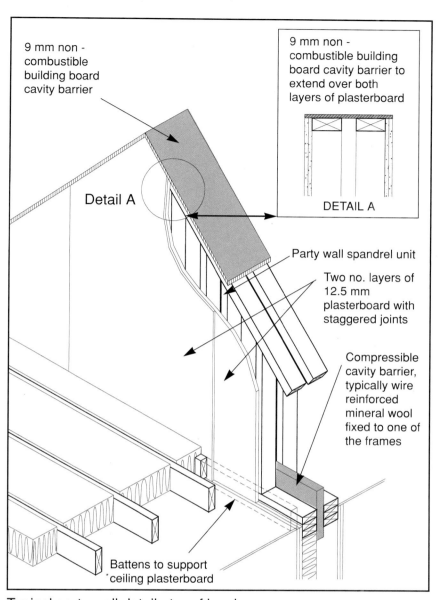

9 mm non - combustible building board cavity barrier

9 mm non - combustible building board cavity barrier to extend over both layers of plasterboard

DETAIL A

Detail A

Party wall spandrel unit

Two no. layers of 12.5 mm plasterboard with staggered joints

Compressible cavity barrier, typically wire reinforced mineral wool fixed to one of the frames

Battens to support ceiling plasterboard

Typical party wall detail at roof level.

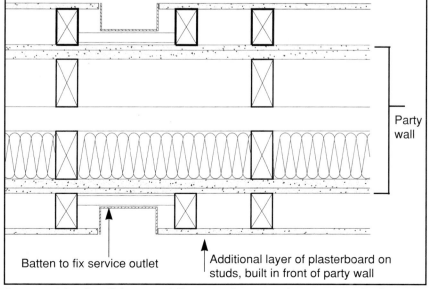

Party wall

Batten to fix service outlet

Additional layer of plasterboard on studs, built in front of party wall

Acceptable detail for providing services on the party wall. Services must not be built into the thickness of the party wall proper.

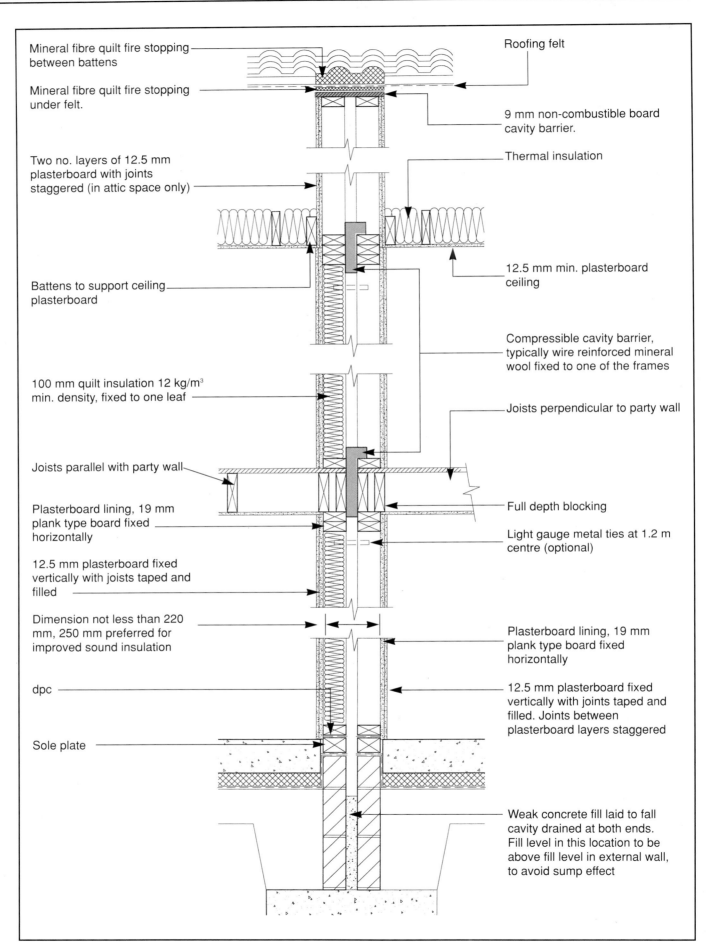

Mineral fibre quilt fire stopping between battens

Mineral fibre quilt fire stopping under felt.

Two no. layers of 12.5 mm plasterboard with joints staggered (in attic space only)

Battens to support ceiling plasterboard

100 mm quilt insulation 12 kg/m³ min. density, fixed to one leaf

Joists parallel with party wall

Plasterboard lining, 19 mm plank type board fixed horizontally

12.5 mm plasterboard fixed vertically with joists taped and filled

Dimension not less than 220 mm, 250 mm preferred for improved sound insulation

dpc

Sole plate

Roofing felt

9 mm non-combustible board cavity barrier.

Thermal insulation

12.5 mm min. plasterboard ceiling

Compressible cavity barrier, typically wire reinforced mineral wool fixed to one of the frames

Joists perpendicular to party wall

Full depth blocking

Light gauge metal ties at 1.2 m centre (optional)

Plasterboard lining, 19 mm plank type board fixed horizontally

12.5 mm plasterboard fixed vertically with joints taped and filled. Joints between plasterboard layers staggered

Weak concrete fill laid to fall cavity drained at both ends. Fill level in this location to be above fill level in external wall, to avoid sump effect

Typical vertical section through party wall where no step or stagger occurs.

PARTY WALLS
continued

The void formed by the slope of the rafters and the horizontal soffit to the eaves must be adequately sealed against fire at each party wall position. This may be achieved by nailing 9 mm non-combustible building board or reinforced mineral wool to the face of the projecting top rails of the spandrel frames. The fire stopping should be cut to suit the profile of the roof slope and be tightly butted to the soffit and fascia board.

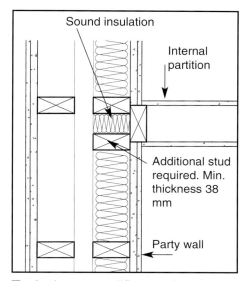

Typical party wall/internal wall junction. This detail will help maintain the integrity of the party wall against fire spread and sound transmission.

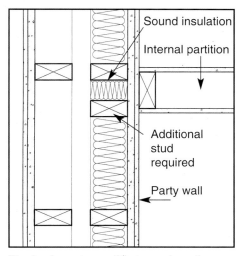

Typical party wall/internal wall junction where plasterboard is carried through on party wall.

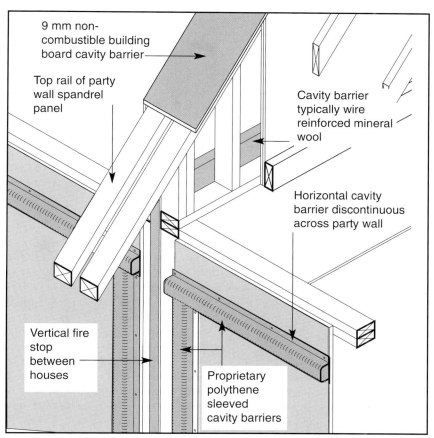

Partially completed party wall at eaves level.

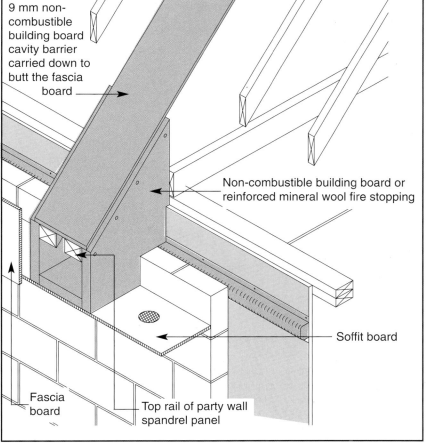

Completed imperforate fire stopping at eaves. No gaps!

PARTY WALLS
continued

The cavity between the timber frame party wall and external masonry leaf must be closed with vertical cavity barriers in the position detailed opposite.

In addition to the cavity barriers, a vertical fire stop seals the junction between the two party wall frames. This is usually achieved by using wire reinforced mineral wool quilt, stapled or nailed to each of the frames. This vertical fire stop must be carried up to the top rail of the party wall spandrel panel.

The two party wall frames generally provide adequate resistance to wind loads on both the front and rear walls. Where the need for bracing is indicated by calculation, this will usually be in the form of sheathing materials. The amount/length of additional bracing required is determined by the amount of extra stiffening required. Generally partial sheathing of the party wall frames is sufficient.

If, by calculation, the whole length of the party wall frame requires sheathing, this may be fixed to the room side of the frame and then covered with the two layers of plasterboard required.

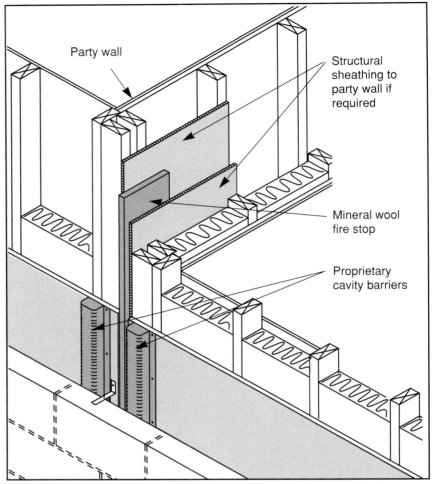

Typical party wall/external wall junction. Note the location of the cavity barrier. Proprietary cavity barriers should be protected with a polythene sleeve.

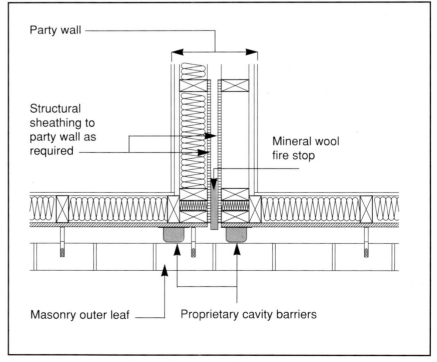

Horizontal section through party wall where no step or stagger occurs.

PARTY WALLS
continued

Steps and staggers: Where steps between dwellings occur that will expose the masonry above the lower roof level, a blockwork core wall between the party wall frames must be constructed to support this exposed masonry, as detailed on page 310.

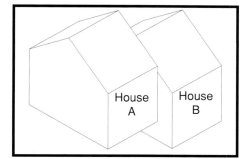

Typical step and stagger

Sound insulation: Airborne sound insulation for timber frame party walls is achieved by a combination of three factors:

◆ Structural isolation, achieved by leaving a 40 mm cavity between the two frames

◆ Dense wall linings. Usually two layers of plasterboard with a minimum thickness of 30 mm on both wall faces, i.e. one layer of 19 mm plank type and one layer of 12.5 mm overlaid to stagger the joints. In the attic area this may be reduced to two layers of 12.5 mm plasterboard on both faces of the party wall when a 12.5 mm plasterboard ceiling is provided

◆ Absorbent quilts, usually mineral wool l00 mm thick, density 12 kg/m³ minimum, fixed securely to one of the frames to prevent sagging. This is a minimum requirement. Thicker and/or denser mineral fibre will provide a higher degree of sound insulation.

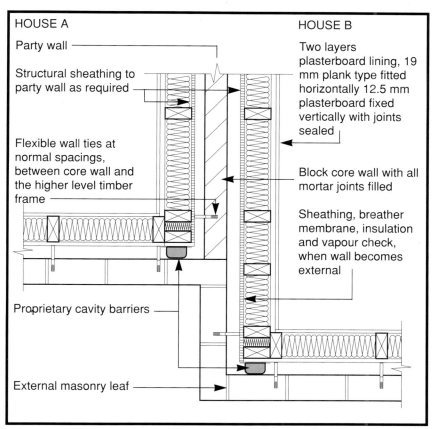

HOUSE A   HOUSE B

Party wall

Structural sheathing to party wall as required

Flexible wall ties at normal spacings, between core wall and the higher level timber frame

Proprietary cavity barriers

External masonry leaf

Two layers plasterboard lining, 19 mm plank type fitted horizontally 12.5 mm plasterboard fixed vertically with joints sealed

Block core wall with all mortar joints filled

Sheathing, breather membrane, insulation and vapour check, when wall becomes external

Horizontal section through party wall, where step and stagger occurs.

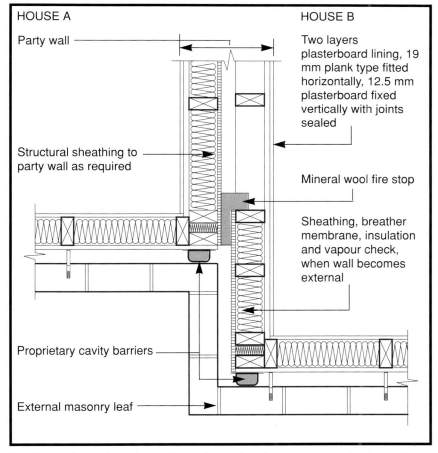

HOUSE A   HOUSE B

Party wall

Structural sheathing to party wall as required

Proprietary cavity barriers

External masonry leaf

Two layers plasterboard lining, 19 mm plank type fitted horizontally, 12.5 mm plasterboard fixed vertically with joints sealed

Mineral wool fire stop

Sheathing, breather membrane, insulation and vapour check, when wall becomes external

Horizontal section through party wall, where stagger but no step occurs.

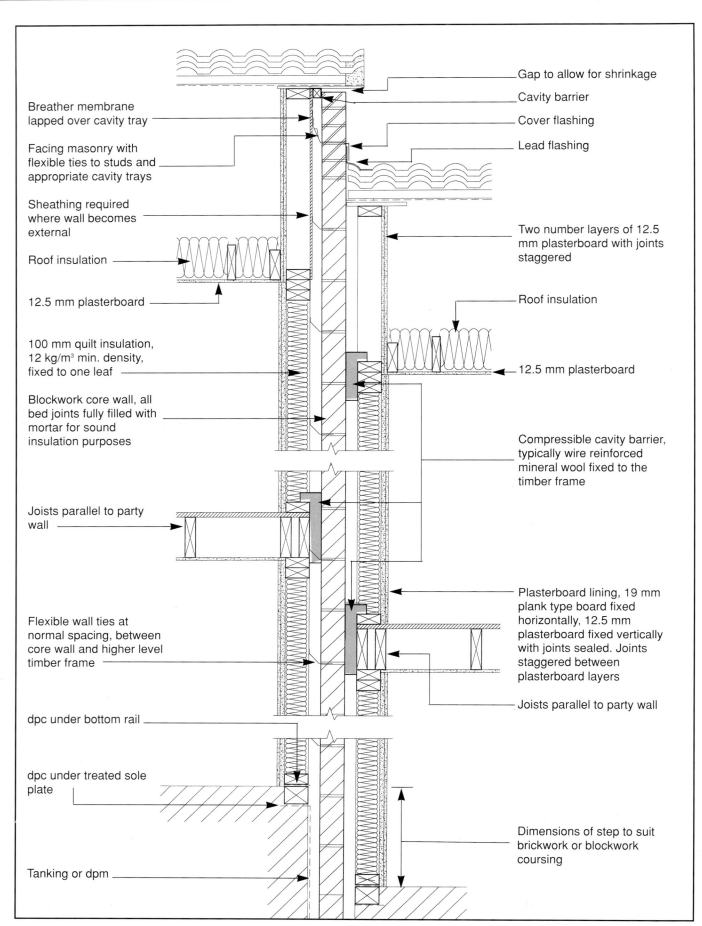

Gap to allow for shrinkage

Cavity barrier

Cover flashing

Lead flashing

Breather membrane lapped over cavity tray

Facing masonry with flexible ties to studs and appropriate cavity trays

Sheathing required where wall becomes external

Two number layers of 12.5 mm plasterboard with joints staggered

Roof insulation

12.5 mm plasterboard

Roof insulation

12.5 mm plasterboard

100 mm quilt insulation, 12 kg/m³ min. density, fixed to one leaf

Blockwork core wall, all bed joints fully filled with mortar for sound insulation purposes

Compressible cavity barrier, typically wire reinforced mineral wool fixed to the timber frame

Joists parallel to party wall

Plasterboard lining, 19 mm plank type board fixed horizontally, 12.5 mm plasterboard fixed vertically with joints sealed. Joints staggered between plasterboard layers

Flexible wall ties at normal spacing, between core wall and higher level timber frame

Joists parallel to party wall

dpc under bottom rail

dpc under treated sole plate

Dimensions of step to suit brickwork or blockwork coursing

Tanking or dpm

Typical vertical section through a stepped party wall.

INTERNAL WALLS

Internal wall construction is very similar to that for external walls, with studs at either 400 mm or 600 mm centres, with noggings. Where sole plates and head binders are used on external walls, they should also be used on internal load bearing walls, to equalise shrinkage and allow a constant stud height to be used throughout.

Where non-load bearing partitions are installed after the structure has been erected, they may be fabricated slightly shorter in height, to allow the ceiling plasterboard to be installed before the partition is erected. Load bearing partitions should be installed prior to the fixing of ceiling plasterboard.

Load bearing partitions are generally prefabricated by the timber frame manufacturer. To prevent undue distortion of these unsheathed wall frames during handling and erection a temporary timber brace may be used on one face of the frame.

Provide a dpc to the underside of all ground floor partitions.

The wall lining to internal partitions is generally 12.5 mm plasterboard, fixed in accordance with the recommendations on pages 136 and 137.

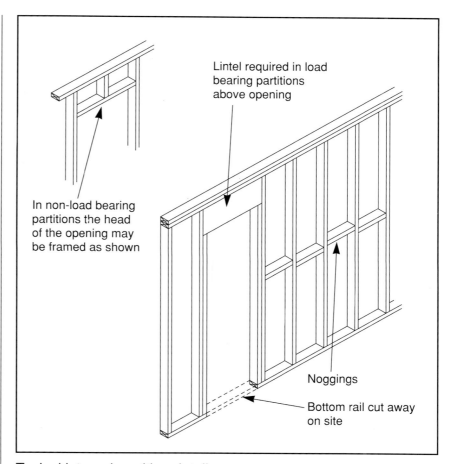

In non-load bearing partitions the head of the opening may be framed as shown

Lintel required in load bearing partitions above opening

Noggings

Bottom rail cut away on site

Typical internal partition details.

INTERNAL WALLS

Internal wall framing & lining junctions

◆ **(A)** All plasterboard junctions must occur on studs or noggings

◆ **(B)** Internal and external corner junctions must be arranged to provide support for both plasterboards and may require an additional stud for this purpose

◆ **(C and D)** Where internal wall junctions occur at a stud centreline, additional studs or battens are required to support adjoining plasterboard edges

◆ **(E)** Where the junction occurs between studs in a wall requiring fire resistance, additional studs must be inserted to support the adjacent plasterboard edges

◆ **(F)** Where no fire resistance is required, the wall and adjacent plasterboard lining can be supported by horizontal noggings set between studs

◆ **(G)** Where the plasterboard is continued through behind the partition, the fire resistance is maintained, but the sequence of work on site may be inconvenienced.

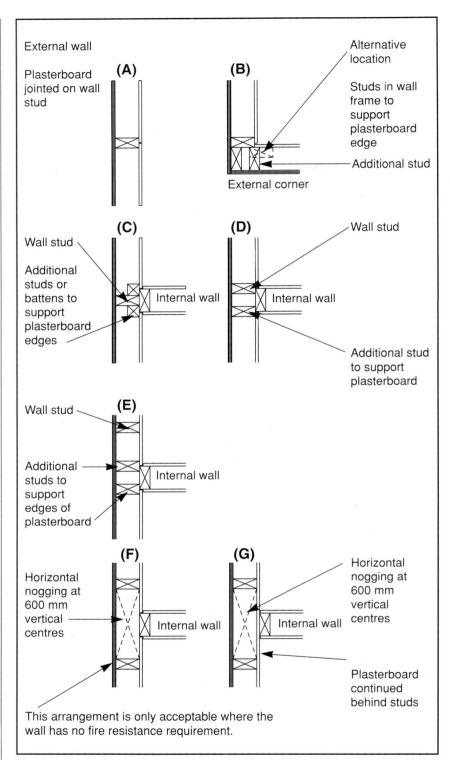

Typical internal/external wall junctions.

FIRST FLOOR CONSTRUCTION

Floor type

The most common type of intermediate floor in domestic timber frame construction is the platform floor, so called because it acts as a working platform on top of the ground floor wall panels, from which the first floor wall panels can be erected. The platform floor is generally factory made.

Where the flooring material is fixed after the first floor wall panels have been erected, floor thickness packers (e.g. treated softwood flooring, plywood or OSB 3) should be used beneath the bottom rail of the wall panels so that internal and external panel heights are constant.

See pages 132 to 135 for details of flooring material types and fixing recommendations.

Where sheathing over the floor edge is not provided, any gaps that may occur between the floor panels, irrespective of their size, must be firestopped. The exposed header joist should be provided with the same preservative treatment as the external wall frames.

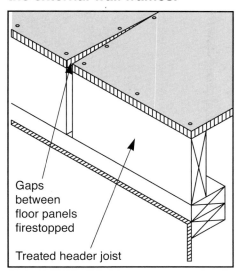

Gaps between floor panels firestopped

Treated header joist

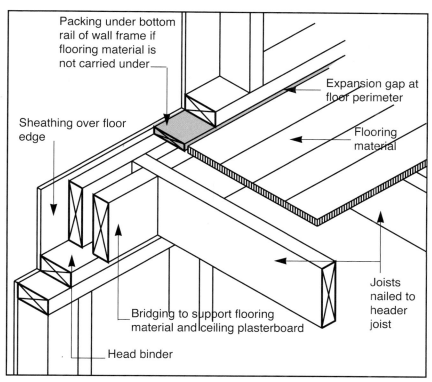

First floor/external wall junction, where joists are at right angles to external wall.

Packing under bottom rail of wall frame if flooring material is not carried under

Expansion gap at floor perimeter

Sheathing over floor edge

Flooring material

Joists nailed to header joist

Bridging to support flooring material and ceiling plasterboard

Head binder

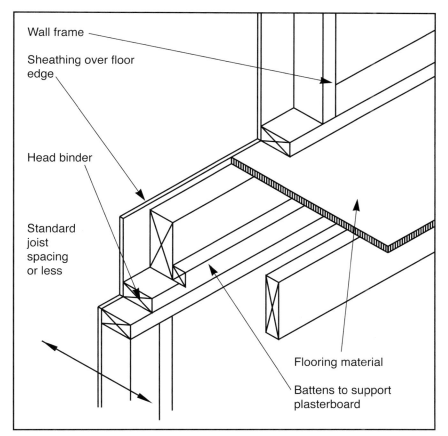

Wall frame

Sheathing over floor edge

Head binder

Standard joist spacing or less

Flooring material

Battens to support plasterboard

First floor/external wall junction, where joists are parallel to external wall. Flooring material carried under wall panel.

FIRST FLOOR CONSTRUCTION

Floor joists

Where a head binder is fitted to the top rail of the wall panel, the floor joists do not necessarily have to coincide with the stud positions. Although trimmers, multiple trusses, beams etc., will usually require additional studs or posts.

Where no head binder is provided, the floor joists must occur over the studs. A small offset is permitted, the extent of which is outlined below. Greater offsets may be obtained subject to design by the timber frame manufacturer.

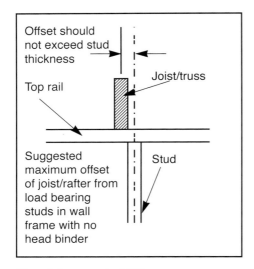

Offset should not exceed stud thickness

Top rail

Joist/truss

Suggested maximum offset of joist/rafter from load bearing studs in wall frame with no head binder

Stud

Notching and drilling

Extreme care should be taken when notching and drilling joists. They should generally only be notched and drilled in the locations and to the extent illustrated on page 131.

In timber frame construction, subject to design by an engineer, joists may be notched and drilled in locations other than those illustrated, including the underside. The engineer must be qualified by examination, be in private practice and possess professional indemnity insurance.

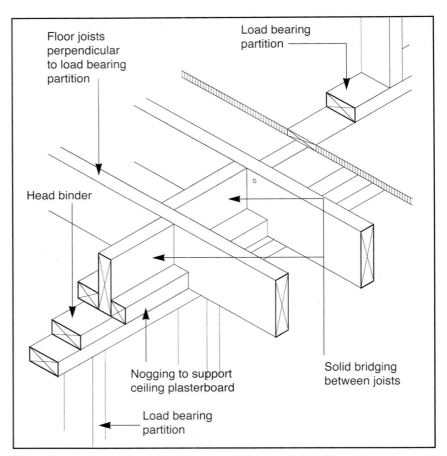

Floor joists perpendicular to load bearing partition

Load bearing partition

Head binder

Nogging to support ceiling plasterboard

Solid bridging between joists

Load bearing partition

First floor/internal load bearing partition junction.

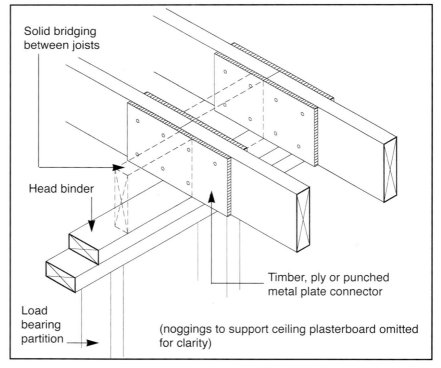

Solid bridging between joists

Load bearing partition

Head binder

Timber, ply or punched metal plate connector

Load bearing partition

(noggings to support ceiling plasterboard omitted for clarity)

Where joists cannot be lapped over a load bearing partition, they should abut, with joints occurring at the centre point. Nominal bearing 45 mm.

FIRST FLOOR CONSTRUCTION

Trimmers and beams

Floor depth beams and trimmer joists can be fabricated by nailing several floor joists together so that they act structurally as one unit.

If a downstand beam is to be avoided, a designed nailing pattern may achieve this. Abutting joists may be supported by joist hangers or by a timber ledger nailed to the face of the double joist and the trimmed joists notched over. Ledger nailing should be designed.

Where beams occur, additional studs or posts will be required in the wall panels to provide support.

Steel beams and specialised composite timber I-beams must be designed by the timber frame manufacturer and installed in accordance with their instructions. Special requirements will apply with regard to fire stopping and fire resistance where such members are used.

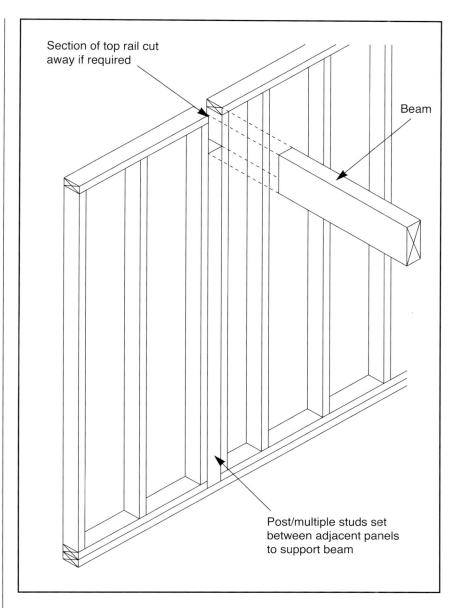

Typical method of supporting a floor beam in a timber frame wall panel, using multiple studs or a post. Multiple studs or posts must occur in the same position in any wall panels below an upper storey panel containing such multiple studs or posts.

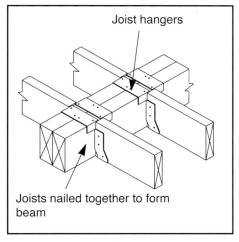

Multiple joists used to form a floor depth beam, designed to suit span and load conditions.

FIRST FLOOR CONSTRUCTION

Support to internal partitions

Where load bearing partitions occur above the floor, their load must be transferred to the partition below. Depending on which direction the floor joists are spanning, this may be achieved as illustrated opposite.

Additional joists may also be required to carry non load bearing partitions which run parallel to the floor joists. Short lengths of non load bearing partition can usually be supported on bridging fixed between joists.

Internal non load bearing partitions at right angles to joist span can normally be carried by the joists, but the additional load imposed must be allowed for, when calculating joist sizes.

TYPICAL METHODS OF SUPPORT FOR LOAD BEARING PARTITIONS, SUBJECT TO DESIGN

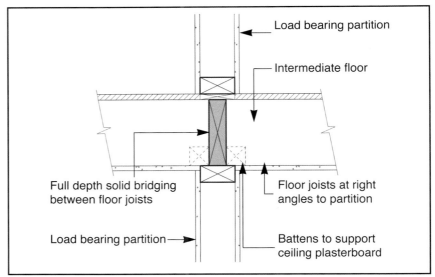

Floor joists at right angles to partitions.

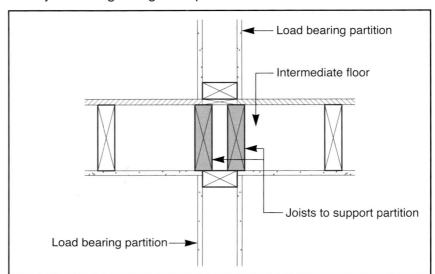

Floor joists parallel to partitions.

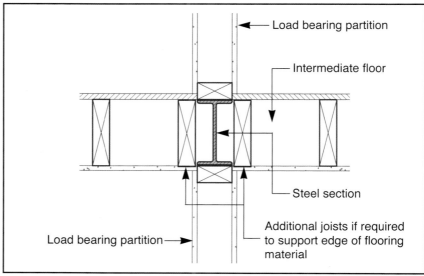

Floor joists parallel to partitions.

FIRE SAFETY

The fire safety requirements for timber frame houses are the same as those for other forms of construction. See Appendix H of this Manual for a comprehensive treatment of the topic.

The nature of timber frame construction does, however, give rise to particular aspects of detail that do not arise in the case of external walls comprised solely of masonry construction. The combustible nature of the timber frame, together with the cavities and voids that are an inherent part of its construction, require that particular provision be made in relation to the installation of cavity barriers.

To meet the recommendations for complying with Building Regulations, cavity barriers should be provided in timber frame walls as follows:

◆ Around all openings, such as doors, windows, vents, openings for extractor fans, meter cupboards, etc

◆ In semi-detached and terraced units, at the junction of party walls and external walls

◆ At eaves level

◆ At verge level at gables.

In addition it is recommended good practice to provide cavity barriers in party walls, at ground and first floor ceiling levels.

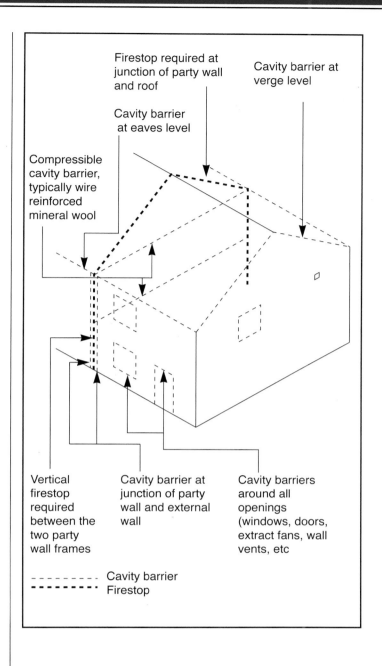

Firestop required at junction of party wall and roof

Cavity barrier at verge level

Cavity barrier at eaves level

Compressible cavity barrier, typically wire reinforced mineral wool

Vertical firestop required between the two party wall frames

Cavity barrier at junction of party wall and external wall

Cavity barriers around all openings (windows, doors, extract fans, wall vents, etc

- - - - - - - - Cavity barrier
▪ ▪ ▪ ▪ ▪ ▪ ▪ ▪ Firestop

FIRE SAFETY
continued

Definitions

Cavity barrier:
A construction provided to close a concealed space against penetration of smoke or flame, or provided to resist the movement of smoke or flame within such a space. Cavity barriers are required to have minimum half-hour fire resistance (i.e. 30 minutes integrity, 15 minutes insulation).

Fire stop:
A seal provided to close an imperfection of fit or design tolerance between elements or components, to restrict or prevent the passage of fire or smoke.

Apart from the cavity barrier practice illustrated in this section, timber frame houses should, as a matter of course, incorporate all other relevant fire safety provisions indicated in Appendix H of this Manual. In particular, the guidance given in Appendix H in respect of the following should be noted:

◆ Means of escape
◆ Wall and ceiling linings
◆ Load-bearing partitions
◆ Integral garages
◆ Roof coverings
◆ Radiation onto boundaries
◆ Rooflights
◆ Heating appliances, hearths, chimneys and flue pipes
◆ Oil storage tanks.

Set out below and opposite are examples of typical fire safety provisions in timber frame housing.

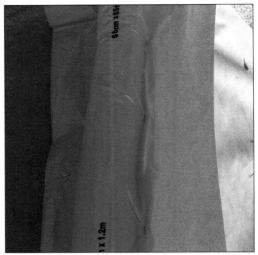
Typical cavity barrier.

Cavity barrier (timber) around sides and head of window frame (cill, when installed, will close cavity at bottom of window).

Cavity barrier around wall vent.

Dpc fitted over timber cavity barriers to sides and head of window opes.

SITE FIXING

The following pages illustrate typical minimum site fixing details. The timber frame manufacturer/design engineer should ensure that site fixing details specific to the project are supplied to the site.

Nails used in the external wall cavity should be corrosion resistant e.g. galvanised, copper or stainless steel.

1. Sole plate to substructure.

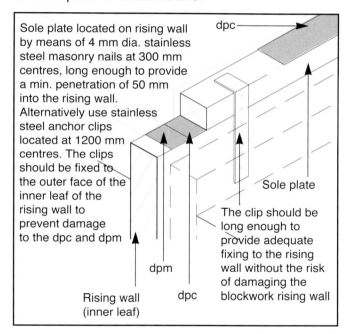

Sole plate located on rising wall by means of 4 mm dia. stainless steel masonry nails at 300 mm centres, long enough to provide a min. penetration of 50 mm into the rising wall. Alternatively use stainless steel anchor clips located at 1200 mm centres. The clips should be fixed to the outer face of the inner leaf of the rising wall to prevent damage to the dpc and dpm

dpc

Sole plate

The clip should be long enough to provide adequate fixing to the rising wall without the risk of damaging the blockwork rising wall

dpm

Rising wall (inner leaf)

dpc

2. Bottom rail to sole plate.

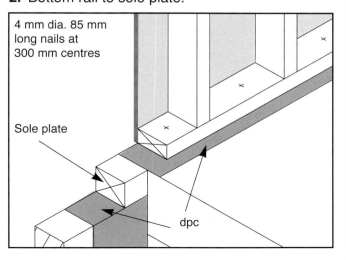

4 mm dia. 85 mm long nails at 300 mm centres

Sole plate

dpc

3. Stainless steel holding down straps.

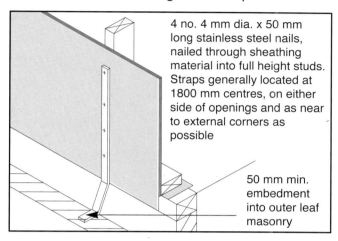

4 no. 4 mm dia. x 50 mm long stainless steel nails, nailed through sheathing material into full height studs. Straps generally located at 1800 mm centres, on either side of openings and as near to external corners as possible

50 mm min. embedment into outer leaf masonry

4. External panel to external panel.

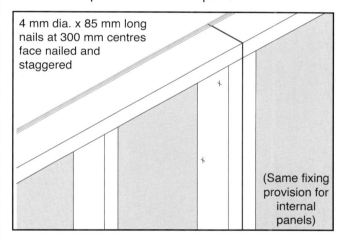

4 mm dia. x 85 mm long nails at 300 mm centres face nailed and staggered

(Same fixing provision for internal panels)

5. Head binder to wall panel.

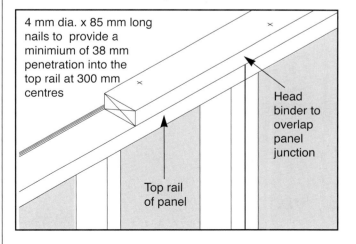

4 mm dia. x 85 mm long nails to provide a minimium of 38 mm penetration into the top rail at 300 mm centres

Head binder to overlap panel junction

Top rail of panel

Note:
Details 6, 7, 8, and 9, form part of a sequence.

6. Header joist to head binder/top rail.

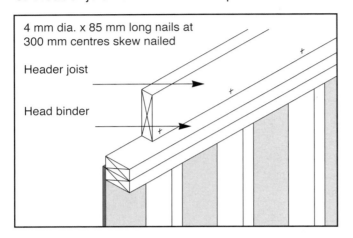

4 mm dia. x 85 mm long nails at
300 mm centres skew nailed

Header joist

Head binder

7. Floor joists to header joist, (see also detail **15**).

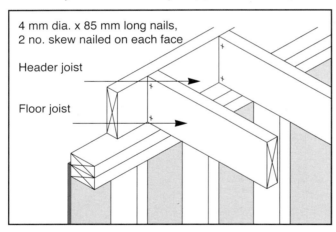

4 mm dia. x 85 mm long nails,
2 no. skew nailed on each face

Header joist

Floor joist

8. Blocking between floor joists.

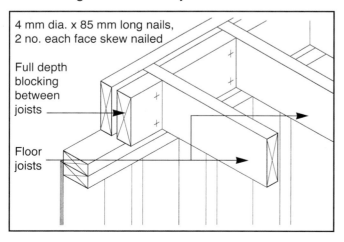

4 mm dia. x 85 mm long nails,
2 no. each face skew nailed

Full depth
blocking
between
joists

Floor
joists

9. Bottom rail to header joist.

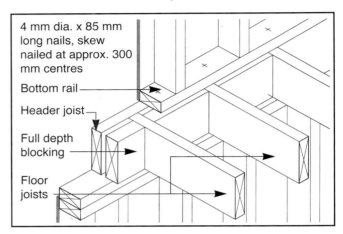

4 mm dia. x 85 mm
long nails, skew
nailed at approx. 300
mm centres

Bottom rail

Header joist

Full depth
blocking

Floor
joists

10. Solid bridging.

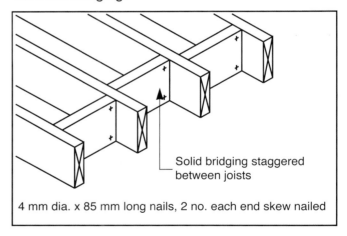

Solid bridging staggered
between joists

4 mm dia. x 85 mm long nails, 2 no. each end skew nailed

11. Herringbone strutting.

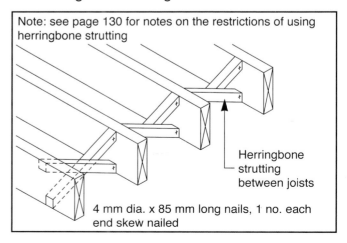

Note: see page 130 for notes on the restrictions of using
herringbone strutting

Herringbone
strutting
between joists

4 mm dia. x 85 mm long nails, 1 no. each
end skew nailed

12. Joists lapped over internal partitions.

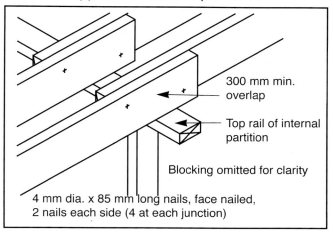

300 mm min. overlap

Top rail of internal partition

Blocking omitted for clarity

4 mm dia. x 85 mm long nails, face nailed, 2 nails each side (4 at each junction)

13. Trimmer (2 members).

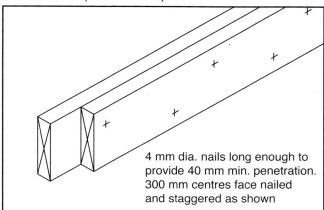

4 mm dia. nails long enough to provide 40 mm min. penetration. 300 mm centres face nailed and staggered as shown

14. Trimmer to trimming joist and joist to trimmer.

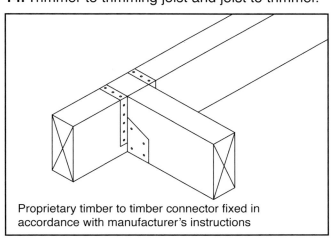

Proprietary timber to timber connector fixed in accordance with manufacturer's instructions

15. Header joist to floor joist.

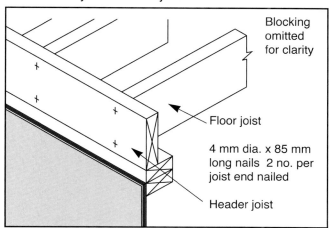

Blocking omitted for clarity

Floor joist

4 mm dia. x 85 mm long nails 2 no. per joist end nailed

Header joist

16. Floor decking to floor joists.

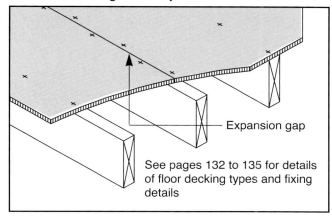

Expansion gap

See pages 132 to 135 for details of floor decking types and fixing details

17. Floor panel to floor panel.

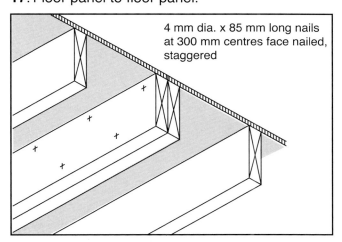

4 mm dia. x 85 mm long nails at 300 mm centres face nailed, staggered

18. Trussed rafter to head binder or top rail over studs.

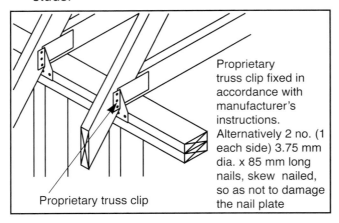

Proprietary truss clip fixed in accordance with manufacturer's instructions. Alternatively 2 no. (1 each side) 3.75 mm dia. x 85 mm long nails, skew nailed, so as not to damage the nail plate

Proprietary truss clip

19. Spandrel panel bottom rail to top rail/head binder of wall panel.

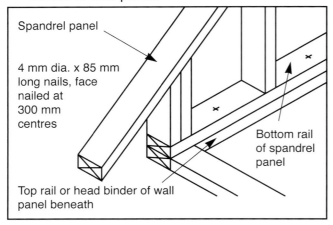

Spandrel panel

4 mm dia. x 85 mm long nails, face nailed at 300 mm centres

Bottom rail of spandrel panel

Top rail or head binder of wall panel beneath

20. Gable ladder to spandrel panel.

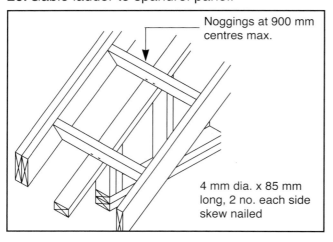

Noggings at 900 mm centres max.

4 mm dia. x 85 mm long, 2 no. each side skew nailed

21. Plasterboard fixing to walls.

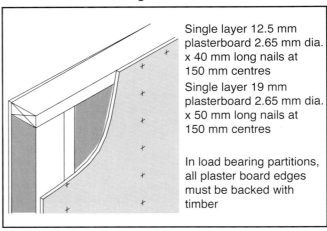

Single layer 12.5 mm plasterboard 2.65 mm dia. x 40 mm long nails at 150 mm centres

Single layer 19 mm plasterboard 2.65 mm dia. x 50 mm long nails at 150 mm centres

In load bearing partitions, all plaster board edges must be backed with timber

22. Plasterboard fixing to party wall.

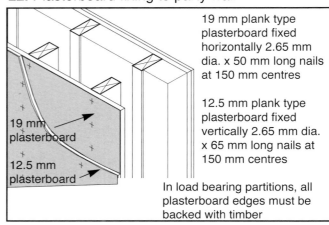

19 mm plank type plasterboard fixed horizontally 2.65 mm dia. x 50 mm long nails at 150 mm centres

12.5 mm plank type plasterboard fixed vertically 2.65 mm dia. x 65 mm long nails at 150 mm centres

19 mm plasterboard

12.5 mm plasterboard

In load bearing partitions, all plasterboard edges must be backed with timber

The following pages contain a checklist compiled by the Timber Quality Bureau of Ireland as part of their Quality Approval Scheme for Timber Frame Buildings.

Site Name			Builder	
Site Address			Manufacturer	
No. of Houses			House Type	

Name of site supervisor:

SECTION 1: DOCUMENTATION	Signed	Date	Comment
Site plans/elevations			
Location... [ ]	....	....	
Finished floor level .... [ ]	....	....	
Individual house drawings			
Foundation plans (including baseplan)........................... [ ]	....	....	
Panel layout plan.. [ ]	....	....	
Architectural drawings... [ ]	....	....	
Specifications			
Materials... [ ]	....	....	
Timber treatments.. [ ]	....	....	
Standard drawings			
General construction details... [ ]	....	....	
Roof bracing .... [ ]	....	....	
Tank supports .... [ ]	....	....	
Site fixing schedule.. [ ]	....	....	
Site Instruction Form .... [ ]	....	....	
Manuals etc.			
HomeBond Manual.. [ ]	....	....	
Manufacturers erection manual...................................... [ ]	....	....	
Site log book.. [ ]	....	....	
Certificates			
Design .... [ ]	....	....	
Manufacture .... [ ]	....	....	
Treatment .... [ ]	....	....	
SECTION 2: SITE STORAGE	**Signed**	**Date**	**Comment**
General			
Level & well drained .... [ ]	....	....	
Panel storage			
Off ground.. [ ]	....	....	
Supported properly... [ ]	....	....	
Sheathing face up .... [ ]	....	....	
Covered & ventilated .... [ ]	....	....	
Loose timber joists			
Off ground.. [ ]	....	....	
Supported properly... [ ]	....	....	
Roof trusses			
Off ground.. [ ]	....	....	
Supported properly... [ ]	....	....	
QA marked correctly... [ ]	....	....	
Plasterboard and Insulation			
Dry & covered... [ ]	....	....	
SECTION 3: SITE DELIVERY			

Undamaged...	Record in Site Log Book with date,
As per specification	signature and any comment.

HOUSE No._____

Site Name		Builder	
Site Address		Manufacturer	
House Type			

Name of site supervisor:

SECTION A: SUBSTRUCTURES AND GROUND FLOORS			Signed	Date	Comment
RISING WALLS	Dimensions (see baseplan) Widths.....lengths.... diagonals.........	[ ]	....	....	
Concrete sub-floor/floor	Separation at floors and party wall....	[ ]	....	....	
Timber sub-floor	Heights... ventilated... drainage........	[ ]	....	....	
DPM	Undamaged/repaired.......................	[ ]	....	....	
	Lapped under dpc..........................	[ ]	....	....	
	Joints lapped to maintain integrity.....	[ ]	....	....	
DPC	Undamaged or repaired...................	[ ]	....	....	
	In position and full wall width..........	[ ]	....	....	
Sole plate	Level..	[ ]	....	....	
	Fixed to schedule...........................	[ ]	....	....	

SECTION B: SHELL ERECTION			Signed	Date	Comment
Ground floor wall plan	No damage........................	[ ]	....	....	
	In line, level, plumb..............	[ ]	....	....	
	Nailing as per schedule....................	[ ]	....	....	
	Holding down fixings to schedule......	[ ]	....	....	
	Full support to panel bottom rail........	[ ]	....	....	
	Head binder..	[ ]	....		
Timber floor (use 2 boxes if ground and first floor are timber)	Joists QA marked.............	[ ] [ ]	....	....	
	Joist hangers fully fixed.....................	[ ] [ ]	....	....	
	Fixing to schedule...........................	[ ] [ ]	....	....	
	Notching & drilling............................	[ ] [ ]	....	....	
	Expansion gaps in decking................	[ ] [ ]	....	....	
	No gaps at wall cavities....................	[ ] [ ]	....	....	

Use additional boxes for upper storeys and spandrel panels			Signed	Date	Comment
Upper storey wall panels	No damage........................	[ ] [ ] [ ]	....	....	
	In line, level, plumb..............	[ ] [ ] [ ]	....	....	
	Nailing as per schedule....................	[ ] [ ] [ ]	....	....	
	Holding down fixings to schedule......	[ ] [ ] [ ]	....	....	
	Head binder.......................................	[ ] [ ] [ ]	....	....	
Roof structure	Fixed to schedule...........................	[ ]	....	....	
	Bracing fixed to schedule..................	[ ]	....	....	
Timber frame party wall	No services in wall...........................	[ ]	....	....	
	Fixings to schedule..........................	[ ]	....	....	
	Holding down fixings to schedule......	[ ]	....	....	
	No voids...	[ ]	....	....	
	Plasterboard to detail.......................	[ ]	....	....	
	Thickness, layers, nailing................	[ ] [ ] [ ]	....	....	
	Insulation	[ ]	....	....	
	Vapour check/barrier (see section D)	[ ]	....	....	
	Cavity barriers	[ ]	....	....	
	Firestops (see also section C below)	[ ]	....	....	

HOUSE No._____

SECTION C: EXTERNAL WALLS			Signed	Date	Comment
Breather membranes	Undamaged or repaired..................	[ ]	....	....	
	Stud positions marked......................	[ ]	....	....	
Cavity barriers as per details	At doors and windows......................	[ ]	....	....	
	At max. 10m intermediate spacing in wall (vertical).................................	[ ]	....	....	
	At party wall/external wall...............	[ ]	....	....	
	At party wall floor levels (horizontal).	[ ]	....	....	
	At party wall ceiling level (horizontal)	[ ]	....	....	
	At eaves (horizontal)........................	[ ]	....	....	
	At gable wall verge/eaves level........	[ ]	....	....	
	Cavity fully closed...........................	[ ]	....	....	
	Separate dpc to external leaf............	[ ]	....		
Firestops	Top of party wall.............................	[ ]	....	....	
	Eaves at party wall/external wall.......	[ ]	....	....	
	Vertical at party wall/external wall.....	[ ]	....	....	
Doors and windows	dpc's correctly positioned.................	[ ]	....	....	
	Shrinkage gap at cills......................	[ ]	....	....	
Masonry outer leaf	Cavity drained/weep holes...............	[ ]	....	....	
	Wall ties spacing & built in...............	[ ]	....	....	
	Wall ties fixed to studs.....................	[ ]	....	....	
	Clean & ventilated cavity..................	[ ]	....	....	
	Shrinkage gaps...............................	[ ]	....	....	
SECTION D: INTERNALS AND FIRST FIXING			Signed	Date	Comment
Notching and drilling	Permitted size.................................	[ ]	....	....	
	Permitted location............................	[ ]	....	....	
Insulation	No gaps or voids.............................	[ ]	....	....	
	Correctly supported.........................	[ ]	....	....	
Vapour check	Undamaged or repaired....................	[ ]	....	....	
	All gaps sealed...............................	[ ]	....	....	
	Neat service holes...........................	[ ]	....	....	
	All laps timber backed......................	[ ]	....	....	
Vapour check plasterboard	Undamaged	[ ]	....	....	
	Neat service holes	[ ]	....	....	
	All gaps sealed	[ ]	....	....	
	All joints timber backed	[ ]	....	....	

SECTION E: ADVERSE WEATHER AND GENERAL COMMENTS... Use the site log book if extra space is needed

Site Name	
Site Address	
House Type	

Builder	
Manufacturer	

Name of site supervisor: HOUSE No._____

SECTION F: ROOF STRUCTURE	Signed Date Comment	Signed	Date	Comment
Roof structure				
Trusses				
Correctly positioned . . . . [ ]		....	....	
Centres and plumb . . . . [ ]		....	....	
Certification tag . . . . [ ]		....	....	
Fixed to schedule. . . . . [ ]		....	....	
Bracing. . . . . [ ]		....	....	
Tanks supported correctly . . . . [ ]		....	....	
Girder trusses fixed together as per specification . . . . [ ]		....	....	
Cut roofs				
Rafter/ceiling joist dimensions . . . . [ ]		....	....	
Rafter/ceiling joist spacing. . . . . [ ]		....	....	
Rafter/ceiling joist QA marked . . . . [ ]		....	....	
Seated and positioned correctly . . . . [ ]		....	....	
Ceiling ties lapped and nailed . . . . [ ]		....	....	
Rafter/ceiling tie fixed as required . . . . [ ]		....	....	
nails as per specification. . . . . [ ]		....	....	
nails as per schedule . . . . [ ]		....	....	
Purlins (where required)				
Size as specification . . . . [ ]		....	....	
Correctly located . . . . [ ]		....	....	
Timber QA marked. . . . . [ ]		....	....	
Struts bearing on support . . . . [ ]		....	....	
Collars fixed correctly . . . . [ ]		....	....	
Hangers and binders fixed correctly . . . . [ ]		....	....	
Hip roofs				
Girder trusses fixed together as per specification . . . . [ ]		....	....	
Hangers for supporting mono trusses correctly fixed . . . . [ ]		....	....	
Hip rafters bearing on girder truss . . . . [ ]		....	....	
Hip rafters correctly bearing at wall corners . . . . [ ]		....	....	
Wallplate strap fixed at wall corners . . . . [ ]		....	....	
Ledger fixed to apex of first truss. . . . . [ ]		....	....	
Cut roof section . . . . [ ]		....	....	
Rafter/ceiling joist dimensions . . . . [ ]		....	....	
Rafter/ceiling joist spacing . . . . [ ]		....	....	
Rafter/ceiling joist QA marked . . . . [ ]		....	....	
Jack rafters/ceiling joists tied into main roof as per detail . . . . [ ]		....	....	
Battens				
Size . . . . [ ]		....	....	
Over at least 3 supports. . . . . [ ]		....	....	
No damage . . . . [ ]		....	....	
Water tank supports				
Over 4 trusses . . . . [ ]		....	....	
Size as per specification . . . . [ ]		....	....	
Timber QA marked. . . . . [ ]		....	....	

VENTILATION AND CONDENSATION

INTRODUCTION

Ventilation of a dwelling is necessary to provide an adequate supply of fresh air for persons using the dwelling, to remove water vapour and prevent harmful condensation. The need for ventilation is a consequence of higher modern standards of insulation combined with an increase in activities generating water vapour within the building. There has also been a reduction in natural ventilation within buildings due to improved draught proofing.

In order to prevent the harmful consequences of condensation it is necessary to ventilate the building adequately to remove the air bearing the water vapour.

Ventilation should be provided in accordance with the guidance given on the following pages. See also the detailed guidance on roof space ventilation given on pages 183 to 188.

The ventilation system should:

◆ Provide an adequate supply of fresh air for persons using the area

◆ Achieve occasional rapid ventilation for the dilution of pollutants and of moisture likely to produce condensation in habitable rooms, kitchens and rooms containing sanitary appliances

◆ Extract moisture from areas where it is produced in significant quantities (e.g. kitchen and bathroom).

A ventilation opening can include any means of permanent or controllable ventilation which:

◆ Opens directly to the external air

◆ Has a minimum dimension of 8 mm, except in the case of a screen, baffle, fascia, etc.

Note: A ventilation opening does not include a flue to a chimney.

GENERAL NOTE

Special care should be given to the positioning of air vents in an external wall on either side of the party wall, to ensure a minimum of 650mm between vents, unless the external wall is a cavity wall and the cavity is closed vertically on the party wall line. See Appendix F, Sound.

In cavity wall construction the air vent should be sleeved across the cavity, to prevent ventilation of the cavity. Proprietary ventilators are available for this location. Alternatively, pipes can be used , e.g. a 150 mm diameter pipe.

Ventilation requirements for a typical house,
(see table on next page).

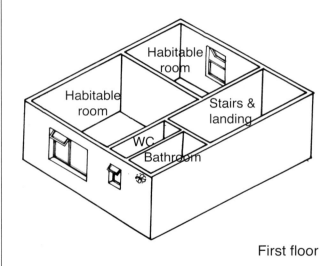

First floor

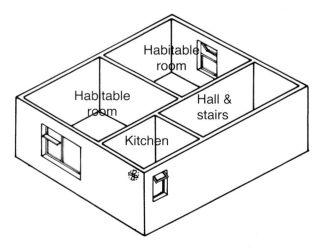

Ground floor

Ventilation requirements for a typical house

Room type	Ventilation requirements*
Habitable rooms i.e. any room used for living or sleeping purposes, including a kitchen, having a floor area of 6.5 square metres or more. **Utility rooms** i.e. any room used for laundry purposes which contains a sink, washing machine, tumble drier or similar equipment and which is not entered solely from outside the building.	◆ Background ventilation having a total area of not less than 6500 mm^2, e.g. a standard 225 x 225 wall vent, located so as to avoid undue draughts or vents in windows, and ◆ Rapid ventilation by one or more ventilation openings, having a total area of at least 5% of the floor area of the room, e.g. opening window(s), or door(s) with some part of the ventilation opening at least 1.75 m above floor level. **Note: Background ventilation means ventilation by means of secure ventilation opening (or openings) consisting of a wall or window ventilator with a controllable ventilation grille and located so as to reduce draughts.**
Small kitchens i.e. kitchens with a floor area of less than 6.5 square metres.	◆ Background ventilation, either 1. having a total area not less than 6500 mm^2 e.g. a 225 x 225 standard wall vent located so as to avoid undue draughts, or vents in windows, **or** 2 by mechanical extract ventilation capable of operating continuously at nominally one air change per hour, and ◆ Rapid ventilation, either 1. by ventilation opening(s) having a total area of at least 10% of the floor area of the kitchen, e.g. opening window(s) with some part of the ventilation opening at least 1.75 m above floor level, **or** 2. by mechanical extract ventilation capable of extracting at a rate of 60 litres per second (or at a rate of 30 litres per second where the ventilation is incorporated in a cooker hood), which can be operated intermittently during cooking. **Note: Background ventilation means ventilation by means of secure ventilation opening (or openings) consisting of a wall or window ventilator with a controllable ventilation grille and located so as to reduce draughts.**
Bathrooms & sanitary accommodation Sanitary accommodation is any space containing a water closet.	◆ Rapid ventilation having a total area of at least 5% of the floor area of the room, e.g. an opening window or door with some part of the ventilation opening at least 1.75 m above floor level, **or** ◆ Mechanical extract ventilation, capable of extracting at a rate of 15 litres per second, which may be operated intermittently.

* These ventilation requirements will be overridden if heating appliances are installed in the rooms.
See page 332 for guidance on minimum ventilation provisions for heating appliances.

AIR SUPPLY TO HEAT PRODUCING APPLIANCES	ROOMS WITH OPEN FLUED APPLIANCES
The following air supply requirements for various heat producing appliances have been derived from Technical Guidance Document J of The Building Regulations, and should be read in conjunction with the ventilation requirements for various room types given on the previous page.	Where habitable rooms or kitchens contain an open flued appliance, reduced rates of extraction may be appropriate. Reference should be made to BRE information paper IP 7/94 Spillage of flue gases from solid fuel combustion appliances.

Appliance type	Air supply requirements
Solid fuel burning open appliance with rated output up to 45 kW e.g. typical open fire.	A ventilation opening (or openings) with a total free area of at least 20,000 mm² of which at least 6,500 mm² is **permanent** ventilation shall be provided. These ventilation requirements are usually met by a combination of opening windows and permanent vents.
Other solid fuel appliances with rated output up to 45 kW e.g. typical domestic stove, range etc.	A permanent air entry or opening with a total free area of at least 550 mm² per kW of rated output above 5 kW shall be provided but in no case less than 6500 mm². Where a flue draught stabiliser is used the total free area should be increased by 300 mm² for each kW of rated output.
Individually flued (non-fan assisted) gas burning appliances with a rated output up to 60 kW (other than balanced flued solid fuel effect appliances) and gas burning cooking appliances e.g typical domestic gas fired boiler, gas cooker.	Any room or space containing a cooker should have an openable window or other means of providing ventilation. If the room or space has a volume less than 10 m³, then, in addition, a **permanent** ventilation opening of at least 5,000 mm² should be provided. Any room or space containing an open flued appliance should have a **permanent** ventilation opening of at least 450 mm² for each kW of appliance input rating, but in no case less than 6500 mm².
Oil burning appliance with a rated output up to 45 kW (other than a balanced flue appliance) e.g typical domestic oil fired boiler.	Any room or space containing an appliance should have a **permanent** ventilation opening of free area of at least 550 mm² for each kW of rated output above 5 kW, but in no case less than 6500 mm².

Note: Permanent ventilators should not incorporate a controllable ventilation grille.

HEIGHT OF HABITABLE ROOMS

Technical Guidance Document F recommends that every habitable room should be not less than 2.4 m in height and the height of such measured beneath any beam in that room and in any bay window shall not be less than 2.1 m. Where such a room is immediately below the roof (e.g. dormer construction) its height should be not less than 2.4 m over an area equal to not less than one half of the area of the room measured on a plane 1.5 m above the finished floor level. See sketches opposite.

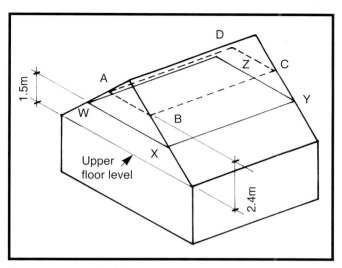

Dormer room height.

Thus: Area of A B C D to be at least half the area of W X Y Z.

Ventilation note:

The ventilation requirements of the Building Regulations as specified in Technical Guidance Document F and also in this section must be adhered to in the construction of dwellings.

HomeBond also advises that if new windows, whether single or double glazed, are being installed in existing houses it is vital that there is sufficient ventilation for the rooms, particularly those with fireplaces, to ensure that the fire, whether an open or closed appliance, has sufficient air to draw and that there will not be a build up of the products of combustion which could be a health hazard.

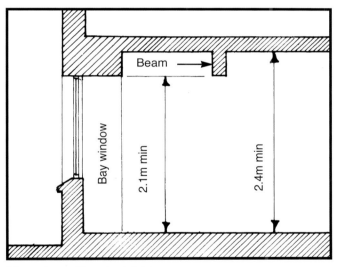

Floor to ceiling height in habitable rooms.

VENTILATION OF HABITABLE ROOMS THROUGH OTHER ROOMS AND SPACES

Two habitable rooms may be treated as a single room for ventilation purposes if there is an area of permanent opening between them equal to at least 1/20th of the combined floor areas.

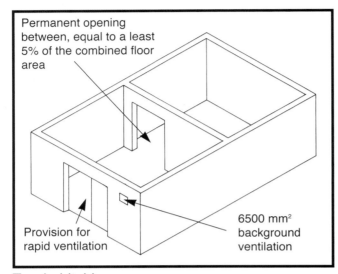

Permanent opening between, equal to a least 5% of the combined floor area

Provision for rapid ventilation

6500 mm² background ventilation

Two habitable rooms.

A habitable room may be ventilated through an adjoining space if:

◆ The adjoining space is a conservatory or similar space

◆ There is an opening (which may be closeable) between the room and the space, with an area not less than 1/20th of the combined floor area of the room and space

◆ Provision is made for:

1. background ventilation to the space, and
2. one or more permanent openings for ventilation purposes between the room and the space, consisting of a wall or window vent, each having a total area not less than 6500 mm² and located so as to avoid undue draughts

◆ Provision is made for rapid ventilation to the space with a total area not less than 1/20th of the combined floor area of the room and space, e.g. an opening window or door

◆ The space is not connected to another room which has no alternative means of natural ventilation other than through the space.

Open doors/windows to provide rapid ventilation to the space with a total area not less than 5% of the combined floor area of the room and space with some part of the ventilation opening at least 1.75m above floor level

Background vent to the space, not less than 6500 mm² or window vents

Conservatory or similar space.

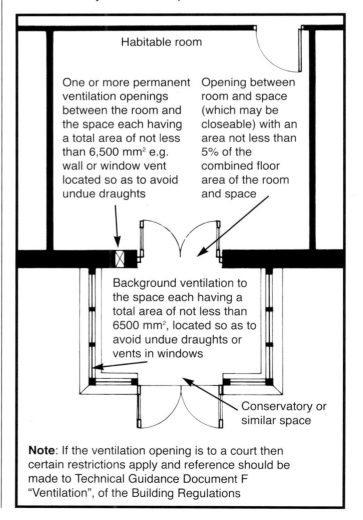

Habitable room

One or more permanent ventilation openings between the room and the space each having a total area of not less than 6,500 mm² e.g. wall or window vent located so as to avoid undue draughts

Opening between room and space (which may be closeable) with an area not less than 5% of the combined floor area of the room and space

Background ventilation to the space each having a total area of not less than 6500 mm², located so as to avoid undue draughts or vents in windows

Conservatory or similar space

Note: If the ventilation opening is to a court then certain restrictions apply and reference should be made to Technical Guidance Document F "Ventilation", of the Building Regulations

CONDENSATION: INTRODUCTION

Condensation occurs when damp air comes in contact with a cold surface, as warm air can hold more water vapour than cold air.

Moisture produced in kitchens and bathrooms (high pressure areas) will find its way into the lower pressure areas such as bedrooms, where it may condense on the colder wall surfaces as indicated in the sketch.

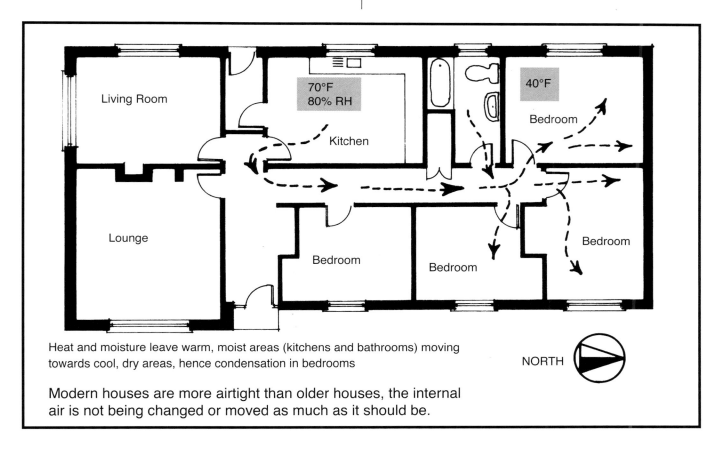

Heat and moisture leave warm, moist areas (kitchens and bathrooms) moving towards cool, dry areas, hence condensation in bedrooms

Modern houses are more airtight than older houses, the internal air is not being changed or moved as much as it should be.

Stagnant air encourages condensation. Stagnant air pockets are very often the first places where condensation will occur. This can be seen in corners, behind furniture, pictures and in cupboards particularly when placed against external walls. The North wall of a house is often the coldest and most prone to condensation. In rooms with severe condensation, it is not uncommon to have to mop up water from the window cill and the jambs every morning due to condensation (condensation channels and weepholes should be provided to all aluminium and timber windows). It is estimated that unheated bedrooms are the cause of at least half of the complaints about condensation.

Sometimes the mould growth can be most severe at the base of a wall, often being confused with rising damp.

Condensation in old houses:
Older houses tend to have more ventilation, larger rooms and higher ceilings, badly fitting doors, windows and floor boards as well as more fireplaces, all of which result in better ventilation. Windows are now draught proofed, doors are factory made incorporating draught excluders and better fitting. Floors are now concrete or timber covered with carpets or vinyl covering, thereby eliminating draughts.

MOULD GROWTH

Once a serious ongoing dampness problem due to condensation has been established mould fungus (mildew), a parasite freely available in the air (pollen and yeast etc.), can develop on walls, furnishings, bedding clothes, leather goods, shoes, handbags, golf clubs, etc.

Mould first appears as spots or small patches which may spread to form a furry layer usually grey-green, black or brown in colour. There are many types of mould growth, but all grow and spread under similar conditions and require similar remedial treatment. Three conditions are necessary for mould growth to occur. These are:

1. A source of infection.
   The spores are freely present in the air.

2. A source of nourishment.
   Dirt, dust, grease, or some organic material is needed in small amounts, and so almost all surfaces will sustain growth.

3. A damp environment.
   Mould growth requires an atmospheric relative humidity level (RH) in excess of 85%, sustained for periods up to 12 hours per day. This will result in serious and widespread growth. At lower levels its growth is slower and it ceases below 70% RH. Mould growth is more marked on North facing walls and in areas where stagnant air pockets exist. As conditions 1 and 2 above cannot easily be avoided, the deciding factor is relative humidity.

Cleaning of the mould using a suitable fungicidal wash is required prior to redecorating, but it must be stressed that such removal is cosmetic and not to be recommended as a cure to the overall problem. Cleaning and sterilisation of the materials on, or in which it has occurred is necessary. It is not always possible to decide whether mould is growing only on the surface, in a top coat of paint, or if it has penetrated further. Where decorations can be stripped off it is usually best to do so.

LIMITING CONDENSATION RISK

Key points for householders:

◆ Contain steam at source

◆ Minimise the use of oil and gas heaters

◆ Increase ventilation levels

◆ Maintain reasonable levels of heat

◆ Avoid drying clothes indoors - if it is necessary, do so in a well ventilated room.

Mould growth due to condensation in corner of room.

Mould growth due to condensation in hall.

CONDENSATION

Condensation is probably the main cause of dampness and mould growth in dwellings. As a result of continuing condensation, walls, ceilings and sometimes floors become damp, discoloured and unpleasant due to mould growing on their surfaces. The following notes explain how condensation occurs and what householders can do to prevent or cure serious outbreaks of it in their homes.

Why condensation occurs
Condensation occurs when warm moist air meets a cold surface. The likelihood of condensation therefore depends on how moist the air is and how cold the surfaces of the room are. The moistness of the air and coldness of the surfaces depend on a range of factors, many of which are determined by the way the house is used.

When condensation occurs
Condensation usually occurs in winter. This is because the building surfaces are cold, more moisture is generated within the house and, because windows are opened less, the moist air cannot escape.

Where condensation occurs
Condensation, which is visible, occurs for short periods in bathrooms and kitchens because of the steamy atmosphere. It also occurs for long periods in unheated bathrooms and sometimes in wardrobes, cupboards or corners of rooms where ventilation and air movement may be restricted. Condensation can occur on materials which are out of sight, for example in roofs.

Condensation forming at junction of walls and ceiling.

What is Important?

In order to prevent or cure condensation problems the following four precautions are important.

1. Minimise moisture production within the dwelling and confine it as far as possible to specific areas, e.g. kitchen, bathroom, scullery.

2. Prevent moist air spreading to other rooms from the kitchen, bathroom or scullery or from where clothes are dried.

3. Provide some ventilation to all rooms so that moist air can escape.

4. Provide some level of heating.

Minimise moisture production
a) Dry clothes externally when possible.

b) If using a clothes dryer, provide venting to the outside.

c) Limit the use of movable gas or paraffin heaters as these types of heaters release large amounts of water vapour into the air and greatly increase the risk of condensation.

d) Reduce cooking steam as far as possible, e.g. keep lids on saucepans, do not leave kettles etc. boiling for long periods.

Prevent spread of moist air
a) Good ventilation of kitchens is essential when cooking or while washing clothes. If that is an extract fan in the kitchen, use it when cooking, washing clothes and particularly if the windows mist up.

b) In the absence of an extract fan, open the kitchen windows and keep the doors between the kitchen and the rest of the house closed as much as possible.

c) After taking a bath, keep the bathroom window open and the bathroom door shut until the bathroom dries.

d) Do not use unventilated cupboards for drying clothes.

e) If clothes are dried in the bathroom or kitchen, run the extract fan if one is present. Do not leave the door open or the moist air will spread to other parts of the house.

f) If a movable gas or paraffin heater must be used, make sure the room in which the heater is located is well ventilated and sealed off from the rest of the house.

Provide some ventilation

The easiest method of reducing the moisture content of room air is to provide some ventilation. Ventilation removes the stale moist air and replaces it with fresh air which contains less moisture.

a) In older houses a lot of ventilation occurs through fireplaces and draughty windows. However, in many modern houses and flats, sufficient ventilation does not occur unless a window or ventilator is open for a reasonable time each day and for nearly all the time the room is in use. Too much ventilation in cold weather is uncomfortable and wastes heat. All that is needed is a slightly open window or ventilator. Where possible, open the top part of the window about 10 mm.
If more than two people sleep in a bedroom the window should be opened wider, particularly during the night. Do not block up the wall or window vents.

b) If condensation occurs in a room where there is a heater connected to the chimney, have the installation checked as the chimney may have become blocked.

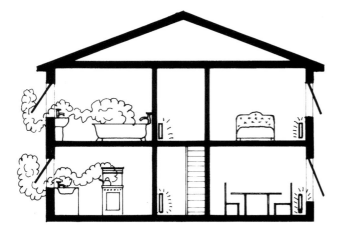

Prevent spread of moist air. Provide ventilation and some heating.

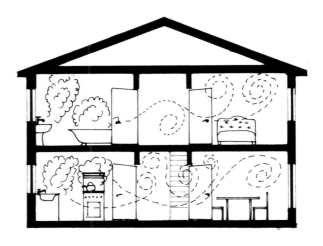

Lack of heating or ventilation facilitates the spread of moist air.

Provide some heating

a) Try to ensure that all rooms are at least partially heated. Condensation most often occurs in unheated bedrooms. If a room has to be left unheated, keep the window open slightly and the door shut.

b) Heating helps prevent condensation by warming the room surfaces. It takes a long time for the cold room surface to warm up. It is better to provide a small amount of heating for long periods than to provide a lot of heat for a short period. Houses and flats left unoccupied and unheated during the day become very cold. Whenever possible, try to provide a constant low level of heating all the time.

c) In houses, the rooms above a heated living room benefit from the heat rising through the floor. In bungalows and some flats this does not happen. Some rooms are especially cold because they have large areas of outside wall and windows or because they lose heat through the roof as well as the walls. Such rooms are most likely to have condensation. Some heating is necessary in these rooms. Condensation is likely if the rooms are not kept above 10°C. When living-rooms are in use they should be heated to 20°C if possible.

d) Insulation reduces the rate of heat loss and helps raise the temperature. However, even in a well insulated house, some heating may be necessary in cold rooms with no indirect heat input.

Condensation on car windscreen.

Condensation is not unique to houses. As illustrated above, it can also occur in cars, especially in wet, cold or humid weather. This is not a defect in the design or manufacture of the car and is readily dealt with by opening windows and use of the fan and heater to demist the windscreen. Similarly, condensation in a house is not a design or construction defect, it results as a combination of climatic conditions and use patterns of a household.

Dehumidifers

Dehumidifers are on sale in many electrical stores. They extract water from the air and gather it in a container. They are relatively inexpensive to run and can be used to reduce condensation in extreme cases.

Dehumidifier.

Mould growth

If small black spots appear on the walls or other room surfaces, this is the start of mould growth. Any sign of mould growth indicates the presence of moisture. If the moisture is caused by condensation it is a sign that the level of moisture in the room needs to be reduced or that heating, ventilation or structural insulation, or all three need to be improved.

The mould growth spots should be washed off and the affected area sterilised using a fungicide containing bleach. The cause of the condensation as should be dealt with recommended under "What is important".

New buildings

New buildings can take a long time to dry out and during the first winter more heating and ventilation will be necessary than in subsequent winters. Excessive temperatures should be avoided to prevent warping of new joinery. With certain types of concrete roofs, final drying may only be able to take place inwards. So, do not use waterproof decorations (such as vinyl papers) on the ceiling unless you have been given expert advice that this would not matter.

Effect of extract ventilation on fuel burning appliances

If you propose to fit an extract fan or otherwise change the ventilation of a room which has a gas or solid fuel appliance connected to the chimney, you should obtain advice from the installer of the heating appliance. This is because there may be a risk of drawing toxic fumes back from the appliance into the room.

Mould growth in bedroom due to condensation.

EFFLORESCENCE, SULPHATE ATTACK AND FROST ATTACK IN CLAY BRICKWORK

EFFLORESCENCE EXPLAINED

Efflorescence consists of deposits of soluble salts formed on the surface of new brickwork. Although efflorescence is unsightly it is often harmless and seldom persists unless water is able to percolate into the brickwork.

All bricks contain a small percentage of soluble salts. These salts are generally harmless unless they are present in bricks which are subject to very damp weather conditions. The problem arises when the bricks become saturated with water. As the brickwork dries out, the soluble salts are carried to the brick surface where they crystallise and are deposited as white crystals. This manifests itself as white patches on the brickwork.

The deposit formed is usually composed of the sulphate of sodium, potassium, magnesium and calcium, not all of these salts being present in any one instance. Sodium carbonate can also appear, usually being derived from the cement in the mortar. Sulphates in bricks may be derived from the clay from which they are made and also from the manufacturing process.

When water is added to the cement the gypsum and alkali in the cement react to form small amounts of sulphates. In a concrete mix where all the water stays in the mix until it is set, all the sulphate will, within a few hours, be fixed in an insoluble form by combination with other constituents of the cement, and so will be incapable of contributing to the efflorescence. If, however, the mix is a mortar mix and is placed between dry porous bricks, some of the water will be soaked into the bricks. The sulphate it contains will then be fixed in combined form and will be available to form efflorescence. The characteristic form in which this type of efflorescence appears is as a ring all round the edges of the bricks. Normally, however, the mortar makes only a minor contribution to efflorescence.

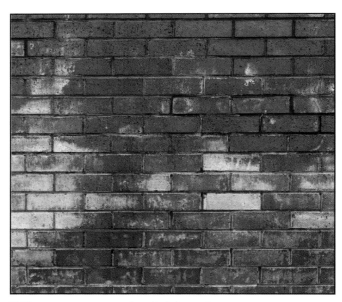

Efflorescence on clay brickwork.

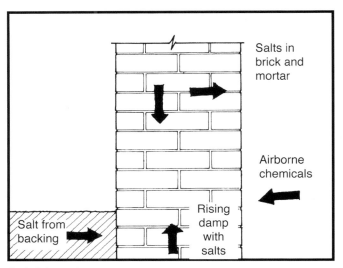

Soluble salt movement.

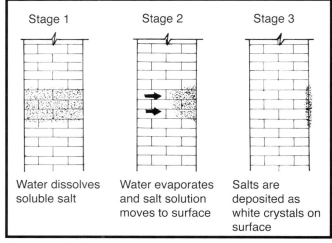

Stages of efflorescence.

WHEN DOES EFFLORESCENCE OCCUR?

Efflorescence is generally a temporary springtime occurrence which appears as new brickwork dries out for the first time. It is sometimes renewed in the second spring of a building's life, but this is usually less marked than the first outbreak.

PRECAUTIONS TO AVOID EFFLORESCENCE

Several precautions can be taken to avoid efflorescence. The main requirement is to avoid moisture getting into the brickwork during the building stages.

◆ Store the bricks in their weather-proof covering in a sheltered area

◆ When bales of bricks are opened and are not completely used up, cover the loose bricks with a damp-proof material

◆ If the bricks become damp, allow them to dry out before use

◆ Protect uncompleted brickwork at night and during rain. One way to do this is to turn back the scaffolding boards against the brickwork to protect the brickface and cover the top of the wall with a damp-proof material

◆ Avoid saturating the brickwork for cleaning purposes

◆ Ensure that all points of the building which are likely to be exposed to continuous saturation are protected by adequate damp proof courses.

If these precautions are followed, and the correct type of brick for the particular climatic conditions is chosen, the possibility of efflorescence is minimised.

REMOVAL OF EFFLORESCENCE

Efflorescence should be allowed to weather away naturally, but it may be removed by brushing with a stiff bristle brush. The deposit should be collected and removed so that it does not enter the masonry at lower levels. Any deposit remaining may be removed or reduced by treatment with clean cold water. Since the deposit is water-soluble, washing down may result in the solution being partially re-absorbed. This may be minimised by using a clean damp sponge, which should be rinsed frequently in clean water. Recurrent efflorescence on older established brickwork may almost always be taken as an indication that considerable quantities of water are entering the masonry as a result of failure of weathering and other protective measures, faulty spouts and gutters and the like.

Chemical methods should never be used for the removal of efflorescence.

Note: IS 51"Clay Building Bricks" 1983 outlines a test for determining amounts of efflorescence, and clarification can be sought from the manufacturer of the possibility of the amount of efflorescence as determined from that test.

This standard also defines the permissible amount of soluble salt content allowed and the manufacturer should be able to confirm that bricks supplied are in accordance with the limits set down.

SULPHATE ATTACK

Incidents of sulphate attack are rare in Ireland. It is caused by a reaction of chemicals in the bricks with chemicals in the mortar solution. The tricalcium aluminate in ordinary Portland cements reacts with the brick sulphate and causes expansion. The source of sulphate is usually the soluble salts present in varying extents in clay bricks, but may also be derived from ground water and from flue gases.

As stated earlier incidents of sulphate attack are rare and are only serious when the design of the building allows continuous saturation of the brickwork. The reaction is firstly an overall expansion of the brickwork, followed, in more extreme cases, by a progressive disintegration of the mortar joints.

The three causes of sulphate attack are tricalcium aluminate in Portland cement, soluble sulphate and water. The possibility of attack should be considered at the design stage of the building and combination of mortars and brick types susceptible to sulphate erosion should be avoided.

Tricalcium aluminate is present in all ordinary Portland cements in amounts from eight to thirteen percent. There is no easy way to estimate the susceptibility of different brand-name cements, so it must be assumed that all ordinary Portland cements are capable of being eroded.

There are a number of ways to safeguard against attack:

◆ Specify richer mortar mixes, for example, I :$^1/_4$:3 or 1:$^1/_2$:4$^1/_2$ or (better still) 1:5-6 with plasticiser in place of lime

◆ Use sulphate-resisting Portland cement

◆ Use bricks with low water absorption percentage

◆ Use bricks with low soluble salt content.

Most types of clay bricks contain soluble sulphates; the amounts vary between different types of bricks. Special quality bricks have limitations on their sulphate content but ordinary bricks have no such limitations. It therefore must be assumed that the use of ordinary bricks will contribute to sulphate attack.

Repeated wetting and drying out of brickwork over a period of years is closely related to sulphate attack. The susceptibility also depends on the exposure to wet weather. Exposed brickwork such as parapets and free-standing walls are most likely to be affected and consideration for this should be made in the building design.

FROST ATTACK ON BRICKWORK

In Ireland frost damage is rare in normal external walls. Trouble can occur, however, in walls exposed to both frost and rain. Frost attack occurs only when brickwork is saturated as well as frozen. So brickwork is more vulnerable in parapets, freestanding and retaining walls where exposure conditions cause continual saturation.

Precautions against frost attack should be taken when choosing the quality of the bricks and mortars.

In extremely exposed conditions, it may be necessary to use special quality bricks which have high compressive strengths and a low water absorption rate. Engineering bricks fulfil these requirements and have known water absorption rates. There is no standard for water absorption rates for ordinary bricks; these can be found only by approaching each manufacturer and asking for results of tests carried out on their bricks.

Choosing a special quality brick could impose limitations on the range of brick colours and textures and this effect should be considered in the choice of materials for all other parts of the building. Despite intensive research over many years, there is no accepted test for frost resistance. The only requirement that the brick manufacturer must satisfy is evidence that bricks of the type required have given satisfactory results for at least three years in the locality concerned, in conditions at least as severe as those proposed. When a suitable brick has been found, one precaution would be to examine all the buildings using this brick in the same weather conditions. Frost attack is likely to affect a building within the first three years, so buildings older than this using the same type of brick would be a good reference.

In particular if bricks which have not been previously used are proposed, or, if the area has a high incidence of freezing and driving rain, it would be advisable to obtain confirmation from the manufacturer that the bricks are suitable for use in that location.

Frost attack on brickwork.

SITE SAFETY

INTRODUCTION

Building work is potentially dangerous. The danger can, however, be minimised by good site management and compliance with the construction regulations.

The Safety Health and Welfare at Work (Construction) Regulations, 1995 address the major causes of serious accidents and provides prescriptions on how to prevent accidents when working at a height, making excavations, using lifting equipment etc.

The construction regulations require all projects to be planned and co-ordinated so that accidents are prevented. For most projects, the client is obliged to appoint a competent project supervisor for both the design stage and the construction stage. The project supervisor must ensure that the project is designed, planned and constructed safely.

Many projects require a safety and health plan and a safety file to be prepared by the project supervisor.

For further information see the guidelines on the Safety Health and Welfare at Work (Construction) Regulations, 1995, available from the Health and Safety Authority at 10 Hogan Place, Dublin 2. Telephone: (01) 614 7000, price £8.

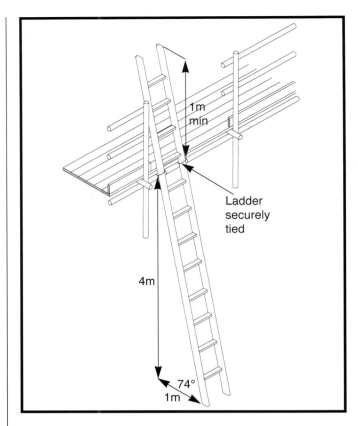

Securing a ladder.

LETHAL LADDERS

Incorrect use of ladders kills a lot of people. Make sure the ladder is:

◆ Right for the job. Would scaffolding or a telescopic platform be better?

◆ In good shape

◆ Secured near the top

◆ On a firm base and footing

◆ Rising at least 1 metre beyond the landing place or that there is a proper hand hold.

Always have a firm grip on the ladder and keep a good balance.

NEVER

◆ Use a makeshift ladder

◆ Lean sideways from a ladder.

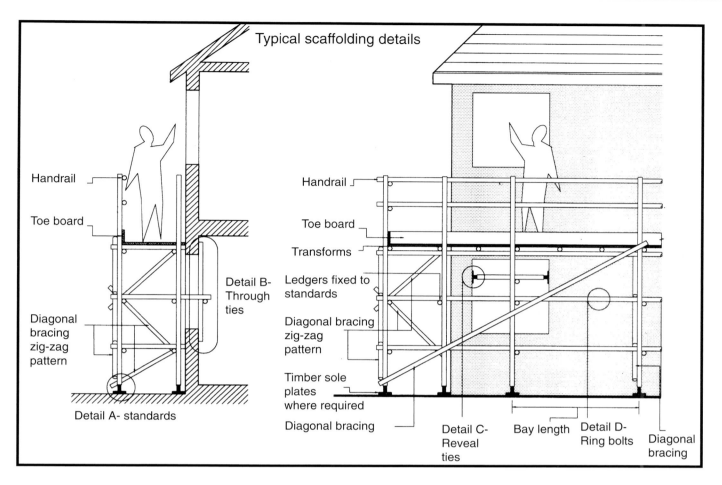

Typical scaffolding details

Handrail

Toe board

Detail B- Through ties

Diagonal bracing zig-zag pattern

Detail A- standards

Handrail

Toe board

Transforms

Ledgers fixed to standards

Diagonal bracing zig-zag pattern

Timber sole plates where required

Diagonal bracing

Detail C- Reveal ties

Bay length

Detail D- Ring bolts

Diagonal bracing

GENERAL ACCESS SCAFFOLDS

Introduction
Scaffolding is used throughout the whole construction industry mainly as a safe platform for working at heights. Its effective use is, however, often reduced due to instability or overloading leading to collapse, or falls of persons or materials due to inadequate guard rails or missing or loose boards. This appendix provides a general overview of the use of scaffolding. References should be made to the Code of Practice for Access and Working Scaffolds, produced by the Health & Safety Authority.

Stability
The stability of a scaffold will be affected by how it is used. Prior to erection, a competent person should assess the likely uses of the scaffold to ensure that the right design of scaffold is erected for the intended work.

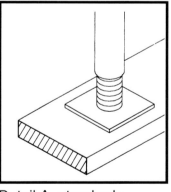

Detail A- standards.

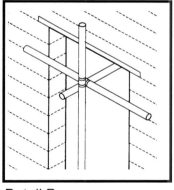

Detail B- Through ties.

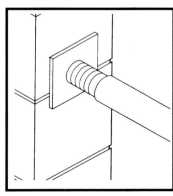

Detail C- Reveal ties.

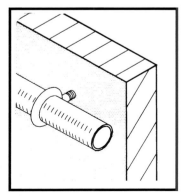

Detail D- Ring bolts.

GENERAL ACCESS SCAFFOLDS

Stability continued

Stability is normally achieved for most scaffolds by tying them to the structure they are serving. The commonly used, independent, unsheeted scaffold may require at least one tie for every standard (vertical member), staggered every second lift. Extra ties may be required where the scaffold is:

◆ Sheeted or netted leading to increased wind loading

◆ Used as a loading platform for equipment or materials

◆ To include attachments such as chutes, hoists, lifting appliances etc.

System or proprietary scaffolding should be tied and erected in accordance with the manufacturer's hand book.

The main types of ties are:

◆ Through tie secured through a window or other opening and bearing against a solid face, (see detail B on the previous page)

◆ Box tie (locking ties) around a column

◆ Reveal tie using a scaffold tube jacked tight into opposing faces of a window opening, (see detail C on the previous page). No more than 50% of the ties can be reveal ties

◆ Drilled in anchor or cast in anchor tie (ring bolt fixing to the structure). This type is not suitable for all materials and the manufacturer's instructions should be complied with, (see detail D on the previous page).

Provide substitute ties, before removing any existing ties so as to maintain the stability of the scaffold.

Rakers or raking struts can be used but they must be adequately braced back to the scaffold to be effective.

All scaffolding requires bracing to prevent collapse. This involves the fixing of diagonal tubes for strength, (see typical scaffold details on previous page).

The uprights (standards) must always rest on steel base plates. The ground should be well compacted and levelled and timber sole plates used to spread the load. Bricks/blocks and loose materials are not suitable for bases.

Guard rails and toe boards

Scaffold platforms from which a person could fall more than 2 m must have guard rails and toe boards fitted. Brick guards, netting or other suitable protection must be fitted where materials may fall from the scaffold.

Loading platforms

Full pallets of bricks or blocks must only be placed on purpose built loading platforms.

GENERAL ACCESS SCAFFOLDS

Working platform
Working platforms should be wide enough and be sufficiently boarded out to allow safe passage of persons along the platform. They should also be capable of resisting the loads imposed upon them.

Where a person is liable to fall more than two metres, the width of the platform should be taken from table 2 of the Code of Practice for Access and Working Scaffolds.

Max. span of scaffold boards

Nominal board thickness (mm)	Max. span between transoms (m)
38	1.50
50	2.60
63	3.25

Overloading
Never overload a scaffold as the consequences can be fatal. The initial assessment of the scaffold design should anticipate the loading in use. Materials loaded on scaffolds should always be distributed to spread the load.

Training
Effective training must be given to scaffolders, supervisors and those using scaffolds. Training is an important control factor in accident prevention. Training in scaffold erection is available from FÁS. Contact local branches for details.

Site access
Ladders used for access must be safe by design, inspected before use and safely erected and secured. Access to unattended scaffolds should be prevented by removing ladders or by providing hoarding around the base of the scaffold.

Inspection of scaffolding
The Safety, Health and Welfare at Work (Construction) Regulations require scaffolds to be inspected by a competent person, before use and at least once a week, or following modification or adverse conditions, to ensure that it remains safe for use e.g.; ties in place, tubes not bent, damaged or undermined, platforms fully boarded, guard rails and toe boards in place and secure, etc.

The inspections must be carried out by a competent person and the results recorded in Register Form CR8 available from H.S.A. A contractor using scaffolding belonging to someone else must examine it for safety before use.

Erection and dismantling of scaffolds
Scaffolds must only be erected or dismantled by competent and trained persons. When dismantling scaffolds, ensure that sufficient ties are in place and do not remove ties until the scaffold is down to that level.

Protecting the public
Do not throw waste materials or scaffolding materials to the ground. Use hoists, lifting appliances, or where appropriate, chutes.

Reference Legislation
Safety, Health and Welfare at Work (Construction) Regulations 1995, SI no.138. See also Guide to the Regulations, available from The National Irish Safety Organisation (NISO).

Further information
National Irish Safety Organisation
10 Hogan Place, Dublin 2. Tel: (01) 662 0399.
Health and Safety Authority
10 Hogan Place, Dublin 2. Tel: (01) 662 0400.
Construction Industry Federation:
Construction House, Canal Road, Dublin 6.
Tel: (01) 497 7487.

Typical general access scaffolds

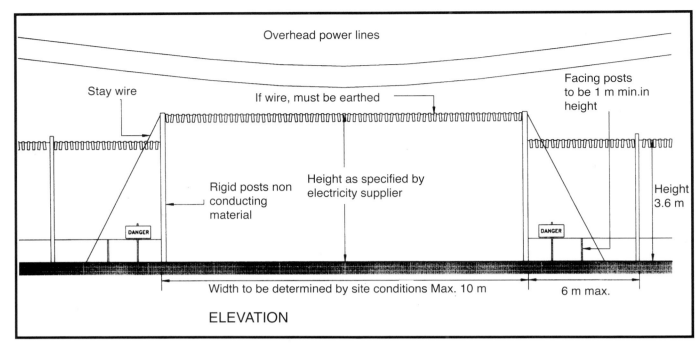

Overhead power lines

Stay wire

If wire, must be earthed

Facing posts to be 1 m min.in height

Rigid posts non conducting material

Height as specified by electricity supplier

DANGER

DANGER

Height 3.6 m

Width to be determined by site conditions Max. 10 m

6 m max.

ELEVATION

A typical layout to prevent contact with overhead power lines. Details of the layout should be discussed with the line owner.

OVERHEAD POWER LINES

Introduction
Overhead power lines must always be regarded as a significant risk especially where plant and vehicles are operating on or adjacent to them. The Safety Health and Welfare at Work (Construction) regulations 1995 require pre-planning and risk assessment of any situation where the risk of contact with overhead lines exists. The details of safety procedures must be included in the Safety and Health Plan and the procedures monitored for effectiveness on an ongoing basis. The key to safety with overhead lines is pre-planning and consultation with the ESB as the hazard can often be eliminated by diverting the lines to a safer location or by the use of access routes to and around the site located away from the danger zones.

Working adjacent to power lines
In situations where no work has to be carried out or where plant need not pass under overhead lines, barriers should be erected parallel to the overhead lines and not less than 6 m distance from them. The distance selected should be subject to consultation with the ESB as the voltage of the lines may determine the distance to be achieved. The barriers should be surmounted by coloured bunting which will act as a further warning. In some situations where access is only possible from one side, then a barrier on that side only may be acceptable.

Plant passing under power lines
Where plant must pass under overhead power lines the access width should be restricted to the minimum possible and should not exceed 10 m.

The access area should be clearly defined by the use of barriers, and goal posts should be erected across the full width of the access route. The goal posts should be of rigid construction and of non conducting material and should be clearly marked to ensure immediate identification.

Notices highlighting the nature of the hazard and indicating the cross bar height should be erected, at the entrance to and along the access route, to warn drivers to lower any jib or load.

OVERHEAD POWER LINES

Plant working beneath overhead lines

If it is necessary to operate plant beneath overhead lines, the ESB should be notified to ensure that the lines are made dead or other precautions taken. Where it is not possible to disconnect the supply, the ESB should be consulted as to the most effective safe system of work to be adopted, including the use of goal posts and other restrictive methods, or by using plant which cannot come into contact with the lines. Under no circumstances should plant be operated beneath overhead lines without first consulting the ESB. The use of insulating guards on jibs, excavators or proximity warning devices are not sufficient or acceptable as safety procedures. The ground level at base of poles or pylons for a distance of 3 m must never be disturbed without the consent of the ESB.

Erection of structures near power lines

Care should always be exercised when erecting scaffolding, elevated platforms, ladders etc. adjacent to power lines. As in the case of plant, the ESB should always be consulted prior to work commencing and where possible the supply disconnected or diverted to a safer location.

Supervision/training

All work adjacent to or beneath overhead lines should be subject to strict supervision by a competent person and adequate training given to all employees and sub contractors likely to be at risk. Training should include the identification of hazards and risk control procedures.

Reference legislation: Safety, Health and Welfare at Work (Construction) Regulations 1995.

Reference material ESB poster; "The avoidance of electrical hazards when working near overhead lines". This poster is available from the ESB.

Further information:

National Irish Safety Organisation,
10 Hogan Place, Dublin 2. Tel: (01) 662 0399.

Construction Industry Federation,
Construction House, Canal Road, Dublin 6.
Tel: (01) 497 7487.

Electricity Supply Board, Head Office, 27 Lower Fitzwilliam Street, Dublin 2. Tel: (01) 702 6759.

SAFETY IN EXCAVATIONS

Serious accidents in trenching and excavations result mainly from collapse of the sides, leading to crushing falls of persons into excavations, contact with buried services or falls of materials on persons working in excavations. Even the most experienced workers can be caught out by the sudden collapse of an excavation, so in all but the most shallow of excavations, (less than 1.25 m deep, subject to ground conditions), planning should include the provision of supports for the sides. Excavations should be risk-assessed prior to work commencing. Detailed controls must be included in a Safety and Health Plan and supervised by a competent person.

Planning

All excavation work must be planned before digging begins on site. A competent person should ensure that sufficient props, walings, or other suitable materials are available to support the length of the excavation to be exposed. An additional supply of materials should be kept to hand for unforeseen events, e.g. poor ground conditions. The trench supports should be installed without delay as the excavation progresses. Before digging, make sure that the location of underground pipes and services is first established.

NEVER WORK AHEAD OF SUPPORT.

Supervision

All excavation work should be supervised by a competent person and all operatives trained and instructed in safe working procedures. All excavations deeper than 1.25 m must be shored or sloped back to a safe angle.

Inspecting excavations

Excavations should be inspected by a competent person at least once a day, when persons are working in it, and thoroughly examined by a competent person (including the support system) at least once a week. Records should be kept on the approved form available from the Government Publications Sales office, Sun Alliance House, Molesworth Street, Dublin 2. Tel: (01) 661 3111.

Other causes of accidents

- Workers may be injured as a result of being struck by falling materials, rocks, etc. Loose materials should be stored away from the excavation and a scaffold board wedged along the side of the excavation. Safety helmets must be worn by all persons engaged on excavation work

- Workers or members of the public may fall into the open excavations. Suitable barriers should be erected and secured into the ground. Barriers should be high enough and sufficiently robust to prevent falls

- Unsafe access and egress can also lead to falls. Ladders or other suitable access methods should be employed and secured to prevent sliding or slippage

- There is a danger that construction vehicles may be driven into excavations or cause the sides to collapse. Adequate stops or blocks should be employed to prevent vehicles approaching the sides of the excavation

- Asphyxiation or poisoning may result from exposure to combustion gases from plant or naturally decaying matter. Explosive concentrations of naturally occurring gases may also build up in excavations. Safety controls should include provisions and procedures for entry into confined spaces.

Further information:

National Irish Safety Organisation,
10 Hogan Place, Dublin 2.
Tel: (01) 662 0399

Health and Safety Authority,
10 Hogan Place, Dublin 2.
Tel: (01) 662 0400

Construction Industry Federation,
Construction House, Canal Road, Dublin 6.
Tel: (01) 497 7487

THE ROOF: A RISKY PLACE TO BE

One in five deaths on sites arise from roof work. Many of these accidents happen in the course of routine maintainence. Almost all of them could be prevented. Very simply:

◆ Always inspect a roof before walking on it

◆ Use proper roofing ladders/crawling boards for access to sloping or fragile roofs

◆ Where work is being carried out, provide a barrier or scaffold platform along the edge side of the roof

◆ If there are others working underneath the roof, make sure debris cannot fall on them.

GENERAL

◆ One of the most dangerous places in a building under construction is around the stairwell and lift shafts in apartments. Make sure that the area is well protected, and that temporary guard rails and balustrades are in place to prevent people falling down

◆ Don't carry passengers in a vehicle that is not designed for passengers

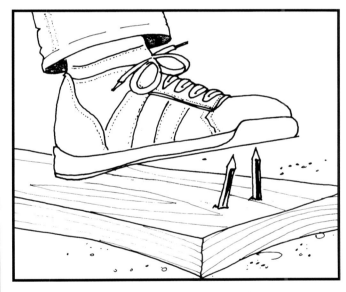

◆ Always ensure nails are removed or hammered down

◆ Safety helmets must be worn on all construction sites

◆ Hard-toed footwear with protective soles must be worn

◆ Goggles, ear defenders and gloves may be necessary.

ELECTRICITY, A KILLER WHEN MISUSED ON SITE

Electrical accidents, many of which are fatal, are often caused by contact with:

◆ Underground or overhead power lines

◆ Unsuitable or badly maintained equipment

◆ Bad connections to the supply.

Here's how to handle electricity on site:

◆ Have power lines re-routed or turned off where possible

◆ Treat electricity with respect

◆ Check constantly that cables are not damaged or worn

◆ Keep trailing cables off ground and away from water

◆ Never overload or use makeshift plugs and fuses

◆ For mains voltage, screened cables must be used and circuits must be protected by proper circuit breakers.

PORTABLE POWER TOOLS = PORTABLE POWER DANGER:

◆ Always use the right tool for the job, and don't make do with a defective tool

◆ Check all tools before use (ensure they are properly earthed)

◆ Don't adjust power tools unless the supply is disconnected

◆ Always be careful with angle grinders and power saws, and check that suitable guards are fitted and used

◆ They must operate at a reduced voltage (110V).

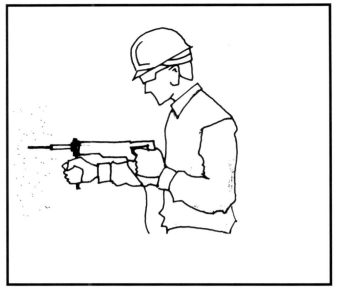

Cartridge operated tools:

◆ Always follow maker's instructions

◆ Keep in secure place when not in use

◆ You should be trained to use the tools

◆ If working on hard material wear goggles. Do not be blind to the risk.

LIFTING BY HAND CAN DAMAGE YOUR BACK

Lifting weights that are too heavy for you, or just lifting weights the wrong way, will do your back permanent damage. You may feel the damage straight away or, more likely the back pain will show up over time. It's very easy to avoid this back damage. It just takes commonsense.

◆ Workers should not be required to carry loads in excess of 25 kg

◆ Get a good grip, keep the load close to your body

◆ Keep the back straight

◆ Bend your knees, lift with your leg muscles, not your back

◆ If it's too heavy, get help

◆ Start lifting sensibly, if you don't want to end up permanently disabled with a bad back before you're 30

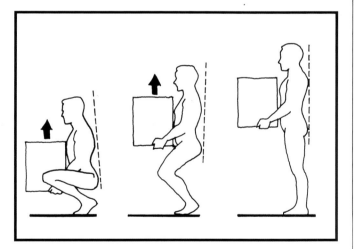

◆ Use mechanical aids such as pallet trucks, hand carts, cranes/lifting gear etc. to reduce manual lifting to a minimum.

ADDITIONAL INFORMATION.

Advice on all aspects of site safety is available from:

Health and Safety Authority (HSA) and National Irish Safety Organisation (NISO),
10 Hogan Place,
Grand Canal St.,
Dublin 2.
Tel: (01) 662 0400, 662 0399.

The detailed legal requirements in respect of site safety are set out in the:

◆ Safety Health and Welfare at Work Construction Regulations 1975

◆ Safety Health and Welfare at Work Act, no. 7, 1989

◆ Safety Health and Welfare at Work (General Application) Regulations 1993 (SI 44 of 1993).

Each of the above is available from:
Government publications,
Sales Office,
Sun Alliance House,
Molesworth St.,
Dublin 2.
Tel: 01 661 3111.

NOTE: For any aspects of site safety or safety in the work place not covered by the above publications additional information can be obtained from Health and Safety Authority.

SOUND

INTRODUCTION

Sound is a form of energy which can be transmitted from its source through a medium such as air or a solid element of construction e.g. a wall or a floor. The types of sound to be considered are airborne and impact sounds. In each case, the sound can be transmitted directly or indirectly, see sketch below.

The principal methods of isolating the receiver from the source are:

♦ Eliminating pathways along which sound can travel, and

♦ Using barriers formed of materials of sufficiently high mass which will not easily vibrate.

In practice sound insulation is usually achieved by using a combination of both methods.

Note:

♦ There are no sound requirements for detached houses

♦ Sound requirements for semi-detached and terraced houses relate mainly to the party wall

♦ There are no sound requirements for floors in single family dwelling houses

♦ The information in this Appendix is for single family dwelling houses, and reference should be made to Technical Guidance Document E of the Building Regulations for sound insulation provisions for flats and apartments, including the provision of resilient layers in floors .

Transmission of sound

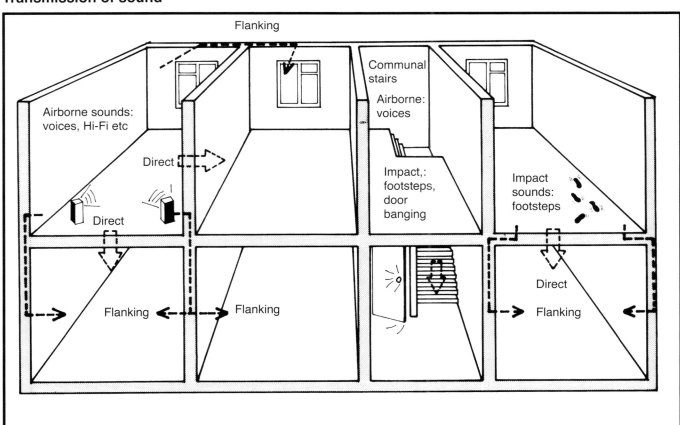

TRANSMISSION OF SOUND

As can be seen from the sketch on the previous page, there are two sources of sound energy:

◆ Airborne sources: voices, hi-fi, tv's etc.,

◆ Impact sources: footsteps, doors banging, etc.

Both these types of sound can be transmitted directly or indirectly.

Direct transmission of sound

Direct transmission means the transmission of sound directly through a wall or floor from one of its sides to the other.

Walls should reduce the level of airborne sound. A solid masonry wall depends on its mass; being heavy, it is not easily set into vibration. Walls with two or three leaves depend partly on their mass and partly on structural isolation between the leaves.

With masonry walls the mass is the main factor but stiffness and damping are also important. Cavity masonry walls need at least as much mass as solid walls because their lower degree of stiffness offsets the benefit of isolation.

Air-paths must be avoided. Therefore, porous materials and gaps at joints in the structure must be sealed. Joints in blockwork in party walls should be filled with mortar. It is preferable that party walls should also have a wet plaster finish to eliminate air-paths from sound transmission through the wall. Resonances must also be avoided; these may occur if some part of the structure (such as a dry lining) vibrates strongly at a particular sound frequency (pitch) and transmits more energy at this pitch.

Flanking transmission of sound

Flanking transmission means the indirect transmission of sound from one side of a wall or floor to the other side.

Because a solid element may vibrate when exposed to sound waves in the air, it may cause sound waves in the air on both sides. Flanking transmission happens when there is a path along which sound can travel between elements on opposite sides of a wall or floor. This path may be through a continuous solid structure or through an air space (such as the cavity of an external wall). Usually paths through structures are more important with solid masonry elements, whereas paths through an air space are more important with thin panels (such as studwork and ceilings) in which sound waves do not travel as freely.

WALLS AND FLOORS

The location of walls and floors which are required by regulations to have good sound insulation.

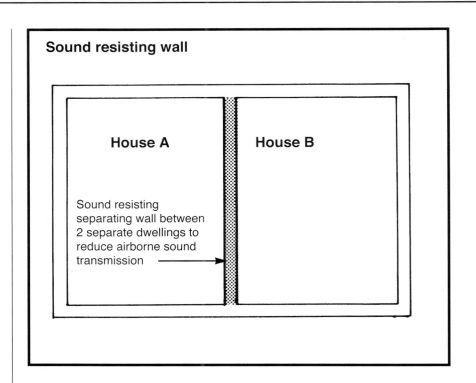

Sound resisting wall

House A

House B

Sound resisting separating wall between 2 separate dwellings to reduce airborne sound transmission →

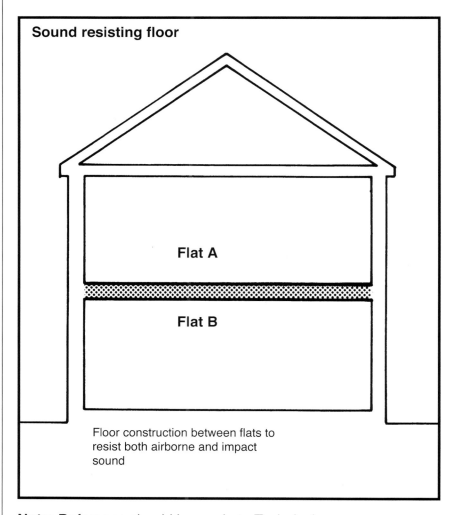

Sound resisting floor

Flat A

Flat B

Floor construction between flats to resist both airborne and impact sound

Note: Reference should be made to Technical Guidance Document E of the Building Regulations for the detailed sound requirements for flats and apartments.

TYPES OF WALL

One of the methods of reducing sound transmission is to use materials in the wall of sufficiently high mass that they will not vibrate easily. The four more widely used wall constructions are:

1) Solid masonry party wall

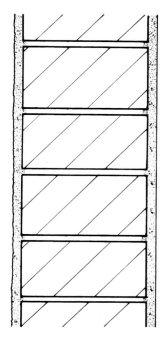

Concrete blockwork or concrete brickwork plastered on both faces

The average mass of the wall (including the plaster) should be at least 415 kg/m². The thickness of the plaster should be at least 12.5 mm on each face. Use blocks which extend to the full thickness of the wall, i.e. blocks laid on their flat.

Example:
215 mm concrete block, 112.5 mm coursing, 12.5 lightweight plaster on each face, block density 1860 kg/m³ gives the required mass.

Points to watch
Fill the joints between the bricks or blocks with mortar, and seal the joints between the wall and the other parts of the construction (to achieve the mass and to avoid air paths).

Workmanship and detailing should be given special attention to limit the pathways between the walls and opposite sides of the sound resisting wall (to reduce flanking transmission).

2) Cavity masonry party wall

Two leaves of concrete blockwork or concrete brickwork plastered on both faces

The width of the cavity should be at least 50 mm. The average mass of the wall (including the plaster) should be at least 415 kg/m². The thickness of the plaster should be at least 12.5 mm on each face.

Example:
102 mm leaves, 225 mm coursing, lightweight plaster; block density of 1965 kg/m³ gives the required mass.

Points to watch
Fill the joints between the bricks or blocks with mortar, and seal the joints between the wall and the other parts of the construction (to achieve the mass and to avoid air paths).

Maintain the separation of the leaves and space them at least 50 mm apart. Connect the leaves with butterfly pattern wall ties.

If a cavity in an external wall is completely filled with an insulating material other than loose fibre, care should be taken that the insulating material does not enter the cavity in the separating wall.

3) SOLID MASONRY PARTY WALL WITH DRY—LINING

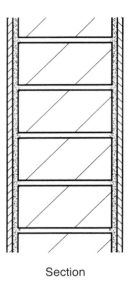

Section

Concrete blockwork or concrete brickwork, plastered on both faces, with plasterboard dry-lining attached to plaster on both faces.

The average mass (including plaster and plasterboard) should be at least 415 kg/m². 12.5 mm plasterboard dry- lining attached directly to plaster (**no cavity or air gaps)**. Use blocks that extend to the full thickness of the wall.

Example
215 mm blockwork, 112.5 mm coursing, lightweight plaster, block density 1860 kg/m³ gives the required mass.

Another acceptable option is the block wall described above, plastered on both sides with gypsum perlite plaster (or similar) not greater than 750 kg/m³, with 12.5 mm plasterboard dry-lining fixed to battens.

Points to watch
Fill the joints between the blocks with mortar and seal the joints between the wall and other parts of the construction, in order to achieve the required mass and avoid air paths. Plasterboard joints should be sealed. Workmanship and detailing should be given special attention, to limit the pathways across which sound can travel.

4) TIMBER FRAME PARTY WALL

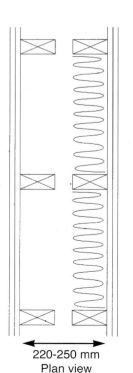

220-250 mm
Plan view

The resistance to airborne sound depends on the isolation of the frames plus absorption in the air space between.

Proprietary forms of construction **underwritten by recognised testing houses,** which include details of frame construction and connections, absorbent materials and linings to satisfy fire resistance, would be suitable methods of achieving the requirement of "reasonable resistance to airborne sound".

A typical example of such a party wall should incorporate plasterboard in two layers with joints staggered, of a minimum thickness of 30 mm, on both faces. The combined width of both faces should not be less than 220 mm, but a greater width of 250 mm will improve sound insulation. 100 mm quilt insulation, 12 kg/m³ min. density, should be fixed between the studs of one leaf.

See Appendix B for timber frame party wall construction details.

KEY JUNCTIONS IN THE CONSTRUCTION

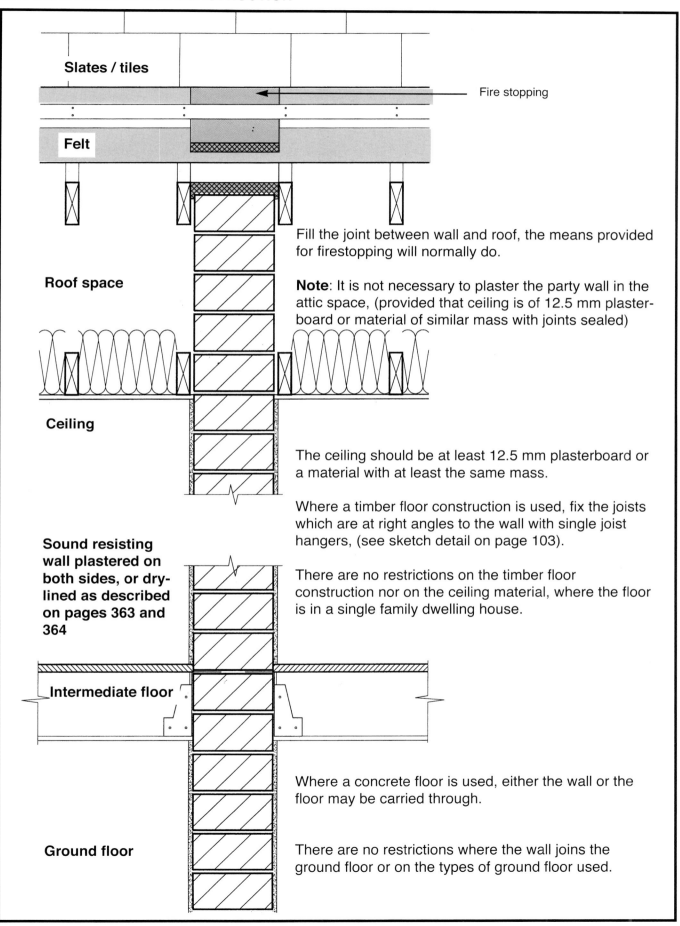

Slates / tiles

Fire stopping

Felt

Roof space

Fill the joint between wall and roof, the means provided for firestopping will normally do.

Note: It is not necessary to plaster the party wall in the attic space, (provided that ceiling is of 12.5 mm plasterboard or material of similar mass with joints sealed)

Ceiling

The ceiling should be at least 12.5 mm plasterboard or a material with at least the same mass.

Where a timber floor construction is used, fix the joists which are at right angles to the wall with single joist hangers, (see sketch detail on page 103).

Sound resisting wall plastered on both sides, or dry-lined as described on pages 363 and 364

There are no restrictions on the timber floor construction nor on the ceiling material, where the floor is in a single family dwelling house.

Intermediate floor

Where a concrete floor is used, either the wall or the floor may be carried through.

Ground floor

There are no restrictions where the wall joins the ground floor or on the types of ground floor used.

KEY JUNCTIONS IN THE CONSTRUCTION
continued

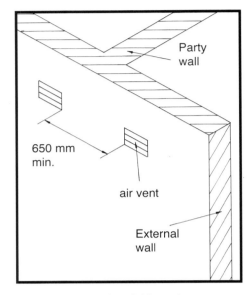

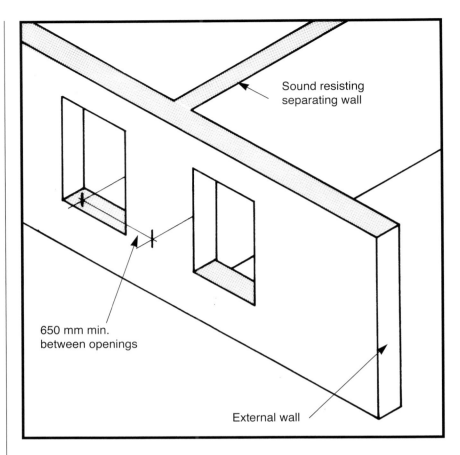

Special care should be given to the positioning of air vents in an external wall on either side of the party wall, to ensure a minimum of 650 mm between vents, unless the external wall is a cavity wall with the cavity closed vertically on the party wall line.

There must be at least 650 mm between openings in the external wall on either side of the party wall, unless the external wall is a cavity wall with the cavity closed vertically on the party wall line.

Where the external wall is of cavity construction, there are no restrictions on the masonry outer leaf.

The masonry external wall (either a solid wall or the inner leaf of a cavity wall) should be either bonded to the sound resisting wall or butted to it and secured with wall ties (or similar) spaced no more than 300 mm apart vertically.

DRAINAGE

INTRODUCTION

The following section deals with drainage above and below ground and all the information contained is in accordance with Technical Guidance Document H of the Building Regulations.

DEFINITIONS.

Surface water: Run-off of rainwater from roofs and any paved surface around the building.

Soil water: Water containing excreted material i.e. from W.C. pans.

Waste water: Used water from waste appliances i.e. sink, baths, showers, WHB's. Used water from washing machines and dishwashers is waste water.

Foul water: Any water contaminated by soil water or waste water.

Traps

All points of discharge into the drainage system should be fitted with a water seal (trap) to prevent foul air from the system entering the building. Any trap not part of a removable appliance should be removable, or fitted with a cleaning eye.

Table 1 gives minimum trap sizes and seal depths for the most commonly used appliances.

Ventilation—To prevent the water seal from being broken by the pressures which can develop in the system the branch discharge pipes should be designed as described on page 369.

Access for clearing blockages— If a trap forms part of an appliance, as in a W.C. pan, the appliance should be removable. All other traps should be fitted to the appliance and should be removable or be fitted with a cleaning eye.

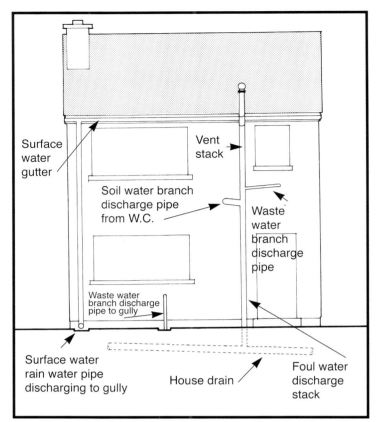

Typical domestic drainage: definitions.

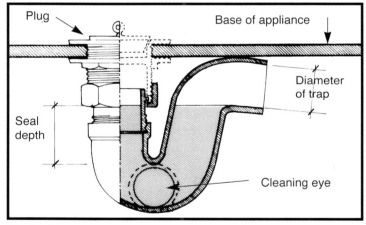

Typical trap.

Table 1 Minimum trap sizes and seal depths.		
Appliances	Diameter of trap (mm)	Depth of seal (mm)
Washbasin, Bidet	32	75
Sink*, Bath*, Shower*. Food waste disposal unit, Urinal bowl	40	75
W.C. pan	100	50
*Where these appliances are installed on a ground floor and discharge to a gully, the depth of seal may be reduced to not less than 40 mm.		

MATERIALS FOR PIPES, FITTINGS AND JOINTS

Any of the materials shown in the table opposite may be used. Pipes should be firmly supported without restricting thermal movement. Reference should be made where necessary to the requirements of Part B of the second schedule to the Building Regulations, 1997 and Guidance in Technical Guidance Document B relating to penetration of fire stopping elements and of fire stopping provisions.

Airtightness

The pipes, fittings and joints must be capable of withstanding an air or smoke test of positive pressure of at least 38 mm water gauge for at least 3 minutes. During this time every trap should maintain a water seal of at least 25 mm. Smoke testing is not recommended for uPVC pipes.

Materials for sanitary pipe work	
Pipe material	Irish/British standard
uPVC	BS 4514
Polypropylene	BS 5254
Plastics	BS 5556, BS5255
ABS, MUPVC Polyethylene	IS 134, IS 135
Trap material	
Plastics	BS 3943

FOUL WATER DRAINAGE PIPEWORK UNDERGROUND

Layout

1. The layout of the drainage system should be as simple as possible.

2. Changes in direction and gradient should be minimised and as easy as practicable.

3. Access points should be provided only if blockages cannot be cleared without them.

4. Connections of drains to other drains or to sewers should be made obliquely, and in the direction of flow. They should be formed using a standard saddle connection.

5. The drainage system should be ventilated by a flow of air. A ventilated pipe should be provided at or near the head of each main drain, and to any branch longer than six metres and on a drain fitted with an intercepting trap. Ventilated discharge pipes can be used, see page 371.

6. Pipes should be laid to even gradients, and any change of gradient should be combined with an access point.

7. Pipes should normally be laid in straight lines.

8. Pipes may be laid to a slight curve providing the curve can be cleared of blockages. The curve should be located as follows:

    a) Close to inspection chambers or manholes,
    b) At the foot of discharge and ventilating stacks.

    Any curves should have as large a radius as possible.

9. Where drains run under or near buildings, on piles or beams, in common trenches or in unstable ground, special precautions should be taken to accommodate the effects of settlement.

MATERIALS FOR UNDERGROUND PIPES AND JOINTING

Any of the materials shown in the table below.

1. Joints in the pipe should be appropriate to the material of the pipes.

2. To minimise the effects of any differential settlement, pipes should have flexible joints.

3. All joints should remain watertight under working and test conditions.

4. Nothing in the pipes, joints or fittings should project into the pipeline or cause an obstruction.

Any of the materials shown in the table below may be used.

Materials for below ground gravity drainage.	
Material	**Irish/British standard**
Rigid pipes	
Fibre cement	IS/EN 588-1
Vitrified clay	IS/EN 295, BS 65
Concrete	IS 6, BS 5911, and for surface water drainage only IS 666
Flexible pipes	
uPVC	IS 424, BS 5481, BS 5556 BS 4660

CLEARANCE OF BLOCKAGES

A sufficient number of suitable access points should be provided for clearing blockages in the drainage system which cannot be reached by any other means. The location, spacing and type of access point will depend on the layout, depth and size of the drainage runs.

The following requirements are for normal methods of rodding, (which need not necessarily be in the direction of the flow), but are not for mechanical means of clearing.

1. Access points should be one of four types:

a) Rodding eyes–capped extensions of the pipes. Provide rodding access to any pipe inaccessible from trap.

b) Access fittings–small chambers on (or an extension of) the pipes but not with an open channel.

c) Inspection chambers–shallow chambers e.g., an armstrong-junction, with working space at ground level.

d) Manholes–large chambers with working space at drain level.

The table opposite shows the depth at which each type of access fitting may be used and the recommended dimensions they should have.

2. Siting of access points– Access points should be provided at all the following locations:

a) On or near the head of each drain run;

b) At a bend and at a change of gradient;

c) At a change of pipe size, and

d) At a junction unless each run can be cleared from an access point.

Minimum dimensions for access fittings and chambers		
Type of access point	**Depth to invert (metres)**	**Internal size length x width (mm)**
Access fittings (e.g. small chambers) Small Large	0.6 or less	150 x 100 300 x 100
A.J.	0.6 or less	300 x 300
Inspection chamber	1.0 or less	450 x 450
Manhole	2.7 or less. Over 2.7	1200 x 750 1200 x 840
Shaft	Over 2.7	900 x 840

Note:
Cover to access fittings and inspection chambers to be same dimension as the fitting/chamber. Cover to manhole to be 600 x 600 mm min.

CLEARANCE OF BLOCKAGES
continued

3. Provide access points to all long drainage runs–the distance between access points will depend on the type of access used but should not be more than that shown in the table opposite for drains up to and including 300mm diameter.

4. Inspection chambers and manholes should have removable non-ventilating covers of durable material such as:

   a) cast iron;
   b) cast or pressed steel;
   c) precast concrete, or
   d) uPVC,

and be of suitable strength.

Inspection chambers and manholes within buildings should have mechanically fixed airtight covers unless the drain itself has water-tight access covers. Manholes deeper than one metre should have metal step irons or fixed ladders.

Maximum spacing of access points in metres				
From	to	Junction	Inspection Chamber	Manhole
Start of external drain			22	45
Rodding eye		22	45	45
Access fitting Small 150 mm dia. 150 mm x 100 mm		12	22	22
Large 300 mm x 100 mm		22	45	45
Inspection chamber, A. J.		22	45	45
Manhole		45	45	90

5. Construction of access points

Materials for access points	
Materials	**Irish/British standard**
Inspection chambers and manholes — Bricks and Blocks	IS 20, IS 91. IS 189.
Vitrified clay bricks	BS 65
Precast concrete	IS 6, IS 166, BS 5911
In-situ concrete	IS 325, IS 326
Plastics	IAB certificates (Irish Agrément Board) BS 7158
Rodding eye and access fittings (excluding frames and cover)	The same as below ground drainage materials, see table on page 374.
The construction of access points should be such that they contain the foul water under working and test conditions and they resist the entry of rainwater/ground water.	

CLEARANCE OF BLOCKAGES
continued

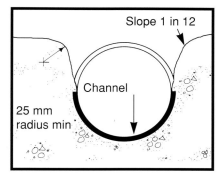

6. Channels and branches should be benched up at least to the top of the outgoing pipe and at a slope of 1 in 12. The benching should be rounded at the channel with a radius of at least 25 mm.

7. Where half round channels are used in inspection chambers and manholes, the branches should discharge into the channel at or above the level of the horizontal diameter.

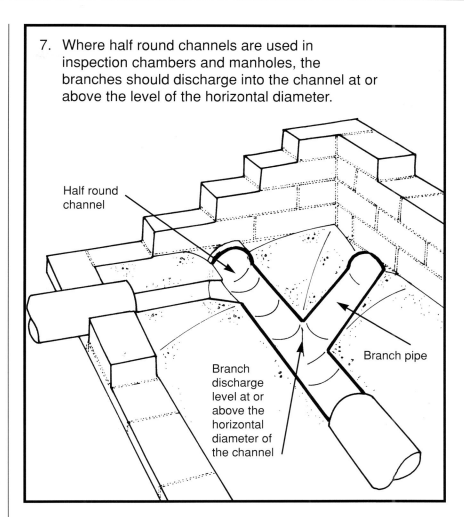

8. Where the angle of the branch is more than 45°, a three quarter section branch should be used.

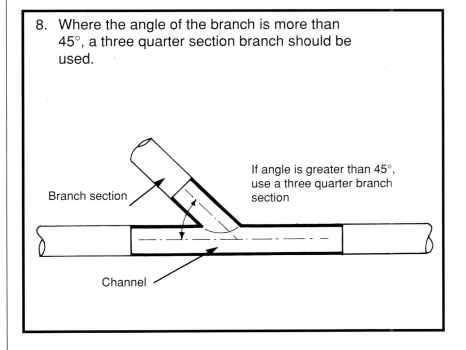

TRENCH EXCAVATION

1. Trenching should not be carried out too long in advance of pipelaying. Backfilling should take place as soon as possible.

2. The bottom of the trench should be kept as narrow as practicable, but must allow adequate room for jointing, placing and compacting the backfill. Trenches should be excavated with vertical sides to a height of at least 300 mm above the top of the pipe, where flexible pipes are being laid.

3. Excavated spoil should be kept at least 0.5 m back from the edge of the trench, and all loose stones should be removed from the heap.

4. The bottom of the trench should be at a level which will accommodate laying the pipes on the prepared underbed. The bottom should be examined for the presence of soft spots or hard objects which should be removed and filled with well tamped bedding materials.

5. Where a delay in pipelaying is envisaged, the bottom layer of 300 mm should not be removed until immediately before laying commences.

6. All excavations deeper than 1.25 m (subject to ground conditions) should be sloped back to a safe angle.

PIPE GRADIENTS AND SIZES

1. Drains should be laid to falls and have sufficent capacity to carry the flows.

2. The minimum allowable diameters and gradients are illustrated in the following diagrams.

A. Small single dwelling:

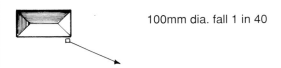

100mm dia. fall 1 in 40

B. Single dwelling discharging to a septic tank or main sewer:

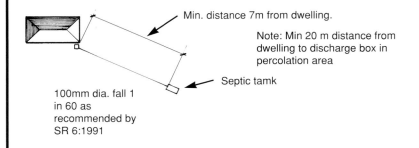

Min. distance 7m from dwelling.

Note: Min 20 m distance from dwelling to discharge box in percolation area

Septic tamk

100mm dia. fall 1 in 60 as recommended by SR 6:1991

C. 2 dwellings:

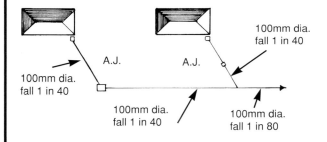

100mm dia. fall 1 in 40

A.J.   A.J.

100mm dia. fall 1 in 40

100mm dia. fall 1 in 40

100mm dia. fall 1 in 80

D. 3 - 8 dwellings:

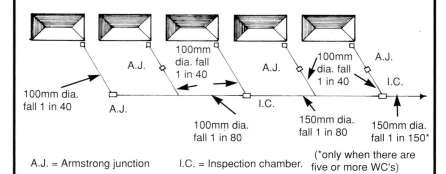

100mm dia. fall 1 in 40

A.J.

A.J.

100mm dia. fall 1 in 40

A.J.

100mm dia. fall 1 in 80

I.C.

100mm dia. fall 1 in 40

A.J.

I.C.

150mm dia. fall 1 in 80

150mm dia. fall 1 in 150*

(*only when there are five or more WC's)

A.J. = Armstrong junction   I.C. = Inspection chamber.

PIPELAYING AND JOINTING

1. The pipes should be joined in the trench and laid on the prepared bed so that they maintain substantially continuous contact with the bed. Small depressions should be left in the bed to accommodate the joints.

   Levelling devices such as bricks or pegs should be removed, and any resulting voids should be filled before backfilling.

2. Particular care should be taken when installing uPVC pipes at temperatures below 3°C. When the temperature of uPVC pipe is below 0°C pipelaying should not be carried out.

Key to diagram opposite

Selected fill free from stones larger than 40 mm, lumps of clay over 100 mm, timber, frozen material and vegetable matter.

Granular material should be 10 mm aggregate conforming to IS 5:1990 having a compaction factor of 0.2 or less when tested in accordance with BS 8310:1985 Appendix D.

Note:
1. Provision may be required to prevent ground water flow in trenches with class N, F or B type bedding.

2. Where there are sockets these should be not less than 50mm above the floor of the trench.

3. The types of bedding and backfilling for rigid pipes of standard strength laid in a trench of any width are shown in the table and diagrams below.

Limits of cover in metres for standard strength rigid pipes in any width of trench								
Pipe bore	Bedding class	Fields & Gardens		Light traffic roads		Heavy traffic roads		
		Min.	Max.	Min.	Max.	Min.	Max.	
100	D or N	0.4	4.2	0.7	4.1	0.7	3.7	
	F	0.3	5.8	0.5	5.8	0.5	5.5	
	B	0.3	7.4	0.4	7.4	0.4	7.2	
150	D or N	0.6	2.7	1.1	2.5	–	–	
	F	0.6	3.9	0.7	3.8	0.7	3.3	
	B	0.6	5.0	0.6	5.0	0.6	4.6	

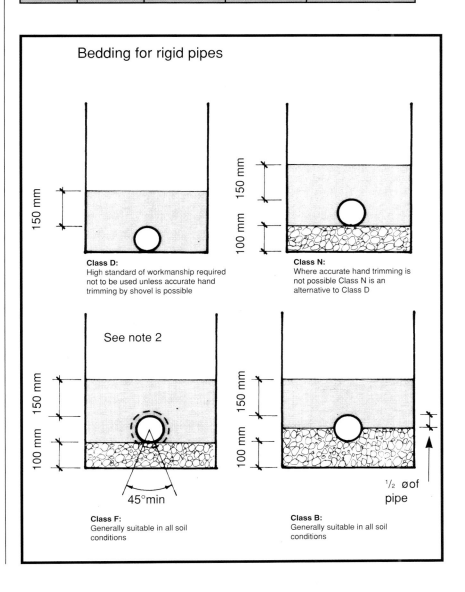

Bedding for rigid pipes

Class D:
High standard of workmanship required not to be used unless accurate hand trimming by shovel is possible

Class N:
Where accurate hand trimming is not possible Class N is an alternative to Class D

See note 2

Class F:
Generally suitable in all soil conditions

Class B:
Generally suitable in all soil conditions

45°min

½ ø of pipe

PIPELAYING AND JOINTING
continued

4. Flexible pipes may become deformed under load and require support to limit the deformation to 5 per cent of the diameter of the pipe. The bedding and backfilling should be as shown opposite.

5. When the pipes have been laid, bedded and surrounded with granular material, the remainder of the backfill may be material excavated from the trench, provided it is free from heavy stones or other objects. It should be compacted in layers.

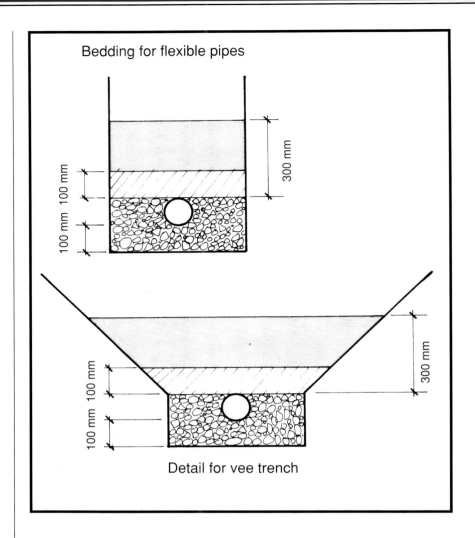

Bedding for flexible pipes

Detail for vee trench

Key to diagram above:

 Selected fill free from stones larger than 40 mm, lumps of clay over 100 mm, timber, frozen material and vegetable matter.

 Selected fill or granular fill free from stones larger than 40 mm.

 Granular material should be 10 mm aggregate conforming to IS 5:1990 having a compaction faction of 0.2 or less when tested in accordance with BS 8310:1985 Appendix D.

FIRE

INTRODUCTION

Part B of the Building Regulations sets out general requirements in respect of fire safety in all buildings, including housing. Technical Guidance Document B, published by the Department of the Environment, gives detailed guidance on how these requirements can be successfully complied with. In addition, Part J of the Regulations sets out requirements relating to heat producing appliances such as central heating boilers, and Technical Guidance Document J gives guidance on compliance with those requirements. On the following pages is set out a brief summary of the principal recommendations of Technical Guidance Documents B and J as they apply to housing. For further details on this topic the reader is directed to the Technical Guidance Documents themselves and to the HomeBond publication "Housing and the Building Regulations".

In all situations where any queries relating to fire safety arise, guidance should be sought from an appropriately qualified professional advisor.

Conventional housing is exempt from the requirement for a Fire Safety Certificate under Building Control Regulations. The need for a Fire Safety Certificate does, however, arise in the case of apartments, including duplex units. In addition, where a house or part of a house is to be used for any other use (e.g. bed and breakfast accommodation), a Fire Safety Certificate is usually required. Further information on the Fire Safety Certificate process is available from individual local authorities.

MEANS OF ESCAPE

In conventional single-storey and two-storey housing, the internal layout will usually provide an acceptable availability of escape routes to occupants. Less conventional layouts can give rise to what are called "inner room" conditions (where one room is entered through another), such as in houses of an "open-plan" design where the stairs to first floor accommodation rises directly from a room at ground floor level, rather than from an enclosed hallway. The floor plans on this page illustrate such a layout.
Note the following:

◆ Stairs to discharge within 4.5 m of external door

◆ Stairs **not** to discharge into kitchen

◆ LD2 detection/alarm system to be provided

◆ All habitable rooms in the upper storey should be provided with windows (or doors) suitable for escape or rescue.

In all houses, regardless of plan form, windows (or doors) suitable for escape or rescue should be provided from inner rooms and bedrooms. A window provided for escape or rescue should provide an unobstructed opening not less than 850 mm high by 500 mm wide, the bottom of which should be between 800 mm (600mm in the case of rooflights) and 1100 mm above floor level and should be located above an area of ground which is:

◆ Free from permanent obstruction which may impede escape or rescue

◆ Suitable for the use of a ladder to provide egress from the window, and

◆ Readily accessible for ladder access to windows by fire brigade personnel.

Where doors are provided for escape or rescue from upper storeys, they should open onto a balcony. Any balcony should be provided with a protective barrier or railings in accordance with Technical Guidance Document K.

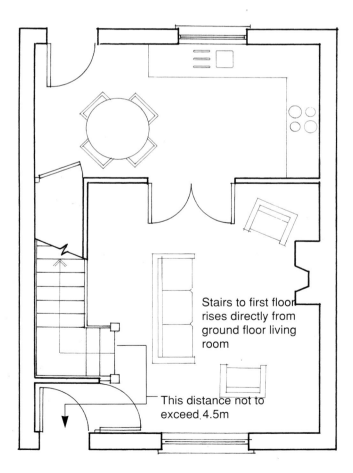

Ground floor.

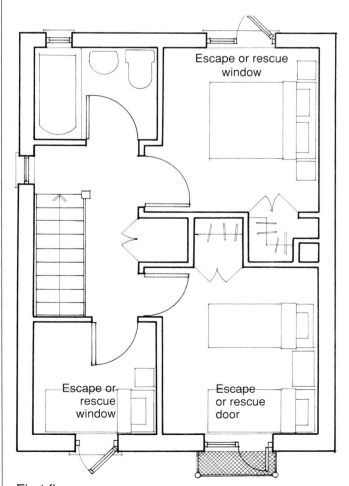

First floor.

MEANS OF ESCAPE
continued

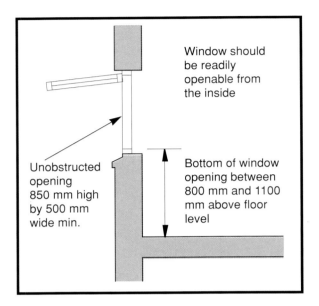

Window should be readily openable from the inside

Unobstructed opening 850 mm high by 500 mm wide min.

Bottom of window opening between 800 mm and 1100 mm above floor level

Escape window.

All bedrooms in all houses should be provided with windows of a type and size that can be deemed escape windows. This includes bedroom windows at ground floor level (e.g. in bungalows).

Example of a suitable escape window.

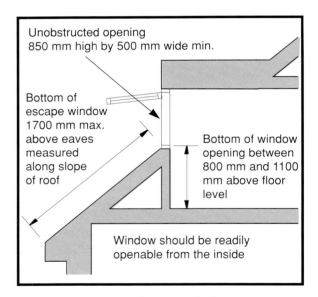

Unobstructed opening 850 mm high by 500 mm wide min.

Bottom of escape window 1700 mm max. above eaves measured along slope of roof

Bottom of window opening between 800 mm and 1100 mm above floor level

Window should be readily openable from the inside

Escape through a dormer window.

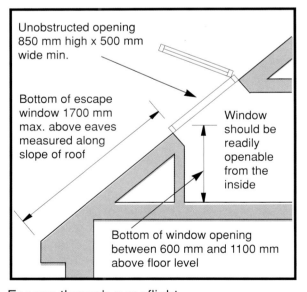

Unobstructed opening 850 mm high x 500 mm wide min.

Bottom of escape window 1700 mm max. above eaves measured along slope of roof

Window should be readily openable from the inside

Bottom of window opening between 600 mm and 1100 mm above floor level

Escape through a rooflight.

MEANS OF ESCAPE
continued

In houses where the design incorporates three storeys of accommodation, additional protection of the hall/stairs/landings areas is considered necessary.

This protection includes the provision of self-closing fire resisting doors (FD 20) and half-hour fire resisting partitions between all rooms and the hall/stairs/landing areas.

It should also be noted that the floors in houses of this configuration are required to have full half-hour fire resistance, (not modified half-hour fire resistance). See page 392 for details of floor construction with half hour fire resistance.

Illustrated on this page are floor plans of a typical three-storey house highlighting the protection of the hall/stairs/landing areas and the location of fire doors. It should be noted that inner room conditions are only acceptable where the floor level of such rooms are not more than 4.5 m above ground or access level (i.e. typically at ground or first floor level).

Where a fire door is used in circumstances such as those illustrated here, care should be taken to ensure that the door as installed complies with the specification as set out in the fire test certificate for the door in question.

All bedroom windows should be escape windows as illustrated on the preceding page.

Three-storey houses should generally be provided with a Type LD3, Grade 3 detection and alarm system, incorporating detectors in the hallways, corridors and staircases.

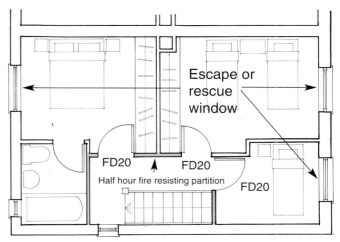

Second floor.

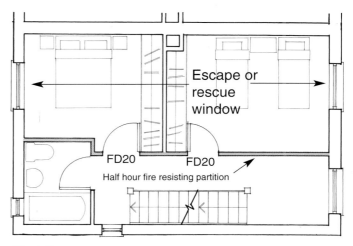

First floor.

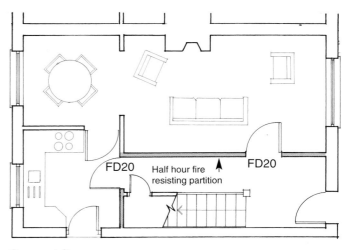

Ground floor.

MEANS OF ESCAPE
continued

A precaution considered necessary as a means of ensuring early escape in case of the outbreak of fire is the installation of a fire detection and alarm system. This should be installed in all houses in accordance with the following guidelines:

◆ Systems should comply with the provisions of BS 5839: Pt. 6: 1995

◆ Number and location of smoke detectors will depend on the type and layout of the house in question. In a typical two-storey, three/four bedroom house, detectors should be provided in the hallway and above the first floor landing. Detailed guidance on this aspect of their installation is given in BS 5839: Pt. 6: 1995. In bungalows, for example, the corridor between living and sleeping accommodation is a suitable location

◆ Locate detectors on ceilings at least 300 mm from walls and light fittings, preferably in a central position

◆ Locate detectors where they are readily accessible for testing and maintenance

◆ Locate detectors in circulation areas so that no door to a habitable room is more than 7.5 m from a detector.

The type and layout of the house will influence the appropriate choice of detection/alarm system. For example, in large houses such as country mansions or houses which have a complex layout it may be necessary to incorporate additional detectors or a more elaborate installation powered from a mains electrical supply.

The table opposite summarises the provisions of BS 5839: Pt. 6: 1995 as regards grades and types of fire detection and alarm systems for houses.

Note:
Grade F (battery powered) systems are not acceptable in new houses. Only mains powered detectors are acceptable.

Minimum grade and type of fire detection and alarm system for protection of life in houses

House type	Minimum type and grade of system	
	Grade	Type
Houses with no floor greater than 200 m² in area.		
Bungalow or other single story unit.	E	LD3
Two-storeys house, with no floor level exceeding 4.5 m in height above ground.	E	LD3
House in which one floor level is more than 4.5 m above ground.	C	LD3
House is which more than one floor level is more than 4.5 m above ground.	B	LD2
Single family dwellings with one or more floors greater than 200 m² in area.		
Single-storey dwelling.	C	LD3
Two-storey house with no floor level exceeding 4.5 m in height above ground.	B	LD3
House in which one or more floor levels are more than 4.5 m above ground.	A	LD2

WALL AND CEILING LININGS

Wall and ceiling linings can contribute significantly to the spread of fire and are therefore controlled. Plastered surfaces are acceptable throughout but some other materials are restricted in their use. Untreated timber sheeting used as a lining may only be used in small panels of 5.0 m² or less. Such panels should be separated by at least 2 m from any other such panel and the total area of such panels in any room should not exceed 20 m² or half the floor area of the room, whichever is less. This relaxation for untreated panels of limited size and disposition applies only to wall linings - it does not apply to ceiling linings.

Alternatively, sheeting may be treated by an appropriate method, such as a fire retardant varnish or paint, to give it a "Class 1" Surface Spread of Flame rating. It should also be noted that the use of timber sheeting applied directly to the underside of floor joists will generally not provide the recommended level of fire resistance of floor. In such instances, the ceiling should be formed by plasterboard in the usual way prior to the fixing of the timber sheeting. The requirements in respect of Class 1 surface spread of flame apply everywhere in houses apart from bathrooms. See sketch opposite.

The use of polystyrene tiles as a ceiling finish is not permitted.

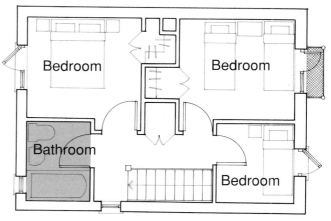

First floor.

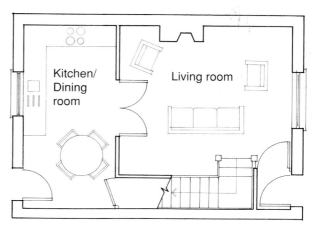

Ground floor.

Typical two-storey house plan. The recommendations for internal wall and ceiling linings are Class 0 or 1 for all rooms except bathrooms or shower rooms which can be Class 0, 1, 2 or 3.

FIRE RESISTANCE

The nature of conventional house construction is such that the standard requirements for fire resistance for such elements as floors and walls are usually automatically met by such construction. However, there are certain situations where particular attention is required to ensure that an adequate level of resistance to fire is incorporated into the construction of houses. These are as follows:

◆ Floors in three-storey houses and over garages should have full half-hour fire resistance, not modified half-hour fire resistance which is normally acceptable in two-storey housing. Attention may be required to the detailed specification of ceiling and floor finishes to ensure that these requirements are met. For example, a timber floor incorporating a ceiling consisting of 12.5 mm plasterboard with all joints taped and filled and backed by timber is deemed to have modified half-hour fire resistance. Such a construction is acceptable in two storey construction, but not in three-storey construction or between a garage and other accommodation. The table opposite sets out a range of common options for the construction of floors with full half-hour fire resistance.

Note: Other means of achieving modified half-hour fire resistance can be found in 'Guidelines for the construction of fire resisting structural elements', a report by the Building Research Establishment.

FLOORS OF 1/2 HOUR FIRE RESISTANCE

Ceiling specification	Floor type (explained below)
one layer of 12.5 mm plasterboard with joints taped and filled and backed by timber	3
two layers of plasterboard with joints staggered and joints in outer layer taped and filled:	
25 mm total thickness	1
22 mm total thickness	2*
19 mm total thickness	3*
one layer of 12.5 mm proprietary fire grade plasterboard with joints taped and filled and backed by timber	1,2,3
one layer of 9.5 mm plasterboard finished with 10 mm min. lightweight aggregate gypsum plaster	2*, 3
one layer of 12.5 mm plasterboard finished with:	
13 mm lightweight aggregate gypsum plaster	1
10 mm lightweight aggregate gypsum plaster	2, 3
5 mm gypsum board finish plaster	2, 3

*supports not exceeding 450 mm centres

Floor types referred to above are as follows:

1. Any structurally suitable flooring of timber or particle boards on timber joists not less than 37 mm wide.

2. Timber floor boarding, plywood or wood chipboard tongued and grooved and not less than 15 mm (finished) thickness on timber joists not less than 37 mm wide.

3. Timber floor boarding, plywood or wood chipboard, tongued and grooved and not less than 21 mm (finished) thickness on timber joists not less than 37 mm wide.

FIRE RESISTANCE
continued

As stated earlier, in three-storey houses additional protection of the hall/stairs and landings is considered necessary. As well as providing fire resisting doors, half-hour fire resisting partitions are required between all rooms and the hall/stairs and landing area.

Depending on whether the partition is load bearing or not, half-hour fire-resisting partitions should be constructed in accordance with the tables opposite. Blockwork partitions will also usually satisfy the requirements for half-hour fire resistance.

Note:
Reference should also be made to pages 136 to 140 which deal with the construction of loadbearing and non-loadbearing timber stud partitions.

The tables on these pages have been derived from 'Guidelines from the construction of fire resisting elements', a report by the Building Research Establishment.

FIRE RESISTANT LOADBEARING INTERNAL TIMBER STUD PARTITIONS

Nature of construction and materials to achieve half hour fire resistance

44 mm min. timber studs at 600 mm centres (except where indicated) faced on each side with:

One layer of 12.5 mm plasterboard with all joints taped and filled.

One layer of 9.5 mm* plasterboard with a finish of lightweight aggregate gypsum plaster – thickness of plaster 10 mm .

*Supports not to exceed 450 mm centres.

FIRE RESISTANT NON-LOADBEARING INTERNAL TIMBER STUD PARTITIONS

Nature of construction and materials to achieve half hour fire resistance

Timber studs at 600 mm centres (except where indicated) faced on each side with:

One layer of 12.5 mm plasterboard with all joints taped and filled.

Two layers of plasterboard with joints staggered, joints in outer layer taped and filled – total thickness for each face 19 mm*.

9.5 mm* thick plasterboard with 10 mm min lightweight gypsum plaster finish.

*Supports not to exceed 450 mm centres.

FIRE RESISTANCE
continued

Doors forming direct connections between garages and areas within houses should be self-closing type FD 30, and should open over a 100 mm upstand or step down from the house to the garage. In addition, any garage attached to a house must be separated from the rest of the accommodation by walls, floors or ceilings having full half-hour fire resistance.

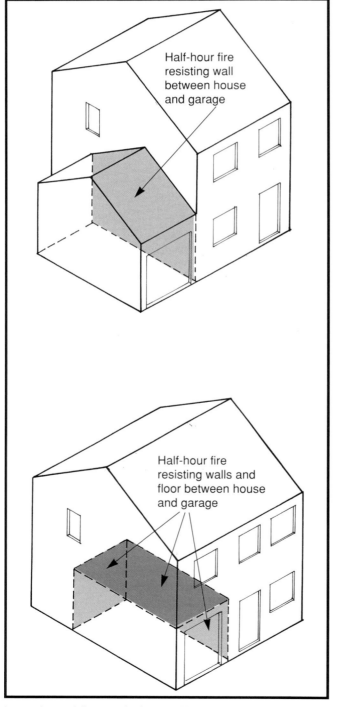

Location of fire resisting walls, floors and ceilings.

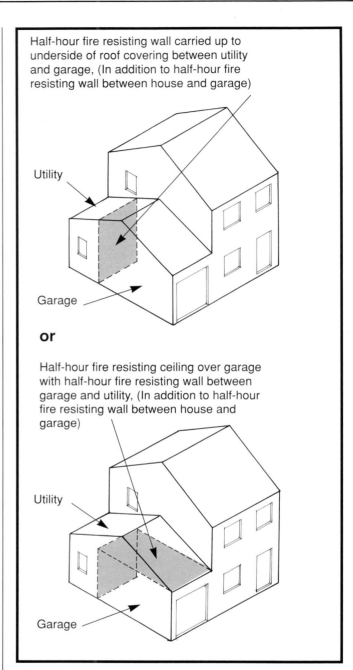

Half-hour fire resisting wall carried up to underside of roof covering between utility and garage, (In addition to half-hour fire resisting wall between house and garage)

or

Half-hour fire resisting ceiling over garage with half-hour fire resisting wall between garage and utility, (In addition to half-hour fire resisting wall between house and garage)

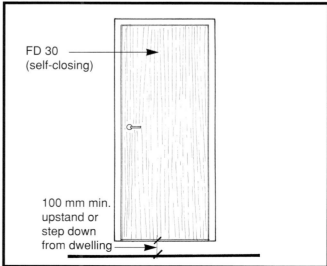

Fire door separating garage from rest of house.

FIRE RESISTANCE
continued

Half-hour fire resisting ceiling with no floor above.

In situations such as illustrated here, it may be necessary to provide half-hour fire resistance in a ceiling which does not incorporate floor boarding on its upper surface. Set out on this page are details of the construction of such ceilings.

Construction specification: Min. 38 mm wide joists with 12.5 mm proprietary fire grade plasterboard, all joints filled and backed by timber, with minimum 150 mm mineral fibre insulation between joists.

Note that the thermal insulation requirements of the Building Regulations may require a greater thickness of insulation material than that deemed necessary to satisfy fire safety requirements.

Note:
Where joists are less than 38 mm wide (e.g. certain roof trusses), it is acceptable to screw fix (with 50 mm long wood screws at 300 mm max. centres) a min. 50 x 25 mm wide batten to the joist to increase the overall width of the joist as illustrated opposite.

Note:
As an alternative to this detail, the wall between the garage and house can be brought up to the underside of the roof-covering in half-hour fire resisting construction.

Note:
A fire door separating a house from a garage should be a door certified by test as being an FD30 door, and should be installed in compliance with the detailed specification as set out in the fire test certificate for the door type in question. See previous page.

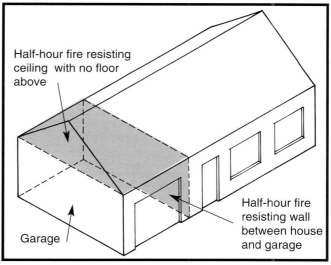

Typical bungalow incorporating garage — a location where a half-hour fire resisting ceiling with no floor above may occur.

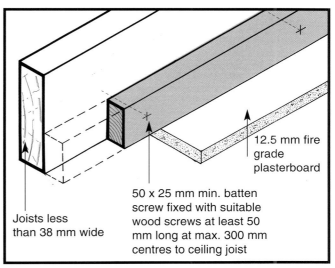

Batten fixing detail.

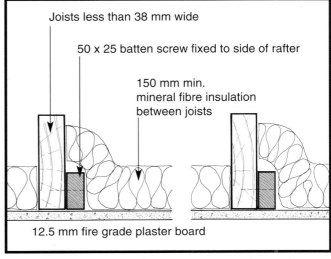

Half-hour fire resisting ceiling with no floor above.

FIRE RESISTANCE
continued

Half-hour fire resisting ceiling with no floor above.

In dormer roofs (and attic conversions) where the floor area abuts an unfloored area, a vertical fire stop should be provided at this junction as illustrated opposite.

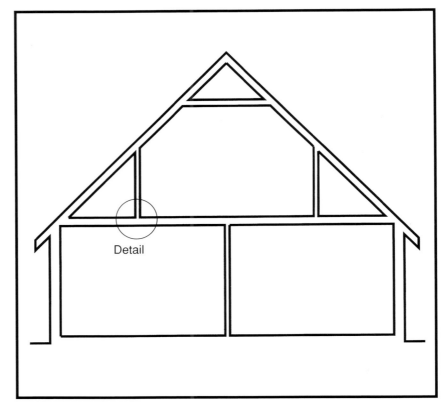

Typical two storey dormer configuration.

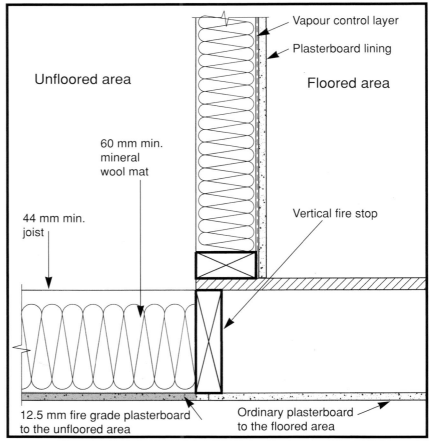

Fire stopping detail.

FIRE RESISTANCE
continued.

Fire-stopping of party walls is an essential part of ensuring that fire does not readily spread from house to house. See pages 104 of this manual for guidance in this area, in particular at the junction of the party wall with the roof at eaves level where it is important to fire-stop the space contained by the fascia and soffit. The practice illustrated on page 365 to ensure adequate sound insulation will also ensure adequate fire resistance by avoiding timber floor joists being built into or through party walls.

In houses of masonry construction, it is not required to provide fire stopping in the form of a vertical cavity barrier at the junction of party wall and external wall, **provided** that the cavity around doors and windows is closed. This can be achieved using the methods illustrated on this page.

Note:

◆ In all situations the cavity must be closed at wall plate level and along the top of the gables

◆ The details shown here are the standard cavity closing details applicable to semi-detached and terraced houses of one or two storey in height

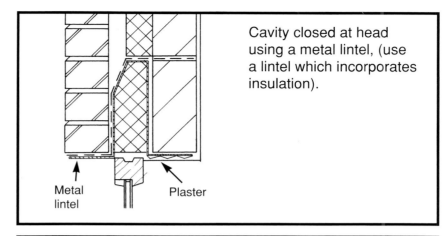

Cavity closed at head using a metal lintel, (use a lintel which incorporates insulation).

Metal lintel   Plaster

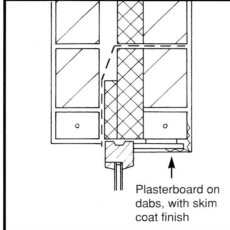

When using pre-stressed concrete lintels, the cavity can be closed by plaster-board fixed by dabs to the underside of the lintel and tight against the window frame with skim coat plaster finish.

Plasterboard on dabs, with skim coat finish

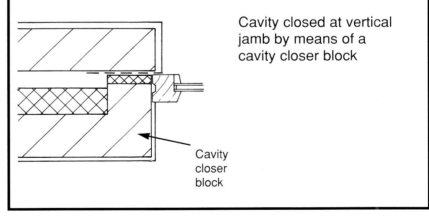

Cavity closed at vertical jamb by means of a cavity closer block

Cavity closer block

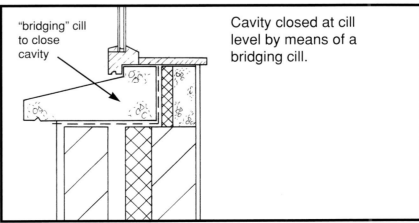

"bridging" cill to close cavity

Cavity closed at cill level by means of a bridging cill.

Typical cavity closing methods.

ROOF COVERINGS

Roof coverings are required to prevent ready penetration of fire and also to limit flame spread on their surfaces. This is achieved by requiring materials to have specified roof "designations". The common roofing materials, such as concrete tiles and fibre cement slates, used in housebuilding readily meet these requirements. Flat roofing materials may need additional protection to achieve compliance. For example, bituminous felt needs to be covered by a finish such as bitumen-bedded chippings in order to be deemed acceptable as a roof finish close to boundaries. Where such materials are being used, the manufacturer's/supplier's guidance should be sought in respect of any surface treatments necessary to achieve the recommended designation.

FIRE FIGHTING ACCESS

Housing estates should be laid out to ensure ready access for fire tenders in the event of a fire. This will require that roads and access generally are adequate for fire tenders. The table opposite summarises the requirements of the Technical Guidance Document B of the Building Regulations in this regard.

The layout of most estates to accommodate everyday vehicular traffic will ensure that these requirements are met.

Vehicle access route specifications	
Appliance type	**Access specification**
Pump	Minimum width of roadway between kerbs 3.7 m.
Pump	Minimum width of gateway between kerbs 3.1 m.
Pump	Minimum turning circle between kerbs 16.8 m.
Pump	Minimum turning circle between walls 19.2 m.
Pump	Minimum clearance height 3.7 m
Pump	Minimum carrying capacity 12.5 tonnes.

FIRE PROTECTION OF STEEL

In some cases, steel members such as RSJ's and Universal Beams are incorporated into the construction of a house. Where such steel gives structural support to floors or walls it is necessary to protect it against fire. In domestic construction a minimum of half-hour or modified half-hour fire resistance is usually required. This can be achieved by encasing the structural steel member with plasterboard. A number of options, including that described below and illustrated opposite, are available for such encasement.

Encasement of steel beams

This method of fire protection involves the encasement of the steel beam using a proprietary system comprising fire grade plasterboard fixed to a framework of lightweight galvanised steel. Precise details will vary depending on the particular proprietary system being used. Manufacturer's detailed recommendations should be rigorously followed. Half-hour fire resistance will normally be achieved by the use of a 12.5 mm thick proprietary fire grade plasterboard, which can be finished to match adjoining finishes.

In addition to plasterboard encasement, other steel protection media include proprietary fire protection boards and intumescent paints. Precise specifications will vary with the period of fire resistance required and the type of steel member being protected, manufacturer's guidance should be sought.

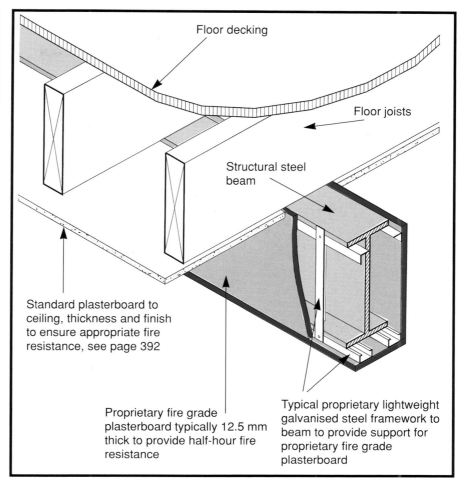

Typical encasement of steel beam using proprietary fire grade plasterboard and lightweight galvanised steel framework.

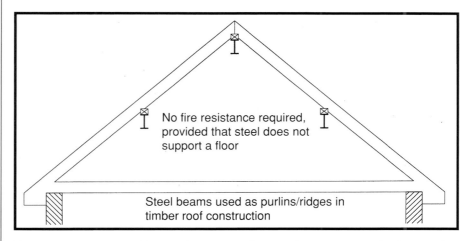

Where steel is used in roof construction and supports only the roof structure it is not necessary to protect the steel. Note however that any steel member in a dormer roof, where it supports any part of the floor, will require protection to ensure that the appropriate level of fire resistance is achieved.

RADIATION ONTO BOUNDARIES

Large openings in external walls, such as doors
and windows, may in the event of a fire give rise
to radiation which may in turn endanger adjoining
buildings and their occupants. To control this risk,
the Technical Guidance Document B limits the
extent of such "unprotected areas" depending on
their distance to boundaries. The accompanying
sketch illustrates the restrictions that apply on
openings within one metre of the boundary.

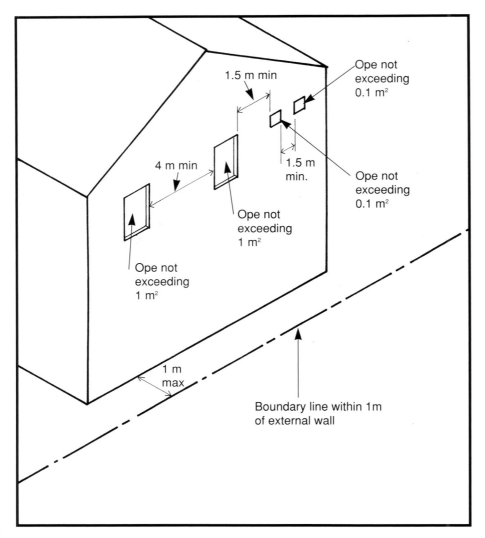

Radiation onto boundaries: unprotected areas
less than 1m from the boundary line – only
unprotected areas of the size and disposition
illustrated here should be used.

RADIATION ONTO BOUNDARIES
continued

In dwellings not exceeding the dimensions illustrated opposite, for openings a metre or more from the boundary, the limit of unprotected areas can be calculated using the table opposite.

Note. The dwelling should not exceed 3 storeys in height (basements not counted) or be more than 24 m in length.

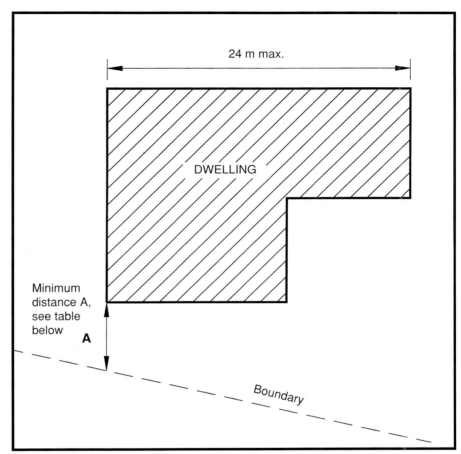

Small residential building. The area in the table below is the total unprotected area to be contained in the walls facing the relevant boundary (could be a notional boundary).

Permitted unprotected areas in small residential dwellings.

Minimum distance (A) between side of building and relevant boundary (m)	Maximum total area of unprotected areas (m²)
1.0	5.6
2.0	12
3.0	18
4.0	24
5.0	30
6.0	no limit

RADIATION ONTO BOUNDARIES
continued

For the purpose of assessing radiation risks, the boundaries in typical housing layout will be as follows.

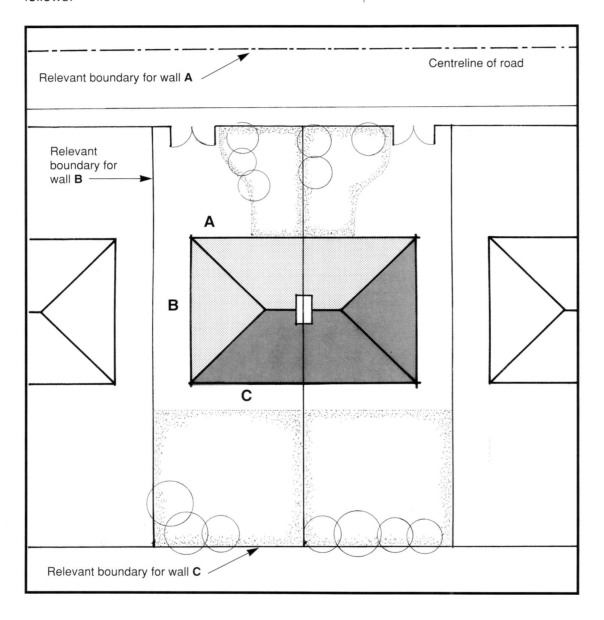

Relevant boundary for wall **A**

Centreline of road

Relevant boundary for wall **B**

A

B

C

Relevant boundary for wall **C**

ROOFLIGHTS

Technical Guidance Document B of the Building Regulations, gives recommendations on the use of glass and plastic rooflights. The principal provisions relevant to housing are summarised below.

Glass rooflights

Any glass in a rooflight within 6 m of a boundary should be at least 4 mm thick unless it is in a rooflight over:

a)   a balcony, verandah, open carport or detached swimming pool

b)   any garage, conservatory or outbuilding whose floor area does not exceed 40 m².

Plastic rooflights

Where translucent plastic materials are used as rooflights they should be type TP(a), or TP(b) as defined in Technical Guidance Document B. Manufacturers and suppliers should be consulted if any doubt exists as to the classification of such materials when used in rooflights.

Single skin plastic rooflights

When materials classified as TP(a) or TP(b) are used in single-skin rooflights, the rooflights should generally be located at least 6 m from any boundary.

Twin-skin rooflights

Where a twin-skin rooflight is made up of two sheets TP(a) or TP(b) material in any combination, the recommendations in the preceding paragraphs for single-skin rooflights apply.

HEATING APPLIANCES

Points to note

The term "room sealed appliance" means an appliance which does not rely on the room in which it is located as a source of air supply e.g. balanced flue appliances. Any appliance in a bath or shower room or in a private garage must be of the room sealed type.

If an appliance is not a room-sealed appliance, the room or space in which it is contained must have a permanent ventilation opening. This ventilation opening should preferably be in an external wall and should be at least the size set out in the table on page 332.

Where an appliance is located in such a way that the room or space cannot be ventilated directly to the open air, the permanent ventilation opening may be to an adjoining room or space, provided that the adjoining room or space has a permanent ventilation opening of at least the same size direct to external air.

Note:

Technical Guidance Document J and the Department of the Enviroment and Local Government Grants Section both require specific provisions to be made for any heating appliance located in a garage. Any such appliance should be:

◆ manufactured for use as a "room-sealed" appliance and installed in strict compliance with the manufacturer's instructions

◆ together with all connections thereto, protected from impact damage by a vehicle either by the provision of suitable barriers or by being located in a position where impact cannot take place

◆ together with its flue pipe, adequately separated from combustible material

◆ fitted with a flue terminal so positioned that flue gases and other products of combustion are prevented from entering the building

◆ fitted with a flue pipe and terminal so positioned and/or shielded so as to minimise the risk of danger to persons through contact.

See page 332 for air supply requirements to heat producing appliances.

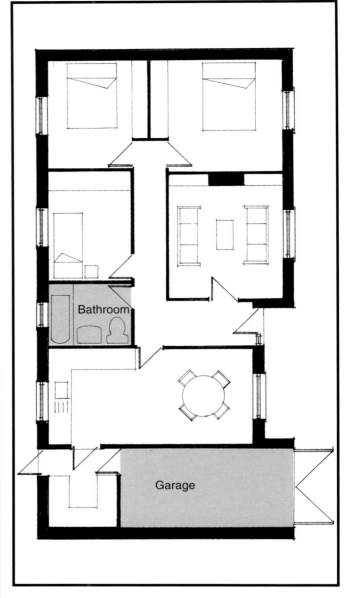

Any appliance in a bath or shower room or in a private garage must be of the room-sealed type.

A heat producing appliance in a garage should be safely located against impact.

FLUE PIPES

For solid fuel appliances, including open fires, and for oil burning appliances where the flue gas temperature is likely to exceed 260°C, flue pipes should only be used to connect appliances to chimneys and should not pass through roof spaces.

Flue pipes should be manufactured from materials as set out in the table below.

Materials for flue pipes

A	B
Flue pipes to solid fuel appliances and oil-burning appliances whose flue gas temperature is **likely** to exceed 260°C .	Flue pipes to gas fired appliances and oil burning appliances whose flue gas temperature is **not likely** to exceed 260°C.
◆ Cast iron to BS 41:1973 (1981) Specification for cast iron spigot and socket flue or smoke pipes and fittings, or ◆ Mild steel with a min. wall thickness of 3 mm, or ◆ Stainless steel with a min. wall thickness of 1 mm, to BS 1449: Part 2:1983, or ◆ Vitreous enamelled steel to BS 6999: 1989.	◆ Sheet metal to BS 715: 1993, or ◆ Asbestos cement to BS 567: 1973 (1989) Specification for asbestos cement flue pipes and fittings, light quality, or BS 835:1973, or ◆ Cast iron to BS 41: 1973 (1981) Specification for case iron spigot and socket flue or smoke pipes and fittings, or ◆ Any material described in column "A" of this table.

FLUE PIPES
continued

Shielding of flue pipes – solid fuel appliances

Where flue pipes are used, they must be shielded from adjoining materials as illustrated here.

Flue pipes from solid fuel appliances should be separated from adjoining materials by at least the distances illustrated below.

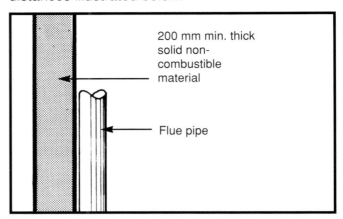

200 mm thick solid non-combustible material. There is no distance requirement between the flue pipe and non-combustible material, or,

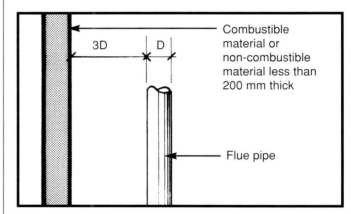

Flue pipe separated from adjoining material by at least 3 times pipe diameter **D**, or,

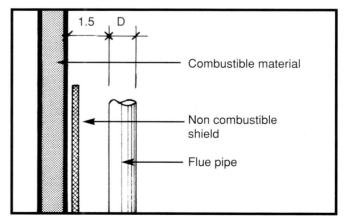

Flue pipe separated from combustible material by a non-combustible shield. There should be a 12.5 mm air gap between the shield and combustible material. The width of the shield should be at least three times pipe diameter **D**.

FLUE PIPES
continued

Shielding of flue pipes – gas burning appliances

Where flue pipes from gas burning appliances pass through a wall, floor or roof, they should be separated from any combustible material by a non-combustible sleeve enclosing an air space of at least 25 mm around the flue pipe as illustrated below, or be at least 25 mm from any combustible material as illustrated opposite.

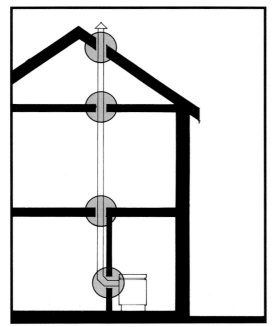

Flue pipe separated from floor, wall and roof by non-combustible sleeve.

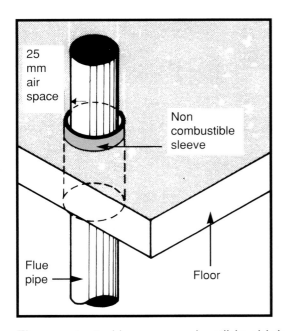

Floor protected by non-combustible shield.

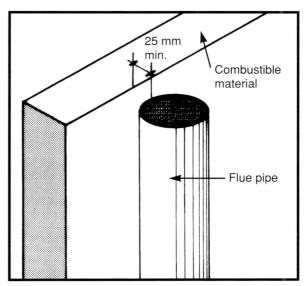

Separation of flue pipe to gas burning appliance from combustible material.

Note: for a double-walled flue pipe, the 25 mm distance may be measured from the outside of the inner pipe, as illustrated below.

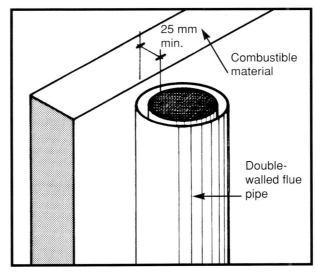

Separation of flue pipe to gas burning appliance from combustible material.

FLUE PIPES
continued

Sizes of flue pipes

Solid fuel appliance:

Generally for solid fuel appliances a 194 mm minimum diameter flue or square section flue of equivalent area (e.g. 172 x 172 mm) is required.

Where a flue serves a closed solid fuel appliance and the flue run incorporates an offset, the size of the flue should be increased to 219 mm minimum diameter or 197 x 197 mm minimum square section flue.

Gas burning appliance

For gas burning appliances, generally the flue should have a cross-sectional area of at least that of the appliance outlet. In the case of gas fires, a round flue of at least 125 mm diameter should be used or a rectangular flue of at least 16,500 mm^2 cross-section with a minimum dimension of 90 mm (e.g. 90 x 185 mm approx. or 130 x 130 mm approx.).

Oil burning appliance

For oil burning appliances discharging into a flue pipe, the flue size should be at least that of the appliance outlet. Where oil burning appliances connect to chimneys, minimum flue size varies with appliance output as outlined in the table below.

Rated output of appliance	Minimum flue size
up to 20 kW	100 mm dia.
20 – 32 kW	125 mm dia.
32 – 45 kW	150 mm dia.

DIFFERENT CALCULATION METHODS

The TGD gives three different ways to calculate compliance with Regulation L1 as regards heat losses through the fabric of a house: (1) The Overall Heat Loss Method; (2) The Elemental Heat Loss Method and (3) The Heat Energy Rating Method.

THE OVERALL HEAT LOSS METHOD (TGD-L ,1.2.1-1.2.2)

A maximum average U-value of all exposed and semi-exposed elements of the dwelling is allowed. This maximum average U-value permitted depends on the ratio between (a) building volume and (b) the total area of exposed and semi exposed elements. In calculating the average U-value, notional U-values equal to 0.75 times the actual U-value are used for semi-exposed elements.

Calculate building volume, and the total area of the exposed and semi-exposed elements. Depending on the ratio between the two, the maximum average U-value (U_m) is set out in Diagram 2 or Table 1, page 7 of the TGD.

The Overall Heat Loss Method also requires maximum average elemental U-values for exposed roofs (0.35 W/m²K) exposed ground floors (0.45 W/m²K), and exposed walls (0.55 W/m²K).

To comply with the Regulations by using the Overall Heat Loss Method, the average U-value of the house must equal or better the maximum average U-value permitted by Table 1. In addition, individual elemental U-values for roofs, walls and ground floors must equal or better those listed.

THE ELEMENTAL HEAT LOSS METHOD (TGD-L, 1.2.3-1.2.7)

This method is suitable for dwellings, material alterations, material changes of use, and extensions.
A maximum elemental U-value in W/m²K is given for each element.

	New Buildings and Extensions	Material Alterations, Material Changes of Use
Exposed roofs	0.25	0.35
Exposed walls	0.45	0.60
Exposed floors	0.45	0.60
Ground floors	0.45	-
Semi-exposed roofs	0.35	0.60
Semi-exposed walls	0.60	0.60
Semi-exposed floors	0.60	0.60
Exposed Windows, personnel doors and rooflights	3.30*	3.30*
Vehicle access doors	0.70	0.70

To comply with the Regulations by using the Elemental Heat Loss Method, the U-value for each building element must equal or better the elemental U-values in the table.
* Permitted average U-value of windows, personnel doors and rooflights may vary. The total heat loss must not exceed that given for the maximum area and U-value specified in the TGD-L, table 3. The following values are taken from that table.

HEAT ENERGY RATING METHOD (TGD-L, SECTION 4)

The Heat Energy Rating of a dwelling is a measure of the annual energy requirements of a dwelling for space heating and domestic hot water for standardised conditions. It forms the new and third method available for complying with TGD-L. The Rating is calculated for standardised room temperatures, levels of hot water use and conditions of operation by the standard method specified in TGD-L Appendix C. For dwellings, an acceptable level of transmission heat loss is demonstrated when the calculated Heat Energy Rating (H.E.R) is less than the Maximum Permitted Heat Energy Rating (MPHER) specified in TGD-L Table 4 page 17.

The calculations address:

- Rate of Heat Loss Through the Building Fabric;
- Rate of Heat Loss due to Ventilation;
- Water Heating;
- Solar and Other Energy Gains;
- Space Heating efficiency, controls and demand.

and calculates energy required to:

- offset transmission and air infiltration losses through the building fabric;
- offset losses associated with ventilation, and
- provide for domestic hot water.

DIFFERENT CALCULATION METHODS - continued

In addition to achieving a HER better than the allowed MPHER **other conditions also have to be met.** These include:

♦ Achieving elemental U-values as stated;

Roofs	0.35 W/m²K,
Walls	0.55 W/m²K,
Ground floors	0.45 W/m²K,

♦ Provisions for thermal bridging as required in TGD-L;
♦ Provisions for air infiltration as required in TGD-L;
♦ Provisions for space and hot water controls as required in TGD-L;
♦ Provisions for insulation of hot water storage vessels, and
♦ Provisions for insulation of pipes and ducts.

Details are given in TGD-L, Section 4, Page 17.

Software to allow the assessment of compliance on basis of Heat Energy Rating is available from the Irish Energy Centre, Glasnevin, Dublin 9.

CALCULATION OF U-VALUES

♦ All three methods require calculation of the U-value for each exposed and semi-exposed element: floor, walls, external wall openings, and roof. With standard construction one can refer to tables in the TGD and avoid detailed calculation.
♦ Select the insulation: glass fibre, extruded polystyrene, polyurethane…
♦ Detail the construction: cavity walls, pitched roofs, double glazing,…
♦ Table 5 on page 19 of the TGD gives the thermal conductivity of common materials, but manufacturers' certified test data should be used in preference. Calculations in this publication use such manufacturers' data.

SLAB-ON-GROUND AND SUSPENDED GROUND FLOORS

♦ Calculate floor area, excluding any unheated spaces outside the insulated fabric such as garages.
♦ Measure the exposed perimeter, including any perimeter between the heated building and unheated spaces.
♦ Calculate the ratio: Exposed perimeter/Area.
♦ Use TGD table 7, page 25 to establish the necessary thermal resistance of added insulation, to achieve the desired U-value (which should be 0.45 or better).
♦ Select the insulation type, and use makers' certified data, or TGD table 5, page 19 to obtain its thermal conductivity.
♦ Multiply the necessary thermal resistance by the thermal conductivity to obtain the required insulation thickness.

EXPOSED INTERMEDIATE FLOORS, WALLS, AND ROOFS

♦ Refer to makers' certified data, or TGD -L,Table 5, page 19 for thermal conductivity of the insulation.
♦ For exposed intermediate floors, see TGD-L, table 19, page 35.
♦ For walls, see tables 14 to 18 at TGD-L pages 33 and 34 for cavity, timber frame and hollow block walls and the insulation thickness needed in each case. TGD-L examples 5,6 and 7 show the calculation.
♦ For roofs, see tables 8 to 12 at TGD-L pages 30 and 31 for the desired construction and required insulation thickness. Refer to TGD-L example 8, page 29 ' pitched roof' to show how tables 8 and 9 are worked out.

SEMI-EXPOSED FLOORS, WALLS, AND ROOFS

♦ Proceed as for exposed elements. Modify the U-values obtained, if the heat loss calculation method permits. This applies to the Overall method, not to the Elemental method, see example 2.

GENERAL COMMENTS

♦ The simplest calculation method is the Elemental Heat Loss Method. However, if one makes additional calculations, more design flexibility is possible. A compact building has a smaller external surface area and loses less heat than a straggling building of the same volume. The TGD recognises this, so the Overall Heat Loss Method requires less rigorous U-values for compact buildings, because of their more efficient shape. Calculation of surface area and volume permits the use of this method.
♦ Windows can help heat gain by way of solar heating. Refer to TGD-L, Appendix C, page 39.

EXAMPLE ONE: HEAT LOSS CALCULATIONS:
DETACHED BUNGALOW

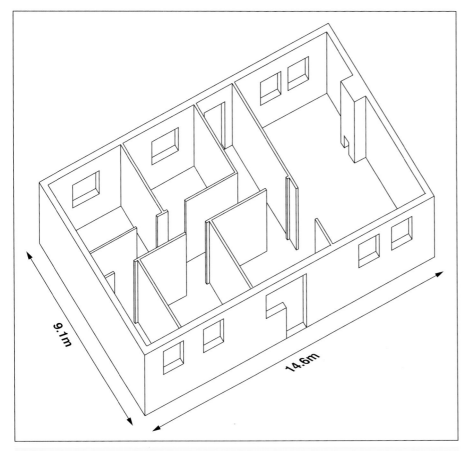

This first example is of a simple kind.

CONSTRUCTION

Ground floor:
- Concrete slab-on-ground expanded polystyrene, DPM.

External walls:
- Two leaves 100 concrete blockwork
- 100 cavity;
- 50 expanded polystyrene-partial-fill;
- External finish: 19 render;
- Internal finish; 13 lightweight plaster.

Windows and external doors:
- Single glazed timber frame.

Roof:
- Pitched tile; felt; ventilated roofspace;
- 150 glassfibre quilt at ceiling level;
- 12.5 plasterboard and skim.

DIMENSIONS

14.6m x 9.1m externally
14.0m x 8.5m internally
2400 floor to ceiling height

Floor area [A]:		**119.00 m²**
Volume [V]:		**285.60 m³**
Perimeter [P]:	14+14+8.5+8.5 =	**45 m**
P/A:	45/119 =	**0.38**

EXTERNAL OPES
[Windows, external doors, rooflights]

North:
2 x (1.2x1.0)+(1.2)x(2.1) + 2 x (1.3)x(1.0) = **7.52 m²**
South:
2 x (1.2x1.0)+(0.9)x(2.1) + 3 x (1.0)x(1.0) = **7.29 m²**
West:
(0.9 x 1.0) = **0.90 m²**

Total: **15.71 m²**

WALL AREA
(14.0 x 2.4 x 2) + (8.5 x 2.4 x 2) = **108 m²**

ALL METHODS: CALCULATE THE U-VALUES

FLOOR:

Concrete slab on ground, 14.0m x 8.5m
Perimeter (P) = 45m
Heated area (A) = 119 sq.m.
P/A = 0.38

Required U-value = 0.45 W/m²K
Necessary thermal resistance of added insulation, from TGD table 7, page 25 by interpolation: 1.02.
Insulation: Expanded polystyrene: thermal conductivity: 0.037 from TGD table 5, page 19.
Required insulation thickness: 1.02 x 0.037 = 38 mm.

WALLS:

Insulation: Expanded polystyrene: thermal conductivity: 0.037 from TGD table 5, page 19.
Wall type: as TGD table 14, page 33: external leaf rendered dense concrete blocks, partial fill insulation, internal leaf dense concrete block with lightweight plaster.
Proposed insulation thickness: 50 mm, from design data.
U-value: 0.50, by interpolation of TGD table 14, page 33.

ROOF:

Insulation: Glassfibre quilt: thermal conductivity: 0.040 from TGD table 5, page 19.
Roof type: as TGD table 8, page 30: tiled pitched roof, ventilated roof space, plasterboard ceiling, insulation between joists at ceiling level.
Proposed insulation thickness: 150 mm, from design data.
U-value: 0.28, by interpolation of TGD table 8, page 30.

WINDOWS:

Single glazed, timber frame: from design data.
Indicative U-value, from TGD table 20, page 36: 4.7.

Having calculated the U-values, decide which calculation method to employ. The following two pages show each calculation method, applied in turn to the design example. It will be seen that a design may be satisfactory using one design method, and unsatisfactory with another.

OVERALL HEAT LOSS METHOD

Calculate area and volume, and average U-value. Floor area, and height to plane of insulation, are as above.

Element	Area	U-value	Area x U-value
Exposed or semi-exposed	m²	W/m²K	W/K
Floor: (14 x 8.5)	119.00	0.45	53.55
Wall: (walls minus opes)	92.29	0.50	46.15
Opes: (Single glazed, wood frame)	15.71	4.70	73.83
Roof	119.00 346.00	0.28	33.32 206.85

Total Area (At)   **346.00m²**
Total AU   **206.85 W/K**

The actual average U-value of the dwelling
$$U_m = \frac{Total\ AU}{A_t} = \frac{206.85}{346.00} = 0.60\ W/m^2K$$

From Diagram 2, TGD page 8, calculate the maximum allowable average U-value, U_m, having regard to the area and volume of the building.
Area of exposed and semi-exposed elements:
$A_t = 346.00\ m^2$
Building volume [V] = 285.60m³ from above.

$$\frac{A_t}{V} = \frac{346.00}{285.60} = 1.21$$

Maximum allowable U_m (from TGD Table 2, page 8) = 0.60 W/m²K.
On this calculation basis the proposed specifications are acceptable.

Now check the maximum average elemental U-values have also been met.

Element	Max. Aver. Elem. U-value	Calculated U-value
Ground floor	0.45 W/m²K	0.45 satisfactory
Walls	0.55 W/m²K	0.50 satisfactory
Roof	0.35 W/m²K	0.28 satisfactory

The design as checked by the Overall Heat Loss Method is satisfactory.

ELEMENTAL HEAT LOSS METHOD

Having worked out the actual U-value of each element, the Elemental Heat Loss Method involves (1) checking the actual U-values against those required, and (2) an examination of the area of window, rooflight and door openings, to see (a) what proportion, if any, must be double glazed; and (b) that the total area of standard double glazing does not exceed 22.5% of the floor area.

(1) Checking out the actual U-values against those required

Element	Max. Aver. Elem. U-value	Calculated U-value
Ground floor	0.45 W/m²K	0.45 satisfactory
Exposed walls	0.45 W/m²K	0.50 not satisfactory
Exposed roof	0.28 W/m²K	0.28 not satisfactory

To lower the U-value for exposed walls to 0.45 W/m²K, increase the quantity of insulation.

To find out by how much, study TGD Table 14, page 33. Conductivity of expanded polystyrene = 0.037 W/mK as before.

Required increase in wall insulation thickness is 9mm. So, use 60 mm insulation in the cavities in lieu of the initially proposed 50 mm.

Using TGD table 9, page 30 with additional insulation over joists, required increase in roof insulation is 25mm. 100mm between joists with 75 over joists against thermal bridging. (not preventing thermal bridging would need further 25mm as TGD table 8).

(2) Area of openings in the external envelope: windows, rooflights, external doors.

Total openings in roof and external walls = 15.71 m² from above: Floor area = 119.00 m² also from above; total proportion of openings area to floor area: 13.2%.

- 13.2% requires U-value of 5.48 W/m²K (TGD table 3, page 8):
- Actual U-value = 4.7 W/m²K, **So glazing is acceptable.**

If the design is checked by the Elemental Heat Loss Method, two changes must be introduced:

[1]   thicker wall insulation, and
[2]   thicker roof insulation.

HEAT ENERGY RATING METHOD (H.E.R.)

Additional data required for the H.E.R method:

The construction is standard with no air sealing.
- 1 large flue (chimney)
- 1 small flue (gas boiler)
- 5 small openings
- No fans
- No draught lobbies
- All sides exposed.

Heat system is a standard gas boiler with radiator distribution system, (pipes insulated and embedded in ground floor slab).
Hot water tank is 120 litres with a foam jacket 40 mm thick. Controls are of a basic nature.

The Maximum Permitted Heat Energy Rating for an

$$\frac{A_t}{V} = 1.21 \text{ is } 138.97 \text{ kWh/m}^2.\text{yr.}$$

The 2 page worksheet on the following pages...

A Heat Energy Rating of 130.6 kWh/m².yr has been achieved.

In addition, the house also complies with:

1. Achieving elemental U-values as stated

Roofs	0.35 W/m²K;
Walls	0.55 W/m²K;
Ground floors	0.45 W/m²K.

2. Provisions for thermal bridging as required in TGD-L;

3. Provisions for air infiltration as required in TGD-L;

4. Provisions for space and hot water controls as required in TGD-L;

5. Provisions for insulation of hot water storage vessels, and

6. Provisions for insulation of pipes and ducts.

Therefore, the house complies.

COMMENT

- Common to all three calculation methods is the requirement to calculate the U-values of the elements: walls, roofs, floors. These U-values do not vary if the construction and materials remain the same.

- This explains the advice in the general Homebond leaflet on the Regulations.

  If one uses:

  - standard pitched roof construction with 175 glassfibre of conductivity = 0.040 W/mK as before.

  - standard two leaf plastered/rendered insulated cavity wall construction with 60 expanded polystyrene of conductivity = 0.037 W/mK.

  - standard ground floor concrete slab on ground with 47 expanded polystyrene of conductivity = 0/037 W/mK.

  - the construction meets the requirements of the Elemental Heat Loss Method and the area of external opes is the only concern. If these are double glazed throughout, the only calculation is to check that the area of external opes is less than 22.5% of floor area.

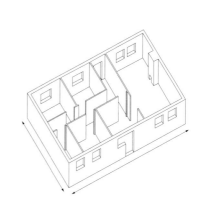

EXAMPLE 1 - DETACHED BUNGALOW - Heat Energy Rating Method•Worksheet•Page 1

DWELLINGS - ASSESSMENT OF COMPLIANCE ON BASIS OF HEAT ENERGY RATING

STANDARD CALCULATION WORKSHEET

1. OVERALL DWELLING DIMENSIONS

	Floor Area (m^2)			Ave. Storey Height (m)			Volume (m^3)		Additional Parts		
Ground Floor	119.00	(1)	x	2.40	(4)	=	285.60	(7)			
First Floor	0.00	(2)	x	0.00	(5)	=	0.00	(8)	Floor Area (m^2)	0.00	(10)
Second Floor	0.00	(3)	x	0.00	(6)	=	0.00	(9)	Volume (m^3)	0.00	(11)

FLOOR AREA (A_t) (1) + (2) + (3) + (10) = 119.00 (12)

VOLUME (V) = (7) + (8) + (9) + (11) = 285.60 (13)

2. RATE OF HEAT LOSS THROUGH THE BUILDING FABRIC

ELEMENTS	Area (A) (m^2)		U-value (U) (W/m^2K)		Rate of Heat Loss (A) x (U) (W/K)		ELEMENTS	Area (A) (m^2)		U-value (U) (W/m^2K)		Rate of Heat Loss (A) x (U) (W/K)	
Roof (type 1)	119.00	(14) x	0.28	=	33.32	(14a)	Rooflights	0.00	(23) x	0.00	=	0.00	(23a)
Roof (type 2)	0.00	(15) x	0.00	=	0.00	(15a)	Window (Type 1)	11.30	(24) x	4.70	=	53.11	(24a)
Wall (type1)	92.29	(16) x	0.50	=	46.15	(16a)	Window (Type 2)	0.00	(25) x	0.00	=	0.00	(25a)
Wall (type 2)	0.00	(17) x	0.00	=	0.00	(17a)	Door (Type 1)	4.41	(26) x	3.00	=	13.23	(26a)
Ground Floor (type 1)	119.00	(18) x	0.45	=	53.55	(18a)	Door (Type 2)	0.00	(27) x	0.00	=	0.00	(27a)
Ground Floor (Type 2)	0.00	(19) x	0.00	=	0.00	(19a)	Other	0.00	(28) x	0.00	=	0.00	(28a)
Other Exposed Floor	0.00	(20) x	0.00	=	0.00	(20a)							
Semi-Exposed element (Type 1)	0.00	(21) x	0.00	=	0.00	(21a)							
Semi-Exposed element (Type 2)	0.00	(22) x	0.00	=	0.00	(22a)							

Area of Exposed and Semi-exposed Elements (A_1): (m^2)

Sum of (A) = (14) + (15) +.........+ (27) + (28) = 346.00 (29)

Rate of Heat Loss through the Fabric: (W/K)

Sum of (A)x(U) = (14a) + (15a) + ...+ (27a) + (28a) = 199.36 (30)

3. RATE OF HEAT LOSS DUE TO VENTILATION

a) Basic Air Change Rate	Air changes per hour (ach)		b) Effect of, Flues, Vents, Fans, etc.		m^3 per hour	
i) effect of type of construction:- standard - 0.4ach			i) Number of large flues/chimneys	1 x 40 =	40.00	(35)
"sealed" - 0.3ach	0.4	(31)	ii) Number of small flues	1 x 20 =	20.00	(36)
ii) effect of height:- ((no. of storeys-1) x 0.1) ach	0.00	(32)	Number of permanent vents			
			iii) - large (opening > 5000 mm^2)	0 x 15 =	0.00	(37)
iii) suspended timber floor:- (0.1/ no. of storeys) ach	0.00	(33)	iv) - small (opening < 5000 mm^2)	5 x 8 =	40.00	(38)
			v) Number of passive vents	0 x 10 =	0.00	(39)
Total Basic Air Change Rate (31) + (32) + (33) =	0.40	(34)	vi) Number of fans	0 x 10 =	0.00	(40)
			vii) Number of ext. doors without draught lobby	2 x 10 =	20.00	(41)

Gross Air Change Rate (34) +(42) = 0.82 (43)

Total air change rate due to chimneys, flues, vents, fans, etc. (ach)

[(35) + (36) + (37) + (38) + (39) + (40) + (41)] /(13) = 0.42 (42)

Adjustment for Degree of Shelter

No. of sides sheltered 0.00 (44)

Shelter Factor 1 - ((44) x 0.075) 1.00 (45)

Adjusted Air Change Rate (43) x (45) = 0.82 (46)

Effective Air Change Rate (allowing for Occupant Controlled Ventilation) Air changes per hour (ach)

For Adjusted Air Change Rate greater than 1: = (46)

For Adjusted Air Change Rate less than 1: = 0.5 + [(46)^2 x 0.5] 0.84 (47)

Rate of Heat Loss due to Ventilation (47) x (13) x 0.33 = 79.17 (48) (W/K)

Specific Heat Loss - Fabric and Infiltration (30) + (48) = 278.53 (49) (W/K)

EXAMPLE 1 - Worksheet•Page 2

4. WATER HEATING

Energy content of heated water   (kWh/yr) | 1851 |(50)
(See Table 21)

Allowance for losses
Distribution Losses (kWh/yr) | 309 |(51)   Storage Losses
(See Table 21)   (for all systems with a hot water tank or cylinder)
(for all systems other than   Tank Volume (litres) | 120.00 |(52)
instantaneous water heating at point of use)   Tank Loss Factor (see Table 22) | 0.00 |(53)
            Tank Losses (kWh/yr)   (52) x (53) = | 455 |(54)

            Primary Circuit losses (kWh/yr)   (See Table 23) | 361.00 |(55)

Total Losses (kWh/yr)   (51) + (54) + (55) = | 1125 |(56)

| Energy for Water Heating   (kWh/yr)   (50) + (56) = | 2976 |(57) |

5. SOLAR AND OTHER ENERGY GAINS

a) Solar Gains

Orientation	Area (m^2)		Flux (W/m^2) (See Table 24)		Shading Correction Factor		Gains (W)	
North	5.00	x	10.00	x	1.00	=	50.00	(58)
Northeast	0.00	x	0.00	x	0.00	=	0.00	(59)
East	0.00	x	0.00	x	0.00	=	0.00	(60)
Southeast	5.40	x	29.00	x	1.00	=	156.60	(61)
South	0.00	x	0.00	x	0.00	=	0.00	(62)
Southwest	0.00	x	0.00	x	0.00	=	0.00	(63)
West	0.90	x	20.00	x	1.00	=	18.00	(64)
Northwest	0.00	x	0.00	x	0.00	=	0.00	(65)
Rooflights	0.00	x	0.00	x	0.00	=	0.00	(66)

Total Solar Gains   (58) + (59) + ...+ (65) + (66) = | 224.60 |(67)

b) Other Energy Gains

            Gains (W)
i) Water Heating
0.114 x (.8 x (56) + .25 x (50)) = | 155.35 |(68)

ii) Lights, appliances,
    cooking, occupants, etc. | 607.85 |(69)
(See Table 25)

Total Other Gains   (68) + (69) = | 763.20 |(70)

Total Gains   (67) + (70) = | 987.80 |(71)   Gains/Loss Ratio   (71)/(49) = | 3.55 |(72)

Utilisation Factor | 0.99 |(73)   Useful Gains   (71) x (73) = | 978 |(74)
(See Table 26)

| Temperature Rise from Gains   (K)   (74) / (49) = | 3.51 |(75) |

6. SPACE HEATING

                                                 kWh/yr
Mean Internal Temperature (K) | 18.45 |(76)   Energy to meet Space Heat Demand   0.024 x (78) x (49) = | 11883 |(79)
(see Table 27)
Base Temperature (K)   (76) - (75) = | 14.94 |(77)   Allowance for losses and equipment energy use
            Distribution Losses (kWh/yr)   (See Table 29) | 180 |(80)
Degree Days | 1777.58 |(78)   Equipment Energy Use (kWh/yr) (See Table 30) | 120 |(81)
(See Table 28)

| Energy for Space Heating   (kWh/yr)   (79) + (80) + (81) = | 12183 |(82) |

7. HEAT ENERGY RATING (HER)

Energy for Space and Water Heating   (kWh/yr)   (57) + (82) = | 15159 |(83)

| Heat Energy Rating   (kWh/m^2/yr)   (83) / (12) = | 127.39 |(84) |

| At/V (29)/(13) = | 1.21 |(85)   Maximum Permitted Heat Energy Rating (kWh/m^2/yr)   (See Table 4) | 138.97 |(86) |

EXAMPLE TWO: HEAT LOSS CALCULATIONS:
TWO STOREY SEMI-DETACHED HOUSE

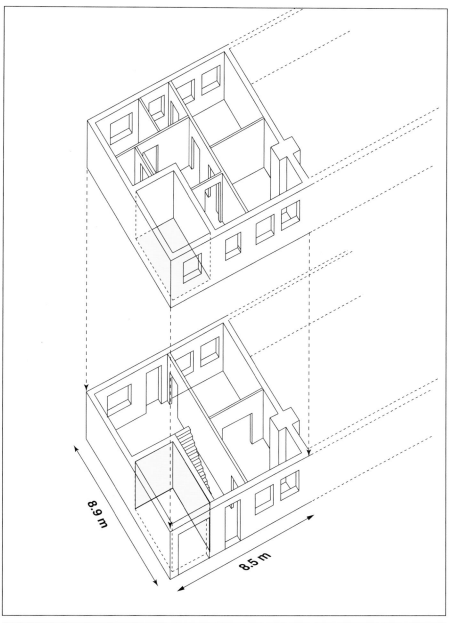

This two storey semi-detached house has an integral, unheated, garage. In accordance with diagram 1, page 6 of the TGD, the coloured walls and floor around and over this garage are treated as semi-exposed elements.

Insulate roof at ceiling level.

CONSTRUCTION

Ground floor:

- Concrete slab-on-ground;
- 45 extruded polystyrene, DPM.

Suspended floor over garage:

- 22 softwood boarding on 175 x 44 joists;
- 100 glassfibre batt between joists, and
- 15 fire-rated gypsum board to soffit.

External walls:

- Single leaf 215 hollow concrete blockwork;
- 60 expanded polystyrene to inner face;
- External finish: 19 render, and
- Internal finish: 12.5 foil-back plasterboard on battens.

Windows and external doors:

- Double glazed, metal frame, 6mm air gap.

Roof:

- Pitched tiled; felt; ventilated roof space;
- 150 glassfibre quilt at ceiling level (100 between joists and 50 over joists), and
- 12.5 plasterboard and skim.

DIMENSIONS

8.5 m x 8.9 m externally.
7.9 m x 8.3 m internally.
2400 floor to ceiling height.
200 deep first floor zone.
5000 floor to top floor ceiling height.

Floor area [A]:		*119.00 m²*
Volume [V]:		*287 m³*
Perimeter [P]: =		*23.9 m*
P/A:	23.9/48 =	*0.50*

EXTERNAL OPES
North: **10.35 m²** South: **10.59 m²**

ALL METHODS: CALCULATE THE U-VALUES

- As example one.
- Exclude unheated area and volume from the calculations.

GROUND FLOOR:

Concrete slab on ground.
Perimeter (P) = (8.3 + 3.4 + 2.4 +3.9 + 5.9) = 23.9 m.
Heated area (A) = (7.9 x 8.3) - (2.4 x 4.2) = 48 sq.m.
P/A = 23.9/48.0 = 0.5

Insulation type, from design data: Extruded polystyrene;
Insulation thermal conductivity: 0.025 from TGD table 5, page 19;
Given insulation thickness, from design data: 46 mm;
Insulation thermal resistance, by calculation: 0.046 / 0.025 = 1.84;
U-value of insulated ground floor, for P/A = 0.50, from TGD table 7, page 25: 0.37.

Note that if insulation thickness was not specified in advance:
Required U-value = 0.45 W/m²K;
Necessary thermal resistance of added insulation, from TGD table 7, page 25: 1.25;
Insulation: Extruded polystyrene: thermal conductivity: 0.025 from TGD table 5, page 19;
Required insulation thickness: 1.25 x 0.025 = 31 mm.

INTERMEDIATE FLOOR:

Insulation: From design data: Glassfibre batt between joists;
Thermal conductivity: 0.035 from TGD table 5, page 19;
Floor type: from design data: as TGD table 19, page 35: insulation between joists;
Proposed insulation thickness: 100 mm, from design data;
U-value: 0.32, by interpolation of TGD table 19, page 35.

EXPOSED WALLS:

Insulation: Expanded polystyrene: thermal conductivity: 0.037 from TGD table 5, page 19;
Wall type: from design data: as TGD table 17, page 34: hollow block wall, rendered externally, plasterboard fixed to timber battens internally, insulation between battens;
Proposed insulation thickness: 60 mm, from design data;
U-value: 0.50, by interpolation of TGD table 17, page 34.

SEMI-EXPOSED WALLS AT GARAGE:

Use notional U-value of (0.75) x (Actual U-value) from TGD paragraph 1.2.1, page 7;
Notional U-value = 0.75 x 0.50 = 0.38.

WINDOWS:

Double glazed, metal frame, 6 mm air gap: from design data;
Indicative U-value, from TGD table 20, page 36: 4.2.

ROOF:

Insulation: Glassfibre quilt: thermal conductivity: 0.040 from TGD table 5, page 19;
Roof type: from design data: as TGD table 9, page 30: tiled pitched roof, ventilated roof space, plasterboard ceiling, 100 mm insulation between joists at ceiling level and additional insulation over joists;
Proposed insulation thickness: 150 mm, from design data;
U-value: 0.25, by interpolation of TGD table 9, page 30.

OVERALL HEAT LOSS METHOD

Calculate area and volume, and average U-value. Floor area, and height to plane of insulation, are as above.

Element Exposed or semi-exposed	Area m²	U-value W/m²K	Area x U-value W/K
Ground floor excl. garage	54	0.37	20
Intermediate floor over garage	10.80	0.32	3.46
Exposed wall	82.52	0.50	42
(Total external wall to heated volume, less external opes and less semi-exposed wall to garage)			
Semi-exposed wall to garage	17.04	0.38	6.48
Windows double glazed, metal frame,doors	20.94	4.20	87.95
Roof	65.57 250.87	0.25	16.39 176.28

Total Area (At)   **250.87m²**
Total AU   **176.28 W/K**

Actual average U-value of dwelling

$$U_m = \frac{\text{Total AU}}{A_t} = \frac{176.28}{250.87} = 0.70 \text{ W/m}^2\text{K}$$

From Diagram 2, TGD page 8, calculate the maximum allowable average U-value, U_m having regard to the area and volume of the building.

Area of exposed and semi-exposed elements:
A_t = 250.87 m².
Building volume [V] = 287.00m³ from above.

$$\frac{A_t}{V} = \frac{250.87}{287.00} = 0.875$$

Maximum allowable U_m (from TGD Table 2, p. 8) = 0.68 W/m²K. On this calculation basis, the proposed specifications are **not acceptable.**

To achieve compliance:
Substitute thermally broken window frames:
Area 20.94
U = 3.60
AU = 75.38
Revised Total AU = 162.25

$$\frac{\text{Revised AU}}{A_t} = 0.65$$

The revised construction now achieves compliance using the overall Heat Loss Method. Average elemental U-values have also been met.

Element	Max. Aver. Elem. U-value	Calculated U-value
Ground floor	0.45 W/m²K	0.37 satisfactory
Walls	0.55 W/m²K	0.51 satisfactory
Roof	0.35 W/m²K	0.25 satisfactory

The revised design as checked by the Overall Heat Loss Method is now satisfactory.

ELEMENTAL HEAT LOSS METHOD

(1) Check the actual U-values against those required.

Element Elem. U-value	Max. Aver. U-value	Calculated
Ground floor	0.45 W/m²K	0.37 satisfactory
Exposed walls	0.45 W/m²K	0.51 not satisfactory
Exposed roof	0.25 W/m²K	0.25 satisfactory
Semi-exposed floor	0.60 W/m²K	0.32 satisfactory
Semi-exposed wall	0.60 W/m²K	0.38 satisfactory

To bring the U-value for exposed walls down to 0.45 W/m²K, increase the insulation:
TGD-L, table 18, page 34.

Conductivity for expanded polystyrene = 0.037 W/mK as before.

Required thickness of insulation is 70 mm, by interpolation on the table.

(2) Examination of the amount of glazing

Total area of openings in external wall
= 20.94 m², from above;

Total floor area
= 119.00 m², also from above;

Total proportion of opening area to floor area: 18%.
18% equates [TGD-L, table 3, page 8] to a required U-value of 4.0

The example would not comply if standard metal frames (U = 4.2 from TGD table 20, page 36.) were used, However, thermally broken frames (U = 3.6, TGD, table 20) will comply.

The 18% proportion of opening to floor area satisfies the maximum allowable opening requirement.

HEAT ENERGY RATING METHOD (H.E.R.)

Additional data required for the H.E.R. method:

The construction is standard with no air sealing.

- 2 storey building;
- 1 large flue (chimney);
- 1 small flue (gas boiler);
- 7 small openings;
- No fans;
- No draught lobbies, and
- Three sides exposed.

Heat system is a standard gas boiler with radiator distribution system (pipes insulated and embedded in ground floor slab).
Hot water tank is 120 litres with a foam jacket 40 mm thick.
Controls are of a basic nature.
The two-page worked example on the following pages gives the detail of the H.E.R. calculation method for this house.
The Maximum Permitted Heat Energy Rating for an

$$\frac{At}{V} = 0.87 \text{ is } 119.59 \text{ kWh/m}^2.\text{yr}$$

A Heat Energy Rating of 111.52 kWh/m².yr has been achieved.

In addition, the house also complies with:

7. Achieving elemental U-values as stated:

Roofs	0.35 W/m²K;
Walls	0.55 W/m²K;
Ground floors	0.45 W/m²K.

8. Provisions for thermal bridging as required in TGD-L.

9. Provisions for air infiltration as required in TGD-L.

10. Provisions for space and hot water controls as required in TGD-L.

11. Provisions for insulation of hot water storage vessels.

12. Provisions for insulation of pipes and ducts.

Therefore, the house complies.

COMMENT

- Using the **Overall Heat Loss Method**, the design, initially unsatisfactory, achieved compliance by the substitution of thermally broken metal window frames instead of the standard frames.

- The same is also true when using the **Elemental Heat Loss Method.** In addition for the Elemental Heat Loss Method however, the wall insulation thickness must be increased to achieve compliance.

- Under the **Heat Energy Rating Method,** which takes account of orientation, solar gain, type of heating system and air tightness / ventilation, compliance can be achieved without changing external walls or windows.

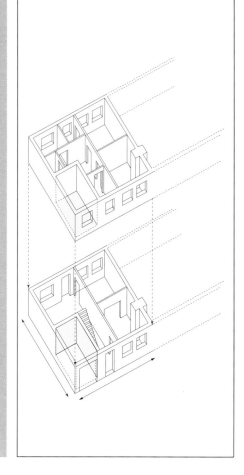

EXAMPLE 2 - WORKSHEET•Page 1

DWELLINGS - ASSESSMENT OF COMPLIANCE ON BASIS OF HEAT ENERGY RATING

STANDARD CALCULATION WORKSHEET

1. OVERALL DWELLING DIMENSIONS

	Floor Area (m²)			Ave. Storey Height (m)			Volume (m³)			
Ground Floor	54.00	(1) x		2.40	(4) =		129.60	(7)	Additional Parts	
First Floor	65.57	(2) x		2.40	(5) =		157.37	(8)	Floor Area (m²) 0.00 (10)	
Second Floor	0.00	(3) x		0.00	(6) =		0.00	(9)	Volume (m³) 0.00 (11)	

FLOOR AREA (A_f) (1) + (2) + (3) + (10) = 119.57 (12)

VOLUME (V) = (7) + (8) + (9) + (11) = 286.97 (13)

2. RATE OF HEAT LOSS THROUGH THE BUILDING FABRIC

ELEMENTS	Area (A) (m²)		U-value (U) (W/m²K)		Rate of Heat Loss (A) x (U) (W/K)		ELEMENTS	Area (A) (m²)		U-value (U) (W/m²K)		Rate of Heat Loss (A) x (U) (W/K)	
Roof (type 1)	65.57	(14) x	0.25	=	16.39	(14a)	Rooflights	0.00	(23) x	0.00	=	0.00	(23a)
Roof (type 2)	0.00	(15) x	0.00	=	0.00	(15a)	Window (Type 1)	20.94	(24) x	4.20	=	87.95	(24a)
Wall (type1)	82.52	(16) x	0.51	=	42.09	(16a)	Window (Type 2)	0.00	(25) x	0.00	=	0.00	(25a)
Wall (type 2)	0.00	(17) x	0.00	=	0.00	(17a)	Door (Type 1)	0.00	(26) x	0.00	=	0.00	(26a)
Ground Floor (type 1)	54.00	(18) x	0.37	=	19.98	(18a)	Door (Type 2)	0.00	(27) x	0.00	=	0.00	(27a)
Ground Floor (Type 2)	0.00	(19) x	0.00	=	0.00	(19a)	Other	0.00	(28) x	0.00	=	0.00	(28a)
Other Exposed Floor	0.00	(20) x	0.00	=	0.00	(20a)							
Semi-Exposed element (Type 1)	17.04	(21) x	0.38	=	6.48	(21a)							
Semi-Exposed element (Type 2)	10.80	(22) x	0.28	=	3.02	(22a)							

Area of Exposed and Semi-exposed Elements (A_t): (m²)

Sum of (A) = (14) + (15) +.........+ (27) + (28) = 250.87 (29)

Rate of Heat Loss through the Fabric: (W/K)

Sum of (A)x(U) = (14a) + (15a) + ...+ (27a) + (28a) = 175.91 (30)

3. RATE OF HEAT LOSS DUE TO VENTILATION

	Air changes per hour (ach)		m³ per hour	
a) Basic Air Change Rate		b) Effect of, Flues, Vents, Fans, etc.		
i) effect of type of construction:- standard - 0.4ach "sealed" - 0.3ach	0.4 (31)	i) Number of large flues/chimneys	1 x 40 =	40.00 (35)
ii) effect of height:- ((no. of storeys-1) x 0.1) ach	0.10 (32)	ii) Number of small flues	1 x 20 =	20.00 (36)
		Number of permanent vents		
		iii) - large (opening > 5000 mm²)	0 x 15 =	0.00 (37)
iii) suspended timber floor:- (0.1/ no. of storeys) ach	0.00 (33)	iv) - small (opening < 5000 mm²)	7 x 8 =	56.00 (38)
		v) Number of passive vents	0 x 10 =	0.00 (39)
Total Basic Air Change Rate (31) + (32) + (33) =	0.50 (34)	vi) Number of fans	0 x 10 =	0.00 (40)
		vii) Number of ext. doors without draught lobby	2 x 10 =	20.00 (41)
Gross Air Change Rate (34) +(42) =	0.97 (43)			
		Total air change rate due to chimneys, flues, vents, fans, etc. (ach)		
Adjustment for Degree of Shelter		[(35) + (36) + (37) + (38) + (39) + (40) + (41)] /(13) =		0.47 (42)
No. of sides sheltered	1.00 (44)			
Shelter Factor 1 - ((44) x 0.075)	0.93 (45)			
Adjusted Air Change Rate (43) x (45) =	0.90 (46)			

Effective Air Change Rate (allowing for Occupant Controlled Ventilation)

Air changes per hour (ach)

For Adjusted Air Change Rate greater than 1: = (46)

For Adjusted Air Change Rate less than 1: = 0.5 + [(46)²x 0.5] 0.91 (47)

Rate of Heat Loss due to Ventilation (47) x (13) x 0.33 = 86.18 (48) (W/K)

Specific Heat Loss - Fabric and Infiltration (30) + (48) = 262.09 (49) (W/K)

EXAMPLE 2 - WORKSHEET•Page 2

4. WATER HEATING

Energy content of heated water   (kWh/yr)   [1857](50)
(See Table 21)

Allowance for losses
Distribution Losses (kWh/yr)   [310](51)   Storage Losses
(See Table 21)   (for all systems with a hot water tank or cylinder)

(for all systems other than   Tank Volume (litres)   [120.00](52)
instantaneous water heating at point of use)   Tank Loss Factor (see Table 22)   [0.00](53)
Tank Losses (kWh/yr)   (52) x (53) =   [332](54)

Primary Circuit losses (kWh/yr)   (See Table 23)   [361.00](55)

Total Losses (kWh/yr)   (51) + (54) + (55) =   [1003](56)

Energy for Water Heating   (kWh/yr)   (50) + (56) =   [2860](57)

5. SOLAR AND OTHER ENERGY GAINS

a) Solar Gains

Orientation	Area (m^2)		Flux (W/m^2) (See Table 24)		Shading Correction Factor		Gains (W)	
North	10.35	x	8.00	x	1.00	=	82.80	(58)
Northeast	0.00	x	0.00	x	0.00	=	0.00	(59)
East	0.00	x	0.00	x	0.00	=	0.00	(60)
Southeast	0.00	x	0.00	x	0.00	=	0.00	(61)
South	10.59	x	28.00	x	1.00	=	296.52	(62)
Southwest	0.00	x	0.00	x	0.00	=	0.00	(63)
West	0.00	x	0.00	x	0.00	=	0.00	(64)
Northwest	0.00	x	0.00	x	0.00	=	0.00	(65)
Rooflights	0.00	x	0.00	x	0.00	=	0.00	(66)

Total Solar Gains   (58) + (59) + ...+ (65) + (66) =   [379.32](67)

b) Other Energy Gains

Gains (W)

i) Water Heating
0.114 x (.8 x (56) + .25 x (50)) =   [144.40](68)

ii) Lights, appliances,
   cooking, occupants, etc.   [610.21](69)
(See Table 25)

Total Other Gains   (68) + (69) =   [754.61](70)

Total Gains   (67) + (70) =   [1133.93](71)   Gains/Loss Ratio   (71)/(49)   =   [4.33](72)

Utilisation Factor   [0.98](73)   Useful Gains   (71) x (73) =   [1111](74)
(See Table 26)

Temperature Rise from Gains   (K)   (74) / (49) =   [4.24](75)

6. SPACE HEATING

Mean Internal Temperature (K)   [18.45](76)   Energy to meet Space Heat Demand   0.024 x (78) x (49) =   kWh/yr [10231](79)
(see Table 27)

Base Temperature (K)   (76) - (75) =   [14.21](77)   Allowance for losses and equipment energy use
Distribution Losses (kWh/yr)   (See Table 29)   [124](80)

Degree Days   [1626.47](78)   Equipment Energy Use (kWh/yr) (See Table 30)   [120](81)
(See Table 28)

Energy for Space Heating   (kWh/yr)   (79) + (80) + (81) =   [10475](82)

7. HEAT ENERGY RATING (HER)

Energy for Space and Water Heating   (kWh/yr)   (57) + (82) =   [13335](83)

Heat Energy Rating   (kWh/m^2/yr)   (83) / (12) =   [111.52](84)

At/V (29)/(13) =   [0.87](85)   Maximum Permitted
Heat Energy Rating   [119.59](86)
(kWh/m^2/yr)   (See Table 4)

DESIGN AND CONSTRUCTION: KEY POINTS

Dwelling Extensions

◆ For extensions of 6.5 m² or less, reasonable provision to conserve fuel and energy is made if the new construction is similar to the existing.

Unheated Conservatories and Garages

◆ Unheated ancillary areas such as conservatories, porches, garages and the like do not require specific provisions to conserve fuel and energy provided such areas are separated from the main building by walls, floors, etc., which meet the requirements of Part L.

Conservatories and Heating

◆ Conservatories may be provided with a heating facility for occasional use and for frost protection, provided that:

- They are separated from the adjacent spaces by walls, doors and other opaque or glazed elements;
- They are clearly intended for occupation on an occasional or seasonal basis;
- They have provision for separate temperature and on/off control of the heating;
- Separating walls and floors are insulated as for semi-exposed walls and floors;
- Separating windows and doors are insulated as per Elemental Heat Loss method and meet the requirements for limiting air infiltration.

◆ Conservatories which do not meet the above requirements must be treated as an integral part of the dwelling and assessed for compliance with Part L accordingly.

Good Practice Reference

◆ See Building Research Establishment Digest 262 "Thermal Insulation: avoiding risks" for guidance on good design and construction practice for insulation generally.

REGULATIONS REVOKED

The 1997 Regulations revoke the following Statutory Instruments:
Building Control Regulations, 1991: S.I. 305 of 1991;
Building Regulations, 1991: S.I. 306 of 1991;
Building Control Act, 1990 (Appeals) Regulations, 1992: S.I. 111 of 1992;
Building Control Act, 1990 (Fees) Regulations, 1992: S.I. 112 of 1992;
Building Control Act, 1990 (Fees) (Amendment) Regulations, 1992: S.I. 182 of 1992;
Building Control (Amendment) Regulations, 1994: S.I. 153 of 1994;
Building Regulations (Amendment) Regulations, 1994: S.I. 154 of 1994.

The 1991 Technical Guidance Documents and the 1994 TGD Supplement are superseded by 1997 editions.

RELEVANT PUBLICATIONS

Building Control Act, 1990 (No. 3 of 1990).
Building Control Regulations, 1997: S.I. 496 of 1997
Building Regulations, 1997: S.I. 497 of 1997.

1997 Technical Guidance Documents Parts:
A: Structure;
B: Fire Safety;
C: Site Preparation and Resistance to Moisture;
D: Materials and Workmanship;
E: Sound;
F: Ventilation;
G: Hygiene;
H: Drainage and Waste Water Disposal;
J: Heat Producing Appliances;
K: Stairways, Ladders, Ramps and Guards;
L: Conservation of Fuel and Energy, and
M: Access for Disabled People.

General Advice and Guidelines for Building Control Authorities, May 1992.
The Building Control System 1992, and Applications for Fire Safety Certificates: A guide for designers, July 1992
Circular letter BCL 6/92, on timber holiday chalets and Part L of the Regulations.

Homebond Publications

Right on the Site:
No.12: Radon
Housing and the Building Regulations, 1997.
Housing Insulation and the Building Regulations, 1997.

Homebond House Building Manual

STANDARD RECOMMENDATION 11 STRUCTURAL TIMBER FOR DOMESTIC CONSTRUCTION

REQUIREMENTS OF SR 11

◆ Maximum moisture content of timber: 22%;

◆ Applicable only to normal domestic houses;

◆ Strength classification, see table opposite;

◆ Stress grading and markings, see page 443.

This Appendix explains SR 11, gives worked examples and reproduces the tables.

STRENGTH CLASSES

SR 11 divides timber in ascending order of strength into three strength classes (SC A, SC B and SC C) depending on the species and grade of timber.

The particular species and grades of Irish and imported timbers that fall into these Strength Classes are set out in the table below.

Softwood Species	Strength classes		
	SC A	SC B	SC C
Irish Timber:			
Sitka Spruce	GS	SS	M75
Norway Spruce	GS	SS	M75
Douglas Fir	GS		SS
Larch		GS	SS
Imported Timber:			
Whitewood*		GS	SS
Redwood*		GS	SS
Fir-Larch**		GS	SS
Spruce-Pine-Fir**		GS	SS
Hem-fir**		GS	SS

* European   ** North American

Timber Grades
The grade abbreviations in the above table as follows:

Visually graded
General Structural: GS
Special Structural: SS

Machine grade:
M75.

STRESS GRADING AND MARKINGS

It is a requirement of SR 11 that all structural timber used shall be stress graded and marked accordingly. The marking system identifies the stress grade and Strength Class of the timber and the registered number of the timber grader and the company. Both the grading and marking of timber by individual companies is subjected to the supervisory control of the Timber Quality Bureau of Ireland, Enterprise Ireland.

On this page are illustrated examples of the markings which occur on stress graded timber in accordance with SR 11.

Span tables

The following page contains the span table for floor joists from SR 11 and examples of its application. The key factor when reading the span tables is to correlate the span, section size and the joist centres applicable with the Strength Class of the timbers. It will be noted that the permissible spans increase from SC A to SC B to SC C for the same section sizes and spacings.

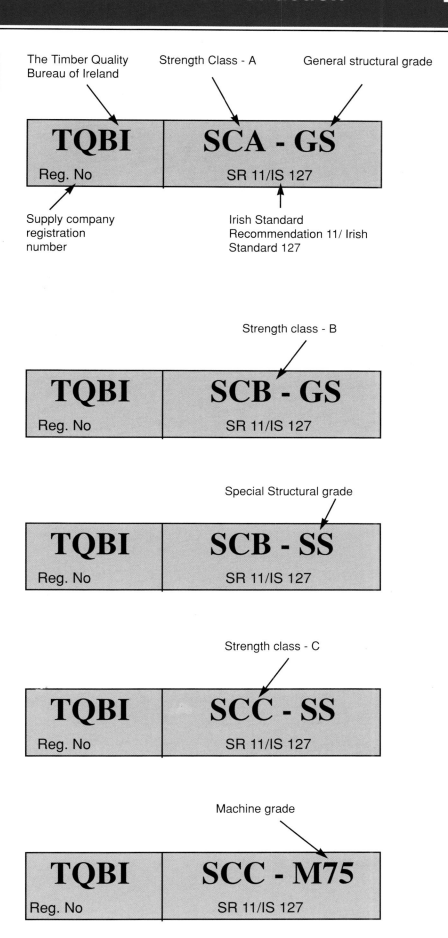

FLOOR JOIST SPAN TABLES

Target size of joist (mm)	Strength Class								
	SC A			SC B			SC C		
	Spacing of joists (mm)								
	300	400	600	300	400	600	300	400	600
	Permissible span of joists in metres								
35 x 100	2.02	1.81	1.48	2.12	1.92	1.67	2.21	2.00	1.74
35 x 115	2.33	2.07	1.69	2.43	2.21	1.92	2.54	2.30	2.00
35 x 125	2.54	2.24	1.83	2.65	2.40	2.09	2.76	2.50	2.18
35 x 150	3.04	2.66	2.17	3.18	2.88	2.51	3.31	3.01	2.62
35 x 175	3.54	3.08	2.51	3.71	3.37	2.93	3.87	3.51	3.05
35 x 200†	4.04	3.50	2.85	4.25	3.85	3.34	4.42	4.01	3.49
35 x 225†	4.51	3.91	3.19	4.78	4.33	3.73	4.98	4.51	3.93
44 x 100	2.19	1.98	1.66	2.26	2.08	1.81	2.39	2.16	1.89
44 x 115	2.52	2.28	1.89	2.63	2.39	2.07	2.74	2.48	2.16
44 x 125	2.74	2.48	2.05	2.87	2.59	2.25	2.98	2.71	2.35
44 x 150	3.28	2.98	2.43	3.44	3.12	2.72	3.58	3.25	2.83
44 x 175	3.84	3.45	2.82	4.02	3.65	3.16	4.18	3.79	3.30
44 x 200	4.38	3.92	3.20	4.59	4.16	3.62	4.78	4.33	3.77
44 x 225†	4.94	4.38	3.57	5.17	4.69	4.08	5.38	4.88	4.24
63 x 150	3.71	3.37	2.91	3.89	3.52	3.07	4.04	3.64	3.20
63 x 175	4.33	3.93	3.37	4.54	4.12	3.58	4.72	4.28	3.73
63 x 225	5.58	5.06	4.28	5.83	5.29	4.61	6.07	5.51	4.80
75 x 150	3.94	3.58	3.11	4.12	3.74	3.26	4.29	3.89	3.40
75 x 175	4.60	4.17	3.63	4.81	4.37	3.80	5.01	4.54	3.96
75 x 225	5.91	5.37	4.67	6.19	5.61	4.89	6.44	5.84	5.09

† This joist requires bridging at intervals of 1350 mm.
The above joist sizes are the minimum permissable sizes at 22% moisture content.
The permissible span is the clear span between supports.

TABLE 5, SR 11: FOR USE IN SIZING DOMESTIC FLOOR JOISTS. THE USE OF THIS TABLE IS ESSENTIAL TO ENSURE PROPERLY SIZED AND SPACED FLOOR JOISTS. NOTE: THIS TABLE DOES NOT ALLOW FOR POINT LOADS SUCH AS PARTITIONS.

SIZING FLOOR JOISTS

The following example illustrates the use of the span tables in sizing floor joists.

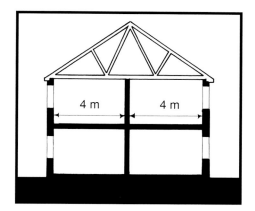

A house with an internal span of 8 m has an internal load bearing wall provided at mid-span as illustrated. The timber specified is Irish grown Sitka Spruce of General Structural Grade (GS).

From the table on page 442 this type of timber is in Strength Class A (SC A).

From the extract of the span tables reproduced below, a floor joist spanning 4 m can be chosen from either 35 x 200 mm at 300 mm centres, or 44 x 225 mm at 400 mm centres, (Note: These joists require bridging at 1350 mm centres).

Strength Class			
Target size of joist (mm)	SC A		
	Spacing of joists (mm)		
	300	400	600
	Permissible span in (m)		
35 x 100	2.02	1.81	1.48
35 x 115	2.33	2.07	1.69
35 x 125	2.54	2.24	1.83
35 x 150	3.04	2.66	2.17
35 x 175	3.54	3.08	2.51
35 x.200†	4.04	3.50	2.85
35 x 225†	4.51	3.91	3.19
44 x 100	2.19	1.98	1.66
44 x 115	2.52	2.28	1.89
44 x 125	2.74	2.48	2.05
44 x 150	3.28	2.98	2.43
44 x 175	3.84	3.45	2.82
44 x 200	4.38	3.92	3.20
44 x 225†	4.94	4.38	3.57
63 x 150	3.71	3.37	2.91
63 x 175	4.33	3.93	3.37
63 x 225	5.58	5.06	4.28
75 x 150	3.94	3.58	3.11
75 x 175	4.60	4.17	3.63
75 x 225	5.91	5.37	4.67

† This joist requires bridging at intervals of 1350 mm.

Depending on the joist span, availability and cost of material, the most economical section can be selected. This also applies to choice of Strength Class provided that this is not specified.

CEILING JOISTS

The permissible span according to SR 11 is the clear span between supports. However, traditional roof construction assumes that a binder/hanger connection supports the ceiling joist, the binder/ hangers being securely fixed to the ceiling joist. Based on this assumption, the span of the ceiling joist would be from the support to the binder connection.

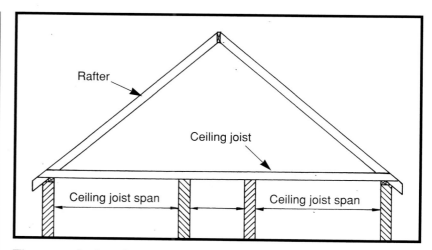

The span is the clear span between supports.

Size of joist (mm)	Strength Class								
	SC A			SC B			SC C		
	Spacing of joists (mm)								
	300	400	600	300	400	600	300	400	600
	Permissible span of joist in metres								
35 x 100	1.42	1.39	1.35	1.84	1.81	1.76	1.94	1.92	1.86
35 x 115	1.82	1.78	1.71	2.24	2.21	2.14	2.37	2.33	2.26
35 x 125	2.10	2.05	1.96	2.53	2.48	2.40	2.67	2.62	2.53
35 x 150	2.88	2.79	2.64	3.26	3.19	3.07	3.45	3.37	3.24
35 x 175	3.74	3.60	3.37	4.05	3.94	3.76	4.28	4.16	3.97
35 x.200†	4.57	4.44	4.13	4.86	4.72	4.48	5.13	4.98	4.72
44 x 100	1.76	1.72	1.66	2.06	2.01	1.96	2.16	2.14	2.07
44 x 115	2.24	2.19	2.09	2.50	2.46	2.38	2.64	2.59	2.51
44 x 125	2.59	2.52	2.40	2.81	2.76	2.67	2.98	2.92	2.81
44 x 150	3.42	3.34	3.20	3.63	3.55	3.40	3.84	3.75	3.58
44 x 175	4.23	4.12	3.93	4.50	4.37	4.17	4.75	4.62	4.39
44 x 200	5.07	4.93	4.68	5.39	5.23	4.95	5.69	5.51	5.20

†This joist requires bridging at intervals of 1350 mm

The above joist sizes are the minimum permissible size at 22% moisture content

Example: If ceiling joists of strength class B are required to span 3 m at a spacing of 300 mm, a 35 x 150 mm joist member can be used.

ROOF RAFTERS WITH INTERMEDIATE PURLIN SUPPORT

Roof angle from 20° to 40°.

The rafter spans shown in the tables are measured on plan and are clear spans from wall plate to purlin or purlin to ridge. The following formula may be used to convert spans on plan to spans on slope:

Span on Slope = Span on plan x K
(Span on Plan = Span on Slope ÷ K)

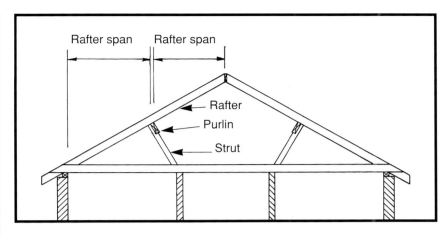

Purlin intermediate support:
The span is either (1) the span between wall plate and purlin measured on plan, or (2) the span between apex and purlin measured on plan.

Roof Pitch (Degrees)	20°	25°	30°	35°	40°
K values	1.06	1.12	1.18	1.24	1.30

Size of rafters (mm)	Strength Class								
	SC A			SC B			SC C		
	Spacing of rafters (mm)								
	300	400	600	300	400	600	300	400	600
	Permissible span of rafters in metres								
35 x 100	2.35	2.03	1.65	2.70	2.35	1.90	2.92	2.53	2.08
35 x 115	2.65	2.30	1.88	3.05	2.65	2.15	3.30	2.85	2.33
35 x 125	2.85	2.47	2.03	3.28	2.85	2.33	3.53	3.08	2.50
35 x 150	3.33	2.90	2.38	3.80	3.30	2.72	4.10	3.58	2.92
35 x 175	3.78	3.30	2.70	4.30	3.75	3.08	4.63	4.05	3.33
44 x 100	2.67	2.30	1.88	3.08	2.67	2.17	3.33	2.90	2.35
44 x 115	3.03	2.63	2.13	3.47	3.03	2.47	3.78	3.28	2.67
44 x 125	3.25	2.83	2.30	3.75	3.25	2.65	4.05	3.50	2.88
44 x 150	3.80	3.30	2.70	4.38	3.80	3.10	4.72	4.10	3.35
44 x 175	4.35	3.78	3.10	4.95	4.32	3.55	5.35	4.65	3.83
44 x 200	4.85	4.22	3.47	5.53	4.82	3.97	5.97	5.20	4.28

The above joist sizes are the minimum permissible sizes at 22% moisture content.

The roof rafters complying with this table are to be single length members continuous over the purlins without splices.

Example: A roof rafter of strength class B is required to span 2.5 m at spacings of 400 mm. A 35 x 115 mm member can be used.

ROOF RAFTERS WITHOUT INTERMEDIATE PURLIN SUPPORT

Roof angle from 20° to 30°.

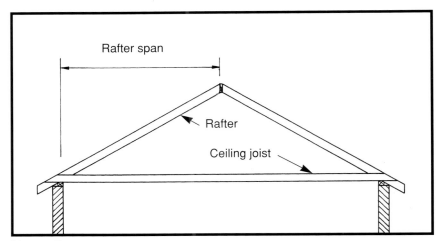

No purlin support:
The span is the span between wall plate and apex measured on plan.

Size of rafters (mm)	Strength Class								
	SC A			SC B			SC C		
	Spacing of rafters (mm)								
	300	400	600	300	400	600	300	400	600
	Permissible span of rafters in metres								
35 x 100	1.67	1.65	1.54	1.72	1.72	1.60	1.91	1.85	1.67
35 x 115	2.02	1.92	1.82	2.16	2.07	1.95	2.21	2.15	2.06
35 x 125	2.28	2.14	2.05	2.39	2.34	2.15	2.47	2.45	2.29
35 x 150	2.88	2.72	2.43	3.04	2.85	2.69	3.21	3.04	2.79
35 x 175	3.47	3.29	2.82	3.68	3.45	3.23	3.84	3.62	3.37
44 x 100	1.84	1.76	1.67	1.97	1.89	1.79	2.11	1.97	1.89
44 x 115	2.25	2.19	2.00	2.39	2.31	2.09	2.49	2.34	2.24
44 x 125	2.46	2.34	2.29	2.66	2.52	2.33	2.80	2.69	2.51
44 x 150	3.17	3.01	2.73	3.34	3.15	2.96	3.48	3.30	3.11
44 x 175	3.77	3.68	3.16	4.01	3.86	3.51	4.25	4.00	3.65
44 x 200	4.46	4.24	3.59	4.77	4.56	4.02	5.01	4.79	4.17

The above joist sizes are the minimum permissible sizes at 22% moisture content.

Example: A roof rafter of strength class C is required to span 4.0 m at spacings of 400 mm. A 44 x 175 mm member can be used.

ROOF RAFTERS WITHOUT INTERMEDIATE PURLIN SUPPORT

Roof angle from 30° to 40°.

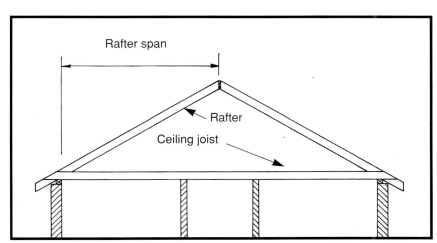

No purlin support:
The span is the span between apex and wall level measured on plan.

Size of rafters (mm)	Strength Class								
	SC A			SC B			SC C		
	Spacing of rafters (mm)								
	300	400	600	300	400	600	300	400	600
	Permissible span of rafters in metres								
35 x 100	1.54	1.45	1.37	1.55	1.58	1.51	1.72	1.60	1.56
35 x 115	1.75	1.70	1.64	1.96	1.80	1.73	1.97	1.97	1.83
35 x 125	2.00	1.99	1.88	2.15	2.05	1.91	2.20	2.14	2.03
35 x 150	2.54	2.43	2.28	2.74	2.61	2.41	2.88	2.77	2.59
35 x 175	3.08	2.95	2.77	3.32	3.15	2.91	3.44	3.29	3.04
44 x 100	1.68	1.63	1.48	1.77	1.73	1.57	1.88	1.79	1.66
44 x 115	1.96	1.93	1.79	2.14	2.01	1.95	2.21	2.12	2.08
44 x 125	2.24	2.16	2.06	2.39	2.30	2.16	2.50	2.44	2.22
44 x 150	2.79	2.69	2.53	3.00	2.86	2.65	3.10	2.98	2.77
44 x 175	3.43	3.30	3.10	3.60	3.51	3.23	3.79	3.61	3.42
44 x 200	4.06	3.91	3.56	4.29	4.06	3.80	4.48	4.34	3.94

The above joist sizes are the minimum permissible sizes at 22% moisture content.

Example: A roof rafter of strength class A is required to span 3.0 m at spacings of 300 mm. A 35 x 175 mm member can be used.

PURLIN SPAN TABLES
STRENGTH CLASS A

Roof angle from 20° to 40°.

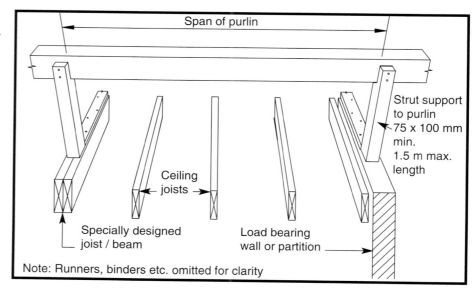

Span of purlin: The purlin span is the clear span between supports.

Purlin size (mm)	SC A								
	Span* of roof rafters in metres								
	1.25	1.50	1.75	2.00	2.25	2.50	2.75	3.00	3.25
	Permissible purlin span in metres								
75x 225	3.16	3.12	2.82	2.63	2.56	2.40	2.35	2.21	2.17
75 x 175	2.63	2.42	2.24	2.17	2.02	1.87	1.73	1.59	1.56
75 x 150	2.26	2.17	1.90	1.84	1.59	1.55	1.42	1.39	1.36
63 x 225	3.03	2.80	2.61	2.43	2.37	2.21	2.16	2.02	1.89
63 x 175	2.43	2.23	2.05	1.89	1.84	1.60	1.56	1.53	1.40
63 x 150	2.17	1.89	1.72	1.57	1.53	1.39	1.36	1.33	1.30

The above purlin sizes are the minimum permissible sizes at 22% moisture content.

*Roof rafter span measured on plan.

Example: A purlin is required to span 2.2 m and is carrying roof rafters with a 1.75 m span.
A 75 x 175 mm member can be used.

The purlin span tables on the following page do not take into account any additional loads, if any, from hangers.

**PURLIN SPAN TABLES
STRENGTH CLASS B**

Roof angle from 20° to 40°.

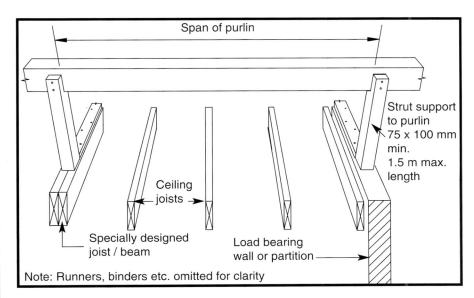

Span of purlin: The purlin span is the clear span between supports.

Purlin size (mm)	SC B								
	Span* of roof rafters in metres								
	1.25	1.50	1.75	2.00	2.25	2.50	2.75	3.00	3.25
	Permissible purlin span in metres								
75x 225	3.22	3.26	3.14	3.04	2.86	2.79	2.63	2.58	2.43
75 x 175	2.64	2.61	2.41	2.34	2.27	2.12	2.07	2.03	1.89
75 x 150	2.34	2.23	2.05	1.98	1.93	1.78	1.74	1.60	1.57
63 x 225	3.07	3.12	2.91	2.82	2.65	2.58	2.43	2.38	2.24
63 x 175	2.62	2.40	2.31	2.14	2.08	2.03	1.89	1.85	1.72
63 x 150	2.24	2.04	1.96	1.90	1.75	1.61	1.57	1.54	1.41

The above purlin sizes are the minimum permissible sizes at 22% moisture content.

*Roof rafter span measured on plan.

Example: A purlin is required to span 2.5 m and is carrying roof rafters with a 3.00 m span.
A 75 x 225 mm member can be used.

**PURLIN SPAN TABLES
STRENGTH CLASS C**

Roof angle from 20° to 40°

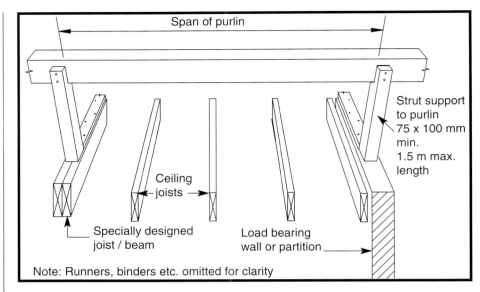

Span of purlin: The purlin span is the clear span between supports.

Purlin size (mm)	SC C								
	Span* of roof rafters in metres								
	1.25	1.50	1.75	2.00	2.25	2.50	2.75	3.00	3.25
	Permissible purlin span in metres								
75x 225	3.38	3.41	3.37	3.16	3.07	2.90	2.83	2.78	2.63
75 x 175	2.86	2.72	2.62	2.53	2.36	2.30	2.25	2.11	2.07
75 x 150	2.55	2.43	2.24	2.17	2.01	1.95	1.91	1.87	1.74
63 x 225	3.31	3.26	3.13	3.03	2.85	2.78	2.62	2.57	2.42
63 x 175	2.73	2.61	2.51	2.33	2.27	2.11	2.06	2.02	1.89
63 x 150	2.44	2.23	2.04	1.98	1.92	1.87	1.73	1.60	1.57

The above purlin sizes are the minimum permissible sizes at 22% moisture content.

*Roof rafter span measured on plan.

Example: A purlin is required to span 2.5m and is carrying roof rafters with a 3.00m span.
A 75 x 225 mm member can be used.

ENTRANCE STEPS TO DUPLEX DWELLINGS

INTRODUCTION

The photographs below illustrate examples of the wide variety of entrance steps to duplex dwellings, incorporating precast concrete steps.

Particular care should be taken at design and construction stage to ensure that:

◆ Moisture penetration is avoided at the junction of the steps and the external wall

◆ Where accommodation is provided under the steps, thermal insulation is provided to the external walls and any ceilings

◆ An adequate step is provided at the threshold

Examples of entrance steps to duplex dwellings.

CONSTRUCTION DETAILS

The sketch below outlines key locations at the junction of the steps and external walls and the sketches on pages 456 and 457 detail the principles of good construction practice at these junctions.

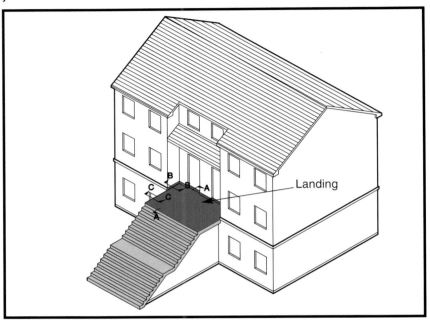

Typical step arrangement at duplex dwelling, outlining key locations at the junction of the steps and the external walls.

As the design and construction of duplex dwellings is so varied, differences in detailing are likely. In this context, the information contained in this appendix should only be used as general guidance. In all cases the requirements of the Building Regulations should be followed.

The incorporation of an asphalt surface on top of the landing, and dressed up the face of any adjoining walls, provides excellent protection against moisture penetration. Where required, suitable tiles can be laid on top of the asphalt. Any asphalt dressed up the face of adjoining walls should be protected by appropriate flashings, see photographs on page 455.

This Appendix will address these issues under the following headings:

◆ APPROACH TO A DWELLING

◆ ACCESS INTO A DWELLING

◆ CIRCULATION WITHIN A DWELLING

◆ SANITARY CONVENIENCES

APPROACH TO A DWELLING

◆ At least one entrance on the boundary of the dwelling plot should have a minimum clear opening of 800 mm.

◆ At least one entrance to the dwelling, preferably the main entrance, should be accessible to wheelchair users. Where it is not practicable to use the main entrance an alternative entrance should be wheelchair accessible.

◆ There should be a clear area at least 1.2 m wide x 1.2 m deep in front of every such entrance.

◆ The approach to the wheelchair accessible entrance from a suitable point of entry on the boundary of the dwelling plot should be suitable for use by wheelchair users.

Alternatively, the approach suitable for wheelchair users may be provided from a point inside the plot where a visitor can conveniently alight from a vehicle, if the distance between the point of access to the site and the wheelchair accessible entrance is greater than 30 m, or the plot gradient is such that relative finished levels between the entrance and point of access to the dwelling site do not allow for the provision of a ramped or sloped approach.

◆ The approach to the wheelchair accessible entrance should have a clear unobstructed width of at least 900 mm, or 3 m where the approach, in whole or in part, forms part of the on site driveway. The approach should have a

firm surface which is suitable for wheelchair use and reduces the risk of slipping.

◆ The approach should be level (max. slope 1:50) or, where plot gradients do not allow this, gently sloping.

◆ Where a level approach is not possible, a sloped approach should be provided and should be as flat as possible. The table below outlines the requirements for sloped approach.

Gradient	Max. length between level landings (measured on plan)
Steeper than 1:20	10 m
Between 1:20 and 1:15 (but not exceeding 1:15)	10 m
Between 1:15 and 1:12	6 m

Requirements for sloped approach

◆ A minimum 75 mm high raised kerb should be provided at any open side of the approach where the ground is not graded to the approach.

Where it is not practicable to provide either a level or sloped approach to the wheelchair accessible entrance, either from the point of entry on the boundary of the dwelling plot, or from a point inside the plot where a visitor can alight from a vehicle, a stepped approach may be used. This may occur where:

◆ The plot gradient of the approach is greater than 1:15.

◆ There is insufficient space for slopes and landings because of the need to conform to the existing building line or other planning requirements, or

◆ The dwelling entrance is not at ground level e.g. duplex buildings or the like.

Where steps are used, the requirements of the sketch on page 462 should be adhered to.

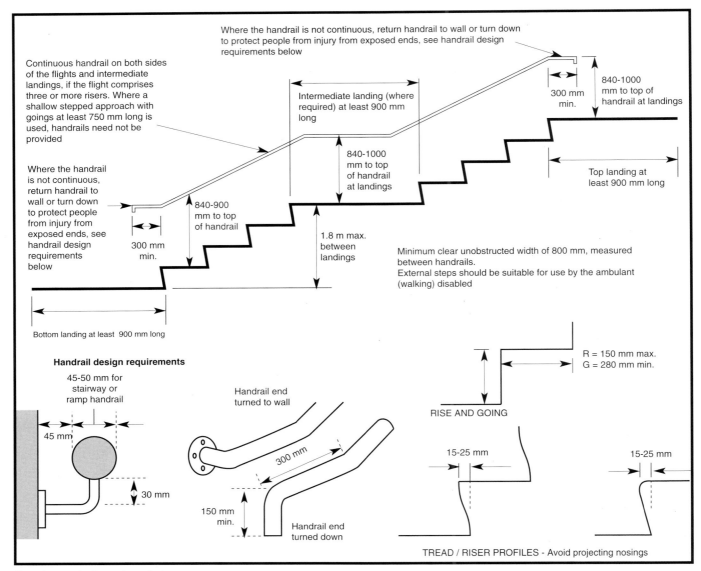

Continuous handrail on both sides of the flights and intermediate landings, if the flight comprises three or more risers. Where a shallow stepped approach with goings at least 750 mm long is used, handrails need not be provided

Where the handrail is not continuous, return handrail to wall or turn down to protect people from injury from exposed ends, see handrail design requirements below

Intermediate landing (where required) at least 900 mm long

840-1000 mm to top of handrail at landings

300 mm min.

840-1000 mm to top of handrail at landings

Top landing at least 900 mm long

Where the handrail is not continuous, return handrail to wall or turn down to protect people from injury from exposed ends, see handrail design requirements below

840-900 mm to top of handrail

300 mm min.

1.8 m max. between landings

Minimum clear unobstructed width of 800 mm, measured between handrails.
External steps should be suitable for use by the ambulant (walking) disabled

Bottom landing at least 900 mm long

Handrail design requirements

45-50 mm for stairway or ramp handrail

45 mm

30 mm

Handrail end turned to wall

300 mm

150 mm min.

Handrail end turned down

R = 150 mm max.
G = 280 mm min.

RISE AND GOING

15-25 mm

15-25 mm

TREAD / RISER PROFILES - Avoid projecting nosings

Requirements for external steps.

ACCESS INTO A DWELLING

Where the approach to a dwelling entrance is level, or sloped, the entrance should be suitable for wheelchair access.

◆ Minimum clear opening width of wheelchair accessible entrance 775 mm, see sketch opposite.

◆ A wheelchair accessible entrance (i.e. level or sloped) should be provided with a level entry, i.e. max. threshold height 15 mm, see sketch on page 463.

◆ Doorbells, entry phones and suchlike should be located a height between 900 mm and 1200 mm above floor level.

The design of the threshold is critical in terms of accessibility and being weathertight. The sketches on page 463 ilustrate typical good detailing practice in this location. The photograph on page 463 illustrates a typical wheelchair accessible entrance.

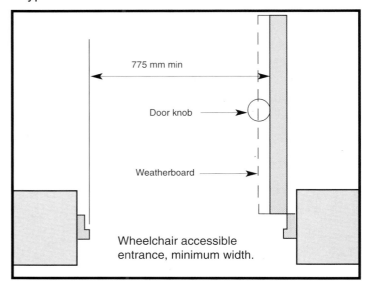

775 mm min

Door knob

Weatherboard

Wheelchair accessible entrance, minimum width.

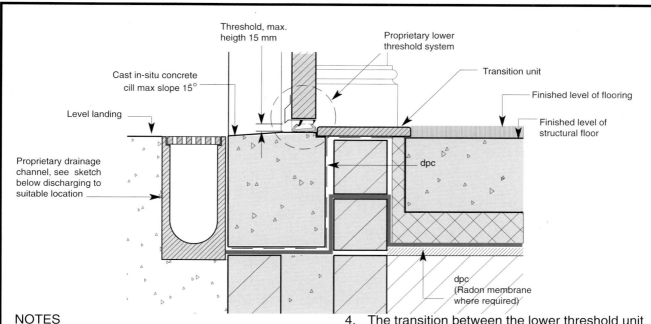

Threshold, max. heigth 15 mm

Proprietary lower threshold system

Transition unit

Cast in-situ concrete cill max slope 15°

Finished level of flooring

Finished level of structural floor

Level landing

Proprietary drainage channel, see sketch below discharging to suitable location

dpc

dpc (Radon membrane where required)

NOTES

1. Proprietary drainage channels should incorporate a grating which will not trap the heels of shoes or pram wheels etc.

2. Drainage channels should be capable of being cleaned and cleared of debris.

3. The use of gravel filled drainage channels is not recommended due to the risk of silting up.

4. The transition between the lower threshold unit and the internal floor level should accommodate accessible transfer for ambulant disabled people and wheelchair users, while permitting occupants the choice of varying the type and thickness of floor covering.

5. The builder needs to take into account the likely occupants choice of floor covering when designing the level of the finished structural floor.

Typical threshold detail at wheelchair accessible entrance.

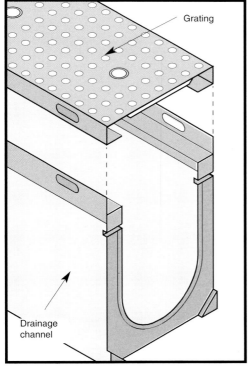

Grating

Drainage channel

Typical proprietary drainage channel assembly

Typical wheelchair accessible entrance.
Note the proprietary drainage channel

CIRCULATION WITHIN A DWELLING

♦ Corridors and doors to habitable rooms in the entry storey should be free of stepped changes of level. Note, where a stepped change of level is provided, e.g. because of the slope of the site, it should be located so that at least one habitable room and the entry level toilet can be accessed from the accessible entrance without the need to negotiate the step(s).

♦ Corridors should have a minimum unobstructed width of 900 mm, see sketch below.

♦ At local permanent obstructions, such as radiators, a clear width of 750 mm should be provided, see sketch below.

Minimum clear opening width (mm)	Minimum unobstructed corridor width (mm)
750	1200 (900 if approached head-on)
775	1050 (900 if approached head-on)
800	900

Clear opening widths of doors to accessible habitable rooms

♦ For minimum clear opening width of doors to accessible habitable rooms, in relation to the adjoining unobstructed corridor width, see table opposite and sketch below. The length of unobstructed corridors should be at least 1200 mm.

♦ Saddleboards, where provided, should be bevelled with a maximum upstand of 10 mm.

♦ Doors to rooms which can only be accessed by the use of steps or stairs, may have a minimum clear opening width of 750 mm, irrespective of the adjoining unobstructed corridor width.

♦ Door handles and light switches should be located between 900 mm and 1200 mm above floor level.

The sketch below illustrates the guidance with regard to minimum widths for corridors and internal doors for convenient wheelchair use.

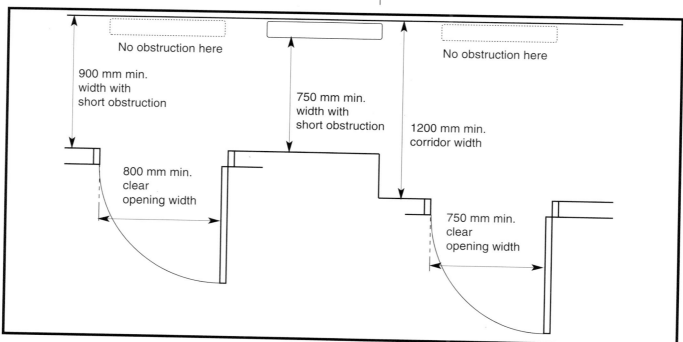

No obstruction here

900 mm min. width with short obstruction

750 mm min. width with short obstruction

No obstruction here

1200 mm min. corridor width

800 mm min. clear opening width

750 mm min. clear opening width

Corridors and internal doors in dwellings

CIRCULARS TO HOMEBOND MEMBERS

NEW BUILDING SYSTEMS / METHODS OF CONSTRUCTION

HomeBond wishes to remind all Members of the importance of ensuring that proposed building systems and/or methods of construction are suitable for use in Ireland. Particular care is required in circumstances where it is proposed to introduce into Ireland building systems or methods of construction which have not traditionally been in use in Ireland.

Care must to taken to ensure:

1. The suitability (including the suitability of design, materials and construction method in "on site" conditions) of any such system or method for use in the particular climatic conditions;
2. The proper training of personnel in the erection of such system or method;
3. Appropriate experienced supervision of the carrying out of work on site.

Recent experience in Canada (British Columbia) highlights the dangers associated with the adoption of building systems and/or methods of construction which do not properly take into account different climatic conditions or the extent of supervision of the works required so that any such systems or methods operate in an appropriate manner to ensure the structural integrity and water tightness of the Dwelling. (It is notable that the climatic conditions in the lower mainland of British Columbia are very similar to the conditions in Ireland.)

Prior to the introduction of any building system or method of construction in respect of any Dwelling, Members must be in a position to produce satisfactory evidence that the proposed system or method of construction in respect of any Dwelling, is of appropriate design and is suitable for use in Ireland, and that the proposed procedures to be adopted will ensure proper and adequate supervision of the construction of the Dwelling.

ROOFING FELTS

HomeBond is aware that new roofing felts are being proposed for use in the roofs of dwellings registered with HomeBond.

Any member intending to use these new roofing felts must ensure that the felt is appropriately certified for use in Irish conditions and that the material is strictly applied in accordance with the requirement of the certificate and manufacturer's instructions.

Items addressed should include the following:

- Is a vapour barrier required?
- What are the roof ventilation requirements of the certificate?
- Can it be draped into the gutter or is a special eaves strip required because the material cannot be exposed to sunlight for long periods?
- Must it be laid out taut or loose?
- Are counter battens required?
- Must the laps be under a batten?
- What are the details at ridges, hips and valleys?

Other aspects considered relevant would be included in the certificate.

HomeBond will require satisfactory evidence such as an appropriate Agrément certificate relating to Irish Building Regulations, Irish climate and Irish construction practices, and confirmation from the member that the felt has been installed in accordance with the conditions of the certificate and manufacturer's instructions.